The Stress Overload Solution

EMOTIONAL BRAIN TRAINING

Laurel Mellin, PhD

Emotional Brain Training (EBT) is a science-based program of emotional neuroplasticity in which people use simple tools to raise their brain's set point for optimal well-being. As with any skills training program, EBT is not without risk and may be unsafe or ineffective for some people. If you have any psychological or medical problems, consult with your physician and other health professionals before beginning this program. EBT is not medical care, but skills training that can be used in support of improved preventive and therapeutic healthcare outcomes. Using the program with the training and support of a Certified EBT Provider is recommended. The outcomes associated with self-study use of EBT are not known. The author, The Solution Foundation (a non-profit corporation), and EBT, Inc. (a California corporation) disclaim all liability for any adverse effects that may result from the use or application of the information contained in this book. The characters discussed in this publication are composites of several individuals and the names of all individuals have been changed to maintain anonymity. Certified EBT Providers may be licensed or registered health professionals. However, they facilitate EBT services outside of their license(s). All providers complete both personal and professional training in the method. To learn more about certification training in EBT, visit ebtbook.com/stressoverload. For a complete list of EBT resources, see "Your EBT Experience" on page 297 If you have questions about the EBT program, please email your inquiry to support@ebt.org.

Editors: Frannie Wilson and Michele Welling. InDesign production: Jamie Holecek. Graphics design: Steven Isakson. Graphics consultant: Jami Spittler. Production: Michael McClure. Technology: Dev Singh and Andrea Singh. Technology design: Joe Mellin. Creative adviser: Walt Rose. Manager: Kelly McGrath. Cover photography: Jamie Rain.

ISBN: 978-0-9864107-5-8
Author: Laurel Mellin, PhD
Published by: EBT Books,
a division of EBT, Inc.
101 Larkspur Landing Circle, Suite 327, Larkspur, CA 94939
WEBSITE: www.ebt.org
BLOG: www.brainbasedhealth.org
E-MAIL: support@ebt.org

Also by Laurel Mellin

The Stress Eating Solution
Wired for Joy
Spiral Up!
The Pathway
The Solution
Shapedown
3-Day Solution Plan

For Mackey and Papa

Contents

Take Charge

Celebrate the Power of One

The Stress Overload Solution Program

This Book **The EBT Online Community**

- EBT Mobile App for stress relief
- Video demonstrations for each day of the challenge
- More courses: Stress Eating, Advanced EBT & more
- FREE workshops and forum boards
- Coaching and telegroups (additional charge)

This book includes a 25% discount on the Online PLUS membership.
To redeem, visit **EBT.ORG** and enter coupon code: **stressoverload**

Introduction

Stress is the #1 epidemic worldwide, as it triggers chemical cascades that cause almost everything that ails us: appetites, excesses, stalls, and overreactions, as well as many health problems. What's more, stress blocks our well-being, and our joy.

Breakthroughs in neuroscience have given us a creative solution to the stress overload nearly everyone experiences these days. Until now, we've been rather stalled about stress, because stress is part of life. What can you do about it? What's more, once the stress response has been activated, we cannot fill enough prescriptions to counter the chemical mayhem that follows. Medications alone cannot put the genie back into the bottle.

The creative solution to stress is to control how we respond to our own particular variety of upsets, temptations, and losses. Our responses are controlled by our wiring, the strings of neurons that make us either stress resilient or stress reactive. Neuroplasticity research has shown that we can target and change these wires, shutting off the ones that make us reactive and trigger harmful chemical cascades, and activating those that promote resilience and unleash healing chemicals.

This approach is surprisingly simple. We only have two kinds of circuits that control how we respond to life. One is the "Stress Circuit," which triggers harmful chemical cascades that cause 75 to 90% of health problems. The other is the "Joy Circuit," which is the solution. It activates surges of healing chemicals that make us happy, healthy, productive, loving . . . and bursting with joy.

This new approach is brain-based healthcare. We change our chemicals by changing our wires. Improved health and happiness naturally follow. It does not replace healthcare, but offers a new resource for making our traditional strategies even more effective. This book will give you a new, science-based way to think about health and tools for applying it. Once you become accustomed to thinking in terms of circuits and reaching for the tools when you want to feel better, this approach is likely to become part of your way of life for one reason: it works!

Joy Circuits

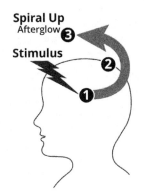

Spiral Up
Afterglow ❸

Stimulus

❶
Accurate Emotions
The circuit activates healing
chemicals and balanced emotions.

❷
Reasonable Expectations
An accurate message guides us (e.g., "I get
my safety from connecting to myself").

❸
Effective Response
We respond in an effective way
(e.g., We connect within) and spiral up
to a state of well-being, with an afterglow.

For example, this morning I was reading the news while having a cup of coffee, and my partner Walt was doing the same. Nearby, our dog Tammy was chasing her favorite stuffed octopus toy around the room. For no particular reason, I had a negative chemical flow going. I was out of sorts. I had the choice of either using the tools in my head, which I do quite often, maybe 10 times a day, or asking Walt to listen to me use them. I said, "I feel bad. Would you listen to me use a tool?" He nodded and settled back in his chair. Walt is familiar with helping me in this way, and I return the favor for him. He sipped his coffee and after about two minutes of using the tools, I spiraled up. My bad mood vanished, and I had a huge smile on my face, and I was laughing out loud, and charged up to start what has become (so far) a great day. That's the power of taking charge of our chemistry by taking charge of these powerful wires!

Approaching health in this "real-time" way is an adjustment, because most of us are not used to rebalancing our body chemistry immediately after the stress chemicals start surging. We're accustomed to waiting until evening to go for a run, meditate, or access support from a friend. Unfortunately, all that waiting is bad for us. The stress chemicals continue to surge, and can impact every cell of our being in significant, negative ways. The tools of Emotional Brain Training (EBT), that you will learn in this book, give you the power to shut off the stress response on the spot. Also, unlike medications, there are no dosing limitations in using the tools so we can switch off those harmful chemical surges and activate healing surges five, 10, or even 15 times a day. That makes for a better day, and for an evening in which we still have plenty of energy to do something that is highly fulfilling, whether it is planting a garden, making love, starting a new business, or walking the dog!

Stress Circuits

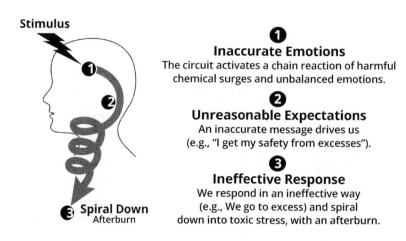

Stimulus

① Inaccurate Emotions
The circuit activates a chain reaction of harmful chemical surges and unbalanced emotions.

② Unreasonable Expectations
An inaccurate message drives us
(e.g., "I get my safety from excesses").

③ Ineffective Response
We respond in an ineffective way
(e.g., We go to excess) and spiral
down into toxic stress, with an afterburn.

③ Spiral Down
Afterburn

Brain-based healthcare is definitely a movement, because we know that these Stress Circuits are a modifiable root cause of health problems, as well as nearly every problem you hear about on the news – whether it is political, emotional, social, economic, spiritual, or behavioral. Until 10 years ago, we did not know that we could rewire these circuits, and it took five separate discoveries in neuroscience to develop EBT.

This new neuroscience approach amounts to a new resource for promoting optimal well-being that would not be possible without the work of thousands of scientists, and most particularly the work of these six scientists whom I consider the pioneers of EBT:

Pioneer #1 – Michael Merzenich, PhD – The father of neuroplasticity
Neuroscientist Michael Merzenich discovered that the brain is soft-wired and proposed that the new science of brain plasticity could transform our lives. Dr. Merzenich is a professor emeritus at UCSF and has contributed to more than 230 scientific articles. As a co-founder and Chief Scientific Officer of Posit Science, Dr. Merzenich heads the company's science team. He holds nearly 100 patents and spearheaded brain training as a new field in healthcare.

Pioneer #2 – Peter Sterling, PhD – The founder of allostasis
Peter Sterling is a neuroscientist from the University of Pennsylvania. In collaboration with biologist Joseph Eyer, he coined the term "allostasis" for the internal process of going to extremes of physiology and behavior, in an attempt to improve the survival of the species. In contrast to "homeostasis," this process often does not cause well-being, and understanding it provides a giant step forward in taking charge of our lives.

Pioneer #3 – Igor Mitrovic, MD – The scientific director
One of the major pioneers in changing circuits is Igor Mitrovic, a UCSF professor, neuroscientist, and physiologist, and the scientific director of EBT. Not only has Dr. Mitrovic brought a new level of scientific rigor to the method, but he advocated that positive emotional plasticity had the potential power to change healthcare. His desire for people to heal, and his bravery in cutting through the reductionism of science to distinguish homeostatic circuits from allostatic circuits, makes it possible to apply the principles of neuroplasticity to the stress response.

Pioneer #4 – Joseph LeDoux, PhD – The emotional brain founder
Joseph LeDoux is the Director of New York University's Emotional Brain Institute and the author of *The Emotional Brain*. His work in collaboration with Elizabeth Phelps, PhD, professor of human neuroscience at Harvard, led to the discovery that fear memories could be reconsolidated if activated by stress. Their work on understanding survival circuits and emotions is fundamental to the effectiveness of EBT.

Pioneer #5 – Elissa Epel, PhD – The psychological stress and aging researcher
Elissa Epel is a professor in the Department of Psychiatry and a health psychologist at UCSF. She has conducted seminal research demonstrating the relationship between psychological stress and cellular aging. Dr. Epel's work with Elizabeth Blackburn, PhD, who was awarded the 2009 Nobel Prize in Physiology and Medicine, has led to greater public awareness of the adverse impact of stress on optimal aging.

Pioneer #6 – Bruce McEwen, PhD – The chief of stress research
The work of neuroendocrinologist Bruce McEwen of Rockefeller University has changed how we think about stress. His concept of stress load ("allostatic load") is central to EBT, as decreasing the stress load by raising the brain's set point is the goal of the EBT program. Dr. McEwen has published more than 700 scientific articles and is known for his work on the effects of environmental and psychological stress, and the role of stress neuroplasticity in improving health.

The Three Steps of the EBT Program

The goal of EBT is to support you at winning at the game of life. It's to equip you with powerful tools, so you can use them to clear away four problems of your choosing, then to raise your set point for lasting results. The program involves three steps.

The EBT Program

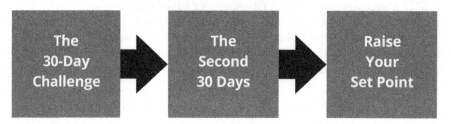

Step 1. The 30-Day Challenge

For 30 days, you will learn one small but important skill each day to rewire Stress Circuits into Joy Circuits. The first week or two, you'll learn how to short-circuit unwanted wires for immediate results. You will learn tools that shut off the Stress Circuit immediately so that overreactions and cravings can fade. Then you will select circuits you want to rewire – a mood, a relationship issue, a work difficulty, and a habit – and learn how to rewire them. The last few days of the program, you'll bring all your skills together with a vibrant, joyful lifestyle and experience optimal well-being.

Step 2. The Second 30 Days

After the 30-Day Challenge, your brain will need time to reorganize itself around this significant improvement in your wiring. Take 30 days to use the tools you've learned and deepen your rewiring, integrating a more vibrant lifestyle. This is a needed respite and gives the brain a chance to make these changes solid. You can continue to use the tools and this book for the Second 30 Days, and when you feel ready for more advanced training, go on to Step 3.

Step 3. Raise Your Set Point

The last step in EBT is to raise the set point of the brain. By completing the first two steps, you will feel much better. You'll experience a "brain reset" which changes the brain's habit. By completing the first steps, we unsettle the brain from its old ways, then continue to raise the brain's set point with our advanced courses to establish new ways that are lasting.

The advanced courses train the brain to move through stress and experience the seven rewards of a purposeful life. There is one advanced course for each of these rewards.

You may want to use this course on your own, but these wires are stored in the emotional brain, which is the social brain. It changes most easily when we are part of a small "tribe" of people who are using the tools, too. Create your own tribe of family members or friends to update your brains for optimal well-being. Also, join the EBT Online Community, as we make anonymous, confidential support easy to access and very convenient.

The 7 Rewards	
• Sanctuary	Peace and power from within
• Authenticity	Feeling whole and being genuine
• Vibrancy	Healthy with a zest for life
• Integrity	Doing the right thing
• Intimacy	Giving and receiving love
• Spirituality	The grace, beauty, and mystery of life
• Freedom	Common excesses fade

Welcome to EBT! During the next 30 days, you can learn about the world of emotional plasticity, and acquire a set of tools that you can use for a lifetime. I designed this course to be a life-changing experience, and hope it is that and more for you!

Welcome

The Power of One

You have a state of connection in your brain that is as close to perfection as humanly possible. In this state, your entire physiology – including your organs, cells, and molecules – is at its best. Elevated emotions flow, such as love, compassion, gratitude, hope, forgiveness, awe, and joy.

We call this Brain State 1.

I gazed outside, and a hummingbird stopped right beside my window. It seemed to look straight at me for a second or two, then it flew away. I was in awe. I was at One.

Last night I was completely exhausted, but I went the extra mile and gave my two-year-old daughter a bath. She was splashing and giggling, and I started laughing. My fatigue disappeared!

"One" is the Optimal State

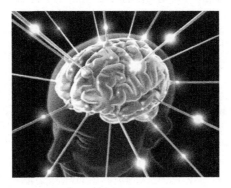

What is the source of these beautiful emotions?

That state of rapture – whether it lasts a second or lingers for hours – is the activation of a Joy Circuit. You have a great many of these wires. Over time, as you use this method, you will create more of them, and the ones you already have will become larger and more powerful. Moments of well-being will appear naturally, and your brain's set point will begin to rise until you are wired at One. You still experience stress, but the default state of your brain is One. That is the goal of EBT. You still need to express negative emotions, but because negative feelings have no Stress Circuits to trigger, a moment of expressing outrage can spiral you up to a bright, shiny state of One.

I realized this phenomenon with a group of scientists who were all studying EBT together. They had changed so much that I thought of them as "spiral up" superstars! Their Stress Circuits had been weakened or cleared, and their Joy Circuits could easily be activated to shut off their Stress Circuits. If they felt stressed, they could simply make a couple of statements about what upset them, express a few robust feelings of anger, and their brain "popped" to Brain State 1. I sensed that they had arrived at this new brain set point because I felt restless. They did not need me anymore. It was time for me to move on. Just a couple of weeks before, I had brought up my concern that this had happened, but each woman was adamant that she had not raised her set point.

So, we had continued to meet. On that evening, three members arrived at the session and reported having had a devastating experience that week. One was passed over for a promotion, and another's grant had been turned down, leaving her work of 20 years in limbo. The third woman's ex-husband, whom she still loved deeply, became engaged. The room was quiet. The woman who had been passed over for a promotion started using the tools, expressing what she was upset about – the unfairness of the situation and her rage about it.

We had all just settled back into our chairs, and were listening to her express her emotions, when she stopped abruptly. She blinked several times, and said, "That's strange. I'm at One."

All eyes met, aware of the way her brain had spiraled up so naturally. Then, the second woman, who was suffering the potential loss of 20 years of scientific inquiry, spoke up. She began describing her situation and belted out a couple of "red hot" anger statements. Then she paused, looking perplexed, and then burst out laughing. She said, "Oh #$%@, I spiraled up to One!"

We were all moved by the experience, and uncharacteristically, silent. Finally, the last woman, whom we expected to take her turn using the tools, instead, looked at me, almost apologetically, and said, "Ditto. I'm at One, too."

This may sound strange to you. It is strange! Yet, that is the power of training the brain for resilience. The brain learns to bounce back. The circuits that trigger us melt away, and we have a profound sense of peace and power from within.

The Power of One is spiraling up
The experience of spiraling up may be as riveting as it is because it releases suppressed emotions, or the "stuffed" feelings held within the circuit when it was encoded. Imagine all those stuffed feelings finally being released! That has to be pleasurable. However, more importantly, it's a sign that we have updated our unconscious expectations so they are more reasonable. The importance of changing our unconscious memories that trigger unreasonable expectations comes straight

from the theories of Sigmund Freud. He understood the immense power of the unconscious mind. In a research meeting at UCSF one day, a psychiatry professor reached for a pad of paper and wrote out this equation:

Stress = Conscious Expectations vs. Unconscious Expectations

He asserted, "Stress is the difference between our conscious expectations and our unconscious expectations." That internal conflict is the primary cause of the chemical and electrical surges that cause many health issues. Until recently, we didn't know that we could update these unconscious memories. Our challenge is to process the unreasonable unconscious wires faster than they can be encoded! It's not keeping up with fashion styles or new downloads of apps that is critical, but keeping up with the influx of information into our unconscious mind, which amounts to 40 million pieces of information per second. In comparison, the conscious mind processes only 20 pieces of information per second. On a daily basis, we have plenty of opportunities to process that emotional data, as stress is plentiful. It can be neatly divided into three types:

Situational stress: "Help, I'm overwhelmed!"

When the overall stress load in the brain crosses a tipping point, the stress switch, the hypothalamus, activates a cascade of stress hormones. Often, it's not just one thing that causes that overload, but a series of stressors that sends us over the edge. The most challenging aspect of situational stress is that we are unable to pinpoint what is causing it! For thinking-oriented people, perfectionists, and those who like to be in control (which is most of us), figuring out what's causing our stress causes secondary stress – feeling stressed about being stressed. Instead, we can keep it simple by processing our emotions, and spiraling up to One.

I'm in tech, and everyone I know is in tech. I was in a frenzy for no reason – always thinking about what I could be doing, if I weren't doing what I was doing. And then my little sister had issues with her boyfriend, and I kept thinking I should commit to MY girlfriend, but I was afraid that she would lose interest, like my last girlfriend did. One day, I was so overwhelmed that I did a blitz of emotional processing. I got to One. It was the first time in my life that I surrendered to my emotions. Now I swear by it.

Trauma wires: "This is a very deep wire!"

Most of our wires are very deep and strong, as they were encoded in childhood. Or the wires are newer, but they feel quite fresh, as if the pain is just below the surface. We feel like we are sitting on a keg of dynamite which could go off at any moment. Our challenge is to trust our primitive emotional processes – and to use them. Although more emotional support from peers is very helpful, and psychotherapy and medications can make the process safer and more effective or some people, there is no substitute for getting to the emotional root cause of the problem, switching off a Stress Circuit, and activating a Joy Circuit. As best stated by psychologist John Gray, "What we feel, we can heal."

I have an overwhelming desire to merge with other people and fix them. My wife is really touchy, and when I start doing it, she screams at me, and says, "I hate it when you try to fix me. Go fix yourself. Stop telling me what to do!" I HATE that, so I started getting to One before I talked to her, and it worked for a while. Then we started talking about our finances, and right when I triggered a very deep wire, I stopped and said to myself, "My job is to get to One." I went for a walk, processed some very gnarly emotions, and spiraled up to One. At that moment, I didn't care about money. I cared about my wife. Besides, if I hadn't been triggered, I would never have broken that wire. Amazing!

Modern life: "The world keeps changing on me!"

The rapid changes in basic expectations about life that we see now are vexing. They impact all of us. Our thinking brain is processing more information now, most of which is cognitive clutter, and that distracts us from the emotional processing that updates our unconscious expectations. What is the solution? The Power of One. You have it, and so do I. We just need to use it!

I was trained as a youngster in some very bizarre attitudes toward people who were different from me. I knew these biases were wrong. Finally, I couldn't live with myself anymore and processed my emotions. The old expectations began to fade. My father's brain was full of bigotry, but mine isn't.

My family is at war against each other because of politics. Each of us is more polarized than the other, and now I don't know what to do. All the expectations of my parents are so strange and morally wrong, and they think the same of me. I started processing my anger about it, and my brain revealed my unreasonable expectation that they would find integrity that same way I would. It was an aha moment, and I spiraled up to One and felt compassion for all of us.

The healing power of One

You might think that this sounds like psychotherapy. After all, we are talking about the unconscious mind, and how EBT is in alignment with the early theories of Freud. I don't see it that way, because resilience is health promoting. The emotional architecture of the brain requires that we crash through some old fear memories in order to promote that optimal state of well-being.

We have a beautiful brain that can do emotional handstands for us if we let it. Harvard professor George Vaillant marveled in his landmark book, *Spiritual Evolution: How We Are Wired for Faith, Hope, and Love*, that our brain evolved such that our conscious mind can light up the pleasure center in our unconscious mind. If we use our inherent emotional capacities well, perhaps we can not only be happy regardless of circumstance, but live a purposeful life.

What's more, neuroscientist Antonio Damasio has proposed that joyous states signify optimal physiology. By venturing out in the world and making our dent it in, then shaking off the residual stress from doing so, and returning to One, we have more than happiness. In fact, accessing the Power of One is a new and natural way to take care of our health . . .

The Missing Link

It was a chance encounter some 10 years ago that made me see EBT with fresh eyes. I realized that medical problems are largely the downstream effects of the cascade of stress hormones.

For most of us, our stress hormone spigot is turned on full blast more often than we would like. Stress negatively and significantly impacts every one of our organs and every aspect of our life. It occurred to me, "Why not go to the source and focus on shutting off the spigot?"

We'd be much happier, healthier and, as physiological stress is the root cause of most problems, it makes sense for the healthcare system to help us shut off our own stress spigot.

Turning off the stress spigot

That idea came to me on a chilly evening in the fog belt of San Francisco, when I was at the university sitting in a classroom awaiting the arrival of faculty members at the EBT group session. They were finding their way through the city from a constellation of hospitals, and running a little late.

Just outside the classroom door, a medical student was rushing down the hallway and bumped into her preceptor physician, and greeted him. Then she stood stone-still, presenting her patient's case to him.

She was speaking in a strong voice, the classroom door was wide open, so I couldn't help but overhear her presentation. The patient was Scott, age 44, a middle-school teacher, father of one teenager, and married to a geology professor at the local junior college. He presented with anxiety, headaches, and stomach aches. His alcohol intake was three drinks per day, and he did not smoke. His presenting complaint was fatigue and being "sick of feeling sick."

The student rattled off a list of medications she had ordered: lorazepam for anxiety, temazepam for sleep, omeprazole for stomachaches, and ibuprofen for headaches. Also, she reported that she had recommended a 12-step program for support with Scott's drinking, but he had said alcohol wasn't a problem. Besides, he didn't believe in a higher power.

The missing link in healthcare is turning Stress Circuits into Joy Circuits.

As I listened to the student present this case, I felt so frustrated. The problem was a few faulty Stress Circuits. Scott could learn the skill of rewiring and use it not only to feel better, but to prevent problems like these from cropping up in the future. I settled back in my chair, closed my eyes, and imagined this student applying brain-based healthcare.

The medical student said, "Scott, all these problems are caused by brain circuits that you can learn how to shut off, or even rewire. If you want prescriptions, I can order them, but you can also learn how to rewire those circuits – or you can do both. What would you like to do?"

Train the brain for resilience

Since that time, enthusiasm about brain-based medicine has grown. Already, there is a national effort to track brain circuits, the NIH Human Connectome Project, which is mapping out the neural circuits that underlie human brain function to aid in the prevention and treatment of common health problems. Some of the titans of medicine are advocating that we stop focusing excessively on pharmacologic treatments, and instead train the brain for resilience – putting Joy Circuits in charge so that our entire physiology is at its best.

Neuroscientist Michael Merzenich, PhD, as part of a course on emotional brain medicine that EBT faculty teach medical students at UCSF, said in 2014, "If there is ever to be a true solution for a medical problem, it will not be chemical. It will be training the brain for resilience."

Thomas Insel, MD, who directed the National Institute for Mental Health for 13 years, is a proponent of rewiring faulty circuits and emphatic that medical care must change. In 2011, he said, "Whatever we've been doing for five decades, it ain't working . . . when I look at the numbers – the number of suicides, the number of disabilities, the mortality data – it's abysmal, and it's not getting any better. Maybe we just need to rethink this whole approach."

The logical brain-based approach of focusing on our wiring made perfect sense. When stress from the external environment or the internal milieu enters the brain, it triggers wires that control our responses to life. If we can step through the portal of the unconscious mind and fiddle with our circuits so that more often than not the circuits that make us healthy and happy become dominant and are activated spontaneously, that should be helpful! My collaborators Igor Mitrovic, Lynda Frassetto, Lindsey Fish, and I had been constructing EBT for some time, when in 2011, we proposed a new brain-based paradigm in healthcare. It was to rewire the stress response. Then, in, 2013, we created a theory that provided a conceptual basis for the new paradigm. It called it emotional plasticity theory, which has four postulates.

Emotional Plasticity Theory
• All living beings have survival drives.
• Emotional circuits evolved to improve survival.
• Circuits can be effective or ineffective.
• Rewiring ineffective circuits improves health.

All living beings have survival drives

The cornerstone of emotional plasticity theory is that all living beings have survival drives. These drives enable us to solve the primitive challenges of life. Imagine if our hunter-gatherer ancestors were out in the bush without their survival drives? They would be eaten by a lion in a fortnight! Survival requires being vigilant, sensing a threat, and, in an instant, organizing body and brain to overcome that peril. Then, after returning to a state of safety, a burst of neurotransmitters rewards us for success. These survival drives live within us all!

Emotional circuits evolved to improve survival

Whatever we did when a lion approached us is valuable information. If we didn't succumb to the lion, then our strategy was pretty effective. Evolutionary biology found a way to bank those responses and instantly replay them when the lion returns. That file cabinet of memories of our past responses is our unconscious ("implicit") memory system. It encodes, stores, retrieves, and rapidly activates these instructions without our awareness (no body feel that a memory is controlling us) or approval. In contrast, the conscious ("explicit") memory system is slow, and we're aware when it is being activated. It's the fast, unconscious memories that are survival memories. They are far stronger, easily overpowering our conscious memories and ruling our responses, particularly when we are stressed. By having a ready bank of proven responses at hand, we avoid overloading our limited "working memory", the active sketch pad that controls incoming data and directs our attention. This "autopilot" function of the emotional circuits enables us to learn faster, progress more easily, and get things done.

I don't have to think about how to drive a car, whip up some scrambled eggs, or really listen to my three-year-old daughter when she is upset about something. I do it automatically.

Circuits can be effective or ineffective

The brain is not discriminating about which circuits it allows to be encoded and stored away for later activation. It takes all comers, virtually any experience we have is automatically stored in long-term memory. Even though we have no awareness that we are learning (such as when someone is put off by a comment we make or when no one laughs at a joke we tell), our emotional circuits are locking that information away in the furthest recesses of our unconscious mind.

A good number of these wires are so completely ridiculous that if we brought them to consciousness, we would laugh until tears ran down our face. This is the problem, they are not conscious, or at least cannot be brought to consciousness by thinking, but only through emotional experiences. The only way we know they are residing in our brain is when we do something that seems completely illogical or ridiculous, and then, despite our best efforts, we keep repeating that pattern. What is the problem? It's an ineffective circuit – a Stress Circuit.

As a little girl, my room was a mess. I liked clutter. It made me feel safe. I'm still doing the same thing, and I'm 39 years old. I tell myself that I am going to stop spending, hoarding, and cluttering, but I keep doing it. That's definitely a wire!

I am drawn to dating women who reject me. I have dated trial attorneys, stay-at-home single mothers, programmers, and teachers. They all look different, but they all trigger the same wire. That wire is ruining my love life. I don't know how I acquired that circuit, but it is at the top of my list for rewiring.

Rewiring ineffective circuits improves health

These wires are highly plastic. We can rewire those ineffective Stress Circuits and improve our physiologic stress, which improves every aspect of our health and well-being.

In healthcare, there are four major methods of avoiding the harm caused by Stress Circuits. Only one of them is to rewire the faulty circuits. The first three do not rewire these circuits, but they can be helpful in the short term. One is to actively cope, such as avoiding situations and people that trigger our faulty wires. It's so helpful! To this day, I don't keep pumpkin pie in the house, as my "I get my love from pumpkin pie" circuit will be triggered. The second approach is cognitive regulation, using effective thoughts to reduce stress and promote healthy responses. That is very effective in low-stress situations, as who doesn't buck up in response to positive self-talk. One of my favorites is, "You don't have to be perfect to be wonderful." The last of the strategies for dealing with stress wires is extinction. It involves building healthy wires (Joy Circuits) without crushing the stress wires. This is effective when stress is low, but when stress levels rise, the Stress Circuit becomes activated, and easily overpowers the new circuit, causing relapse.

Our only hope is to erase the wire, which is called reconsolidation. Here's how it works: you target a wire you don't like and get riled up about this circuit bothering you. By being upset about the wire, the synaptic connections between the neurons become fluid. Basically, they can now change if we deliver a new experience to them. That updates the wire, and after a few hours, that new wire becomes stored in long-term memory, thereby weakening or erasing the old wire. The old Stress Circuit is then less likely to return, and the change can be lasting.

Evidence of reconsolidation in humans has been mounting for many years. In 1978, a novel study by University of Washington psychologist Elizabeth Loftus, PhD had subjects watch a series of slides of an automobile accident, with either a yield or stop sign at the crash scene. Later the story was switched, and the subjects were again presented with slides, but with the opposite sign at the crash. Forty-five percent of the subjects were found later to have updated their memory to the opposite sign, suggesting they had unlocked the memory and changed the memory circuit.

The strategy of breaking apart old circuits and encoding new, updated ones was gaining ground in research on memory circuits. The idea that memories could be updated by dismantling an existing circuit, then encoding a new one to promote lasting changes, has become important in preventing relapse and avoiding the unwanted side effects of medications.

Over 300 papers have been published on reconsolidation in animals in recent years, which largely shows evidence that if a circuit is stress-activated just prior to the arrival of new information, the old circuit changes or is even erased. There have been 13 human studies on reconsolidation during the same period. But research methodology has been challenging, as some of the animal studies used pharmacologically-mediated interventions, such as propranolol. Because that chemical can be harmful to humans, researchers were stumped about how to study reconsolidation in people.

The power to erase circuits

Researchers at New York University and Harvard have led the way on stress circuitry research. Elizabeth Phelps and her colleagues designed a methodology to study reconsolidation in humans. They performed elegant studies published in 2010 to answer the question of whether Stress Circuits ("fear memories") could be erased in humans.

Their methods were novel. Researchers paired a mild shock (unconditioned stimulus) with a colored square (conditioned stimulus). Based on associative learning, the subjects soon activated a stress response when presented with the same colored square without the shock, as evidenced by galvanic skin conductance, measuring how much sweat was being generated due to the activation of the sympathetic nervous system. One day later, researchers repeatedly showed subjects the colored square again but without a shock, until seeing the square alone elicited no stress response – the memory was extinguished. The new memory of the colored card as not threatening was stronger than the old memory that paired the card with a slight shock.

One more variable that had been introduced in the study now became evident. Just before the researchers began showing the cards without the shock to extinguish the "colored card is threatening" memory, some subjects received reactivation of the stress response via a shock alone. Previous studies had shown that stress activation was essential to unlocking the synaptic connections between neurons, making updating the wire and erasing the old one possible. The other subjects received no stress response activation prior to the memory being extinguished, presumably blocking the potential for reconsolidation.

To assess whether or not the Stress Circuit was erased at both three days and one year later, researchers showed the subjects the colored square alone. At both re-testing periods, the memory returned spontaneously for subjects who did not have a stress-activated learning experience. The Stress Circuit was reinstated, even though it had appeared to be erased.

In contrast, at both re-testing periods, the memory was erased and did not return spontaneously for subjects who had a stress-activated learning experience. These studies showed that stress-activation is necessary for lasting change in a circuit, and circuits drive our emotions, thoughts, behavior, and physiology! The take-home finding from these studies was that one must activate the same level of stress, if only for a moment, that one was in when the circuit was encoded. Although the new learning is fragile for up to six hours, after that "reconsolidation window," the old learning is erased and the new learning is encoded in the long-term memory system of the unconscious mind.

Erasing wires requires a spark of emotion

This breakthrough study had major implications for healthcare and public health, in that virtually all methods of treating emotional, relational, and behavioral problems do not stress-activate wires. In fact, they do the opposite, covering over negative thoughts that cause negative emotions with positive thoughts that cause positive emotions, missing the opportunity to use those negative emotions and the stress they cause to erase the offending Stress Circuits. Essentially, we've built a massive intervention effort to treat problems caused by Stress Circuits (depression, anxiety, addictions, obesity, diabetes, heart disease, cancer, and more) by calming down the wires, keeping their synaptic connections locked, and bypassing any hope that we can break apart those faulty circuits and replace them with effective wires. That's a lot to process for health professionals, researchers, and the public. Nearly 10 years later, the hairpin turn to see stress as good for us, and reconsolidation of Stress Circuits as a mainstream activity in America, is just beginning to get underway.

A new paradigm in healthcare

So far, we know that there is a brain state of One in which we are chemically and electrically at our best. Stress Circuits block that state, however, we can transform these wires. We can do that!

This is revolutionary! We can access all the medical care we need, but most problems can be prevented or improved by rewiring a few faulty circuits. With this approach, we have no problems, just have a few wires that are on our "list" to rewire, as we get around to it.

I like that idea. And I love EBT, but it will take a revolution for the EBT tools to appear on milk cartons, for children to learn these powerful stress relief skills in school, and for people to tell their doctors that they want to be their own chemist – rewiring circuits rather than overloading their brain and body with medications, with their toxicities and side effects.

However, change is in the wind. More people are looking for a new approach to well-being. We may be on the verge of a golden age, a time in which natural, brain-based healthcare begins to catch on . . .

It's A Golden Age

Miracles happen, and emotional plasticity may be one of them.

A few years ago, I met with a warm, fatherly psychiatrist to explain the science and methods of EBT. During our conversation, there came a moment when words failed me. I suggested that he try one of the tools, and he demurred, so I volunteered to demonstrate the technique.

I had not been aware of how stressed I was at the time – that I feared that I would never get this method out and would go to my grave with the tools still inside me. However, in the warm womb of his comfy office, I launched into using a tool. I fired up anger that sported a few expletives, made a brief pass through sadness with tears sparkling in my eyes, next touched on fear, and then on guilt.

At that point, the bottom of my reptilian brain opened up. I had unlocked a previously unconscious, completely unreasonable expectation that had taken up residence in my brain. Perfect! Moments later, I had switched that expectation to a reasonable one of my choosing, and a burst of dopamine, oxytocin, and endorphins came over me. I was in joy!

All of this had taken less than four minutes.

He sat quietly. I had no idea what he would say.

Then he gazed straight into my eyes and said, "Nothing in my 40 years of psychiatry has prepared me to explain what I just observed."

Through his eyes, my use of the tools must have seemed strange in two ways. One was that I could self-activate strong negative emotions and rapidly turn them into intense positive feelings. The other was that I had opened my unconscious mind, and transformed a circuit that harmed me into one that healed me. This is something that typically only occurs during an unexpected magical moment over which we have little control, such as a profound insight, a spiritual awakening, or an intimate sharing with a loved one.

Yet it had happened in his office, not by chance, but by choice. I had used such simple tools!

This was emotional plasticity in action. The science is new and the tools are solid, however, we have a lot to learn to realize its potential to help us lead happier, healthier lives. We need a golden age, a time of transformation in which we tap into our greatest resource, our individual power to take charge of our emotional brain, as well as update our healthcare system so that it honors our power, and becomes brain-based.

There has already been a golden age in healthcare. Perhaps we can learn from it . . .

The First Golden Age of Healthcare
A Root Cause of Infectious Diseases: Bacteria

Until about 1900, the leading cause of human death was infectious diseases. The first pandemic in recorded history was in 430 BC, which wiped out two-thirds of the population of Athens. Infectious diseases spread through broad swaths of the world, killing people in droves. Scourges such as syphilis, cholera, salmonella, influenza, typhus, measles, leprosy, and yellow fever exacted heavy tolls on human life.

The Problem: Bacteria

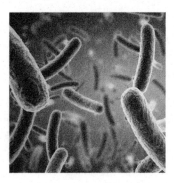

Before 400 BC, our medical defenses were exorcism, magic, potions, enemas, and ointments. Then Hippocrates, the father of modern medicine, coined the Hippocratic Oath and established medicine as a profession. This paved the way for the systematic study of the clinical treatment of health problems.

As clinical medicine evolved, infectious diseases continued their reign of terror. It was not until 1646 AD that Athanasius Kircher, a German Jesuit priest who was caring for plague victims, examined their blood under a microscope. He noted the presence of "little worms," and concluded that the disease was caused by microorganisms or "germs." A competing theory of what was causing these diseases was posited by Lazzaro Spallanzani, an Italian Jesuit priest. He thought that the problem was the rotting of organic matter, which led to "bad air."

Finally, in 1860, amid much drama, the French Academy of Sciences offered 2,500 francs to the scientist who could end the debate between bad air and germ theories. This triggered a flurry of scientific activity until 1862, when Louis Pasteur, a French scientist, conducted a series of elegant experiments proving germ theory. Germ theory is still the basis for treating infectious diseases today.

The Solution: Antibiotics

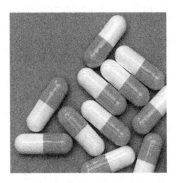

Healthcare in Transition
100 Years Without a Root Cause to Treat

Identifying the root cause of infectious disease launched the golden age of bacteriology. Now there was a modifiable biologic cause of problems! Scientists could explore lock-in-key solutions, such as antibiotics and vaccines to kill "germs" so that many cases of infectious diseases could be resolved. Although far from perfect, this golden age radically reduced the loss of human life.

With infectious diseases being addressed, medicine faced new challenges. People began living longer, long enough to develop chronic conditions, such as asthma, diabetes, heart disease, cancer, obesity, arthritis, anxiety, and depression. These diverse conditions had no unifying modifiable, biologic root cause. Medical advances centered around diagnosing and treating problems, developing medications and procedures, and designing diagnostic and therapeutic devices. It was a highly productive time, however, the more progress that we made, the more we became aware that something might be missing. There were many important successes, but primarily we were managing diseases rather than curing them.

The bubble finally bursts

By the late 1990s, American health and happiness were deteriorating. That downturn has continued. Presently, 45 percent of Americans have at least one chronic disease. Nearly 10 percent of the U.S. population has diabetes, and 35 percent of all adults have metabolic syndrome (a combination of obesity, high blood pressure, type 2 diabetes, and poor lipid profiles). Mental illness and substance abuse affect 20 percent of Americans, and deaths by suicide have increased by about 30 percent since 1999. Despite spending double what other wealthy countries pay per person on healthcare, including the highest per-capita pharmaceutical expense in the world, the U.S. currently ranks last in life expectancy among the 12 wealthiest industrialized nations.

In 1987, the RAND Corporation, a non-profit think tank, reported on a novel study they conducted to evaluate healthcare in America. They discovered a great deal of both over-utilization of care and blind spots where needed care was not administered. This report launched a new movement to make healthcare evidence-based. In the 1990s, organizations including the American Medical Association began stepping up efforts to evaluate treatments, searching for new solutions, revisiting disregarded theories, and questioning accepted ones.

Freud was right: It's the emotional brain

As part of this trend, scientists in the early 2000s used new research methods, molecular medicine, and brain imaging, and were able to validate Sigmund Freud's theory that emotional and behavioral problems are caused by errant pathways in the emotional brain. These pathways or "faulty memories" can be encoded by experiences during childhood and later in life during stress overload. Cognitive neuroscientists showed that the brain regards as solid truth these momentary experiences and encodes them into long-term memory. The brain holds onto these experiences in the form of neural circuits and reactivates them. When we catch ourselves repeatedly doing something completely illogical or feel triggered and experience overwhelming cravings, overreactions, or shutdowns, that's likely to be the result of these faulty memories.

Research methods that could validate Freud's theories were not available during his life. He turned his attention to developing psychoanalysis, with some techniques that were seen by his peers as capricious and impractical, fueling interest in a new, more practical approach: behaviorism.

Stopping short of treating the emotional root cause

A movement away from peering into the unconscious mind and attempting to change it took off in the early 1900s. In 1913, John Watson conceived of behaviorism. The treatment used various conditioning techniques to change behavior, including recording actions, manipulating behavioral antecedents and consequences, and rewarding changes. The fatal flaw in this approach was defining the problem as a behavior, without treating the underlying factors that drive it.

In 1960, American psychiatrist Aaron Beck applied behavioral techniques to changing faulty thoughts, leading to the development of cognitive behavioral therapy (CBT), the most widely accepted and utilized mental health treatment today. However, CBT therapists and others became concerned that the method had lost both its physiologic roots and psychological sensibilities. In 2000, a new wave of behaviorism appeared. This was applying behavioral techniques to change one's approach by using openness, acceptance, and awareness. The most popular modality of contextual behavioral therapy is based on mindfulness, which was launched in the United States by the University of Massachusetts Medical School professor Jon Kabat-Zinn. Despite the appeal of the simplicity of changing behavior and thoughts, the results were not encouraging. Research showed that these methods did not produce lasting or generalized effects. This was also supported by a series of meta-analyses performed in the last decade. For example, a 2012 meta-analysis published in *Cognitive Therapy Research* gave tacit approval to cognitive behavioral therapies but pointed out that supportive data were scarce. Most controlled clinical trials did not have an active control group and failed to follow participants after treatment ended, which are two essential criteria for evaluating effectiveness. However, the number of conditions being treated with these therapies rose at astonishing rates.

In 2006, German researcher Stefan Bornstein authored a whimsical article about the consequences of these approaches. He imagined what Freud might have said on the occasion of his 150th birthday, watching the financial collapse of our healthcare system due to "unprecedented and uncontrollable" rises in metabolic disease, cardiovascular disease, mental health problems, obesity, and other health problems. He argued that the enormous increase in the rates of these conditions was the logical consequence of the wholesale promotion of behavior change without addressing its emotional root cause.

In the 1980s, my own clinical research was based on CBT, and I wanted to improve my patients' results. One day, I struck gold when I discovered an article on obese children and their families published in 1940 by Hilde Bruch, a psychiatrist at Baylor College of Medicine. Her research showed a pattern of missed emotional connection between parent and child, just what I had observed in our clinic. At that time, I was treating families in our earliest EBT intervention, the Shapedown Program. Adding a way for families to create emotional connection seemed like a logical next step, and so I constructed the "magic words" to share feelings and needs, which are the basis for one of the EBT tools today (the Feelings Tool). Soon after I started using this technique, to my astonishment, the mother of a 10-year-old girl with brown curly hair said to me, "What is going on? My daughter has stopped overeating, and instead, she wants to go outside and play!" I had no way to explain what this child had experienced, as the brain science that eventually would explain did not yet exist. I became convinced that we needed to address the emotional root cause of unwanted behavior and went on to expand these emotional tools to adults, not just for obesity, but for all stress-related problems.

Cognitive methods fail the stress test

Researchers remained perplexed about why traditional methods were not causing turnarounds in health problems. A line of inquiry centered around the fact that their common therapeutic feature was reliance on neocortical ("top-down") functioning. Research had already shown that the neocortex relinquishes control to the emotional brain in high stress, to defer to the fast processing of the emotional brain to favor the survival of the species.

For example, when threatened by a lion in hot pursuit, the brain does not use the slow processing of the neocortex. Also, the phenomenon through which retrieving memories is accomplished, "state-specific memory," further undercuts the functioning of the thinking brain when we are stressed. Our ability to remember something is better when we are at the same level of stress as when it actually happened. Learn how to play chess when we're relaxed and happy, and later, when we are stressed out, we won't remember anything about how to play chess! As most top-down methods are learned in low-stress situations, they may not be accessible during high-stress times, right when they are most needed.

In 2013, Candace Raio, Elizabeth Phelps, and colleagues conducted an elegant study that investigated the effectiveness of cognitive techniques to deactivate Stress Circuits during high-stress and low-stress situations. The participants were healthy adults and the study was performed over a two-day period. On the first day of the study, healthy adults underwent fear conditioning, so that when they saw fear-inducing photos, they activated a physiologic stress response and negative emotions. Then participants learned how to shut off stress using cognitive methods. On the second day of the study, the participants were instructed to use the cognitive techniques they had learned the day before to reduce their stress. They were then either stressed (by submerging their hand in cold water), to activate the stress most of us experience in modern life, or not stressed (by immersing their arm in tepid water). Then they were shown the fear-inducing photos again, and emotional and physiologic measures of stress were taken afterward.

As hypothesized, the use of cognitive methods did not reduce stress when participants were under stress. In essence, the cognitive techniques failed the stress test. Also, as predicted, the cognitive methods were effective when the participants were not stressed. Both findings are interesting, because the effectiveness of these techniques during low-stress experiences gives us a false sense of security, making it even more difficult to determine "why" we keep repeating old patterns, which typically occurs during times of stress! According to the researchers, "The finding that cognitive stress reduction techniques are rendered ineffective when we are stressed has broad implications for the efficacy of cognitive regulation to change behavior in everyday life. Importantly, these results offer insight into why even among emotionally healthy people, cognitive strategies taught in the clinic may not generalize to the real world, where stress exposure is ubiquitous."

We need some relief: A culture on meds
With traditional methods not providing the results that we needed, it's no wonder that we turned to chemicals for support. But how well are they working? Some drugs have shown impressive results, such as medications for heart disease, erectile dysfunction, addictive drug overdose, and some types of cancer. However, for others, the mechanism for effectiveness is not known and the results are only marginally better than a placebo and often cause unwanted side effects.

The damage caused by inappropriate prescriptions is staggering. About 1.3 million people went to U.S. emergency rooms in 2014 due to adverse drug effects, and some 124,000 died from those episodes, based on data from the Centers for Disease Control and Prevention as well as the Food and Drug Administration. Opioid addiction currently affects 2.1 million people in the U.S., and an average of 115 Americans die each day from opioid-related overdoses. Perhaps the problem is not the medications, but how much we are forced to overuse them because we have not discovered a treatable root cause of our suffering.

The Second Golden Age of Healthcare
A Root Cause of Chronic Diseases: Stress Circuits
That treatable root cause of our suffering was stress. In the first decade of the new millennium, stress was the buzzword in medical circles. At conferences, people would say, "Well, the problem is stress . . . " and their voices would trail off, as what do you do about stress anyway? It's part of life.

However, the scientists who examine the causes of health problems had been discovering that stress was the root cause of a broad range of health issues. In fact, research conducted by Nobel Prize winner Elizabeth Blackburn and neuropsychologist Elissa Epel showed that psychological stress can shorten the protective ends of our genes and accelerate aging, an underlying cause of cancer, diabetes, and heart disease. This research made it plain that stress had wormed its way under our skin and into our bodies, and that it was killing us.

The science was clear: we needed to find a way to target and oust stress from our brain and body, much the way we would if it were a germ. However, we had no idea how to do that, until five discrete discoveries of the last 50 years coalesced into a novel approach to stress, one that is based on neuroplasticity.

Discovery #1: Allostasis – A new kind of stress

The first discovery that made stress treatable was allostasis. In the mid-1960s, social activist and neuroscientist Peter Sterling was canvassing door-to-door in African American ghettos in Cleveland, Ohio, which were hotbeds of social disruption. Many people who answered their doors had drooping faces or relied on canes to ambulate, possibly due to strokes. In contrast, in more affluent neighborhoods nearby, Dr. Sterling saw no canes or drooping faces. He wondered if stress had become so toxic in these communities that it was causing these strokes.

Four years later, Dr. Sterling, now a young professor at the University of Pennsylvania, met another activist, Joseph Eyer. He was a biologist who was studying population data, just the information Dr. Sterling needed to begin to answer his question. Their collaborations began, and their data analysis confirmed the link between stroke, heart disease, and hypertension, and severe social disruption, including migration, industrialization, urbanization, segregation, unemployment, and divorce. Next, Sterling and Eyer tried to understand how psychosocial stress could impact health. At that time, the way the body was assumed to process stress was based on homeostasis. Physiologist Walter B. Cannon had coined the term in 1926, deriving it from the Greek words "homeo," meaning same, and "stasis," meaning stable. Homeostasis means "remaining stable by staying the same." The defining feature of homeostasis is that it is a *negative feedback loop*, which means it self-corrects, it holds onto a drive to move whatever is out of balance back into balance. If our body temperature goes down too much, we automatically start shivering, an internal mechanism that warms us back up, returning us to a homeostatic state.

The people who were suffering from so much emotional turmoil and social disruption in Ohio must have been so stressed that their bodies could not stay within the gentle limits of homeostasis. The researchers theorized that sometimes the body maintains stability by pulling out all the stops and going to extremes with behavior or physiology. It goes into another gear that is outside of the homeostatic range. In 1988, Sterling and Eyer coined the term for this "pull out all the stops" gear as "allostasis." It was derived from the Greek "allo," which means "variable" so allostasis means "remaining stable by changing."

Allostasis is reserved for the times when we are careening out of control, and our brain tries to do something to stabilize us – with behaviors, such as overeating, drinking too much, or bingeing on videos, or with extremes of physiology, such as high blood pressure, elevated dopamine, or high blood glucose. Although allostasis is effective in the short term, it causes wear and tear. It helps us adapt and establish new normal ranges, even if they are not good for us.

Allostasis was disruptive for scientists! Until the 1980s, it was thought that our homeostatic processes were not controlled by the central nervous system (the brain and spinal cord), but by the peripheral nervous system (all the other nerves). After all, we don't consciously modify our heart rate or keep tabs on our electrolytes! Sterling and Eyer suspected that the central nervous system must be far more engaged in our physiologic activities than we had thought.

To their astonishment, using fluorescence microscopy, the researchers found that the brain was connected to cells throughout the body. This was of great importance in two respects. First, the emotional brain, our unconscious mind, takes in our experiences, without our permission or awareness, including the stress overload of modern life. This is the ultimate invasion of our privacy! The external stress of the world flows into our brain and then right to the cells of our body. Second, based on their research and that of others, the body and brain are in two-way communication. Brain activations influence what happens on the periphery and activities on the periphery influence what happens in the brain. This is the basis for allostasis being a *positive feedback loop* that can careen out of control.

The Problem: Stress Circuits

Stimulus

Spiral Down
Afterburn

Scientific leaders of the time, including Bruce McEwen, Robert Sapolsky, and George Koob, embraced Sterling and Eyer's concept of allostasis, which led to more research. In 1993, Bruce McEwen coined the term "allostatic load" to describe the cumulative impact of repeated episodes of allostasis. High allostatic load lowers the brain's set point, and a set point in stress becomes the brain's habit. With the brain stuck in stress, health problems can become overwhelming, which is why reversing allostatic load and maintaining a high set point is becoming the goal of healthcare.

The discovery of allostasis was monumental. Had it been a germ, legions of scientists would have been eager to study it. However, there was no bacteria or other pathogens to kill. No medication, no vaccination, nor any procedure could provide a ready solution to the problem. What's more, the impact of this stress overload was all-encompassing, impacting every cell of the body! As a result, allostasis was largely ignored by clinical medicine for 30 years.

The Solution: Joy Circuits

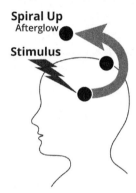

Discovery #2: Neuroplasticity – The brain can change

The second discovery that made stress treatable was neuroplasticity, which was proposed in 1890 by William James, in the first textbook ever written on psychology. However, his idea, like those of the early investigators of infectious disease, was largely ignored. Then in 1949, neuroplasticity was propelled forward when Donald Hebb, a Canadian psychologist, proposed Hebbian theory, that changes in the brain are use-dependent, and neurons that fire simultaneously strengthen the synaptic connection between them. This is also called use-dependent plasticity. For example, if we need love and reach for a handful of cookies, the brain encodes that experience, creating a circuit that associates love and eating sweets. In the future, when the need for love arises, that wire can become activated and trigger a drive to overeat. Hebb's rule, "neurons that fire together, wire together," remains a core principle of neuroplasticity today, however, this breakthrough did not stimulate widespread interest. It was believed that the brains of adults were fixed, immutable, and no longer capable of changing. Neuroplasticity was thought to occur only in children.

Neuroscientist Michael Merzenich was not convinced. He had conducted research on adult monkeys in his post-doctoral studies at the University of Wisconsin-Madison that suggested their brains could change. In 1971, at UCSF, he reconnected with one of his postdoctoral associates, Jon Kaas, of Vanderbilt University, who was experimenting with owl monkeys. Much like Sterling and Eyer had brought about a breakthrough in physiology, Michael Merzenich and Jon Kaas were poised to do the same for neuroplasticity.

The study tested whether or not adult monkeys' brains changed with experience. They cut a nerve in one hand, leaving them with no feeling on the thumb side. If the brain were hardwired and not changed by experience, soon there would be a "black hole" in the brain where it used to receive input via the severed thumb-to-brain nerve. When they examined the monkeys' brains several months later, there was no black hole. In fact, the brain area lit up with activity and had already found a new calling, processing the input from the pinky finger side. They showed use-dependent neuroplasticity in adult monkeys, and other scientists joined in, and by the end of the century, the plasticity of the adult human brain was widely accepted. Dr. Merzenich received numerous awards, including the world's top neuroscience award, the Kali Prize, for his achievements in neuroplasticity.

Discovery #3: Allostatic Circuits – Finally, a "germ" we can treat

The third discovery that made stress treatable was allostatic circuits. We needed to find a way to shut off allostasis and activate homeostasis. Rewiring circuits was the logical strategy, as neural pathways control our responses in daily life. Research at the time focused on identifying specific errant neural wires as the nature of science is reductionistic. Scientists investigate the smallest aspects of a problem, with an eye to assembling a bigger picture over time. In the case of allostasis, that approach may have caused scientists to miss the forest for the trees.

In April 2007, Igor Mitrovic saw the forest. As a neuroscientist and physiologist, he taught physiology to all health science graduate students at UCSF and was passionate about EBT. His wife, a stress researcher with her own lab at UCSF, had given him a book on EBT in 2003, mentioning that another professor at UCSF had written it and that it might help with his anxiety. Soon we met, and Dr. Mitrovic began to guide the method in finding its conceptual neuroscience basis, eventually becoming the method's scientific director.

His breakthrough came during an EBT research meeting, when his face suddenly lit up, and he exclaimed, "EBT is rewiring the stress response!" Then he began marking up a nearby whiteboard, first drawing a simple symmetrical triangle, and calling it a homeostatic circuit. In a flash, he erased the image and drew a misshapen triangle, then several more on top of one another, clearly careening out of control. He called that an allostatic circuit. Those whiteboard drawings, for a physiologist, were the equivalent of the 1848 Eureka moment when gold was discovered at Sutter's Mill in California. If the EBT tools could rewire our stress response, which controls our physiology, then we could offer a new paradigm in healthcare.

Dr. Mitrovic had conceptualized the stress response, the primary controller of our physiology, as two opposing types of circuits. He recognized that instead of seeking to discover specific errant circuits causing particular unwanted responses, what mattered the most was training the brain to choose a homeostatic circuit rather than an allostatic circuit. What was most important was whether we spiraled up to a state of well-being, activating healing chemicals, or spiraled down into toxic stress, triggering harmful chemicals. His creativity, clarity, and decisiveness gave medical science of the 21st century its germ. Instead of treating the downstream effects of stress, we could directly treat stress itself: the allostatic circuit. Soon after that, Igor Mitrovic, Lynda Frassetto, Lindsey Fish, and I authored an article published in the journal *Hypothesis* entitled "Rewiring the Stress Response: A New Paradigm in Healthcare."

Five years later, Joseph LeDoux authored a landmark paper, "Rethinking the Emotional Brain," which documented a wealth of science about allostatic circuits. He proposed that the most extreme allostatic wires, "survival circuits," which evolved to defend life, through actions such as physical defense, the balance of fluids, and reproduction, were vulnerable to corruption through negative emotional plasticity. Other wires could be incorporated into this circuitry, based on Hebbian learning, if they were activated at the same time, locked into unconscious long-term memory systems, then retriggered without our awareness or permission. The implications of this were enormous! Imagine a "fight-or-flight" circuit and a "drinking wine" circuit coactivating to produce a fight-or-flight drive to drink too much. These corrupted wires that drive our responses to daily life are the engine behind being triggered, overreacting, and going to excess. They can encode seemingly unstoppable drives for extremes of emotions, behaviors, sensations, thoughts, or states, or whatever we happen to turn to when we are highly stressed. Thus, the brain can encode circuits that cause us to be addicted to nearly anything!

Discovery #4: Switching Circuits – On-the-spot stress relief
The fourth discovery that made stress treatable was a full set of powerful resiliency tools. We needed tools that could stand up to a fight-or-flight response and stare it down, or better yet, switch it off. Neuroplasticity is use-dependent, so rewiring stress overload and optimizing natural, sustainable well-being takes repeatedly switching off allostatic circuits and activating homeostatic wires in the throes of the stresses of our day. It's not something that "can wait" until we have time to talk with a friend or go for a walk. We need on-the-spot stress relief to wire our brain for resilience.

This is easier than one might think, as evolutionary biology has given us a brain that rapidly alleviates stress by processing emotions. Our Stress Circuits give off steam in the form of negative emotions. By leaning into emotions and processing them effectively, we shut off Stress Circuits and activate Joy Circuits, changing the chemicals in every cell of our being. Emotions are not just psychological; they are our pathway to rapid and profound improvements in our biochemistry.

This concept that emotions were biologic, not just psychological, was initially forwarded in 1872 by Charles Darwin, who proposed that emotional expressions cross species and that facial expressions and body movements conformed to emotions. In the 1960s and 1970s, UCSF psychologist Paul Ekman built on Darwin's theories, showing that human emotions identified by specific facial expressions were universal, the same in diverse Eastern and Western cultures, and even in a remote community in Papua New Guinea, which was separated from other cultures by steep mountains. However, it was in 2003, that Antonio Damasio, a neurologist, and professor at the University of Southern California, took the emotion-physiology link a step further. He proposed the Nesting Principle, that emotions were the product of an elegant, multi-leveled set of inputs from our most primitive immune responses, reflexes, and metabolic regulation, through pain and pleasure, as well as behaviors, all the way to drives and motivations. If emotions were the tip of our iceberg, and we could positively impact that tip, all below it, our entire physiology and experience of life, would follow along.

Developing a system for processing emotions was not an "aha" moment. Igor Mitrovic had prepared his entire life, including three decades of scientific training, to bring about the stroke of insight that all human circuits could be categorized as homeostatic or allostatic. For me, developing an emotional processing system that matched the brain's ways was a step-by-step process over the same period. The first tool was easy to develop, as it is the tool that enables us to bring to consciousness our feelings and needs, taming emotions while in homeostasis. The next two, one used at the tipping point between homeostasis and allostasis, and the other for our initial wandering into allostasis, came soon after that. In developing the second and third tools, we drew upon the work of psychologist John Gray, who pioneered strategies for guiding the flow of negative emotions into positive ones. This process was essential to effective emotional processing, as we had learned from catharsis therapy (wholesale expression of anger) that negative emotions can become stuck and extreme, causing still more stress and problems. With two tools that prevented negative emotions from becoming stuck and harmful, and instead caused them to flow into positive emotions, we could accomplish our goal of switching circuits in real time.

There was only one problem at this point, which was the world was changing. The shared stress load of modern life had increased, and even the healthiest and happiest people had Stress Circuits rattling around at the bottom of their brain. Technology made this more pronounced as processing emotions requires feeling them, and feeling them takes a few moments, during which time at least four texts might arrive! Artificial, addictive temptations were sprouting up everywhere, and their use corrupted our brain's reward center, so we needed to retrain it to enjoy natural pleasures.

This led to adding two more tools to the set in 2007, one for stress overload and another to promote high-intensity natural pleasure. The resultant EBT 5-Point System for Emotional and Behavioral Regulation mirrors both neurophysiology, drawing upon understandings of emotional processing in the brain, and attachment theory, modeling the tools on the resilience methods used by parents of securely attached children. The work of Allan Schore, a neuropsychologist at the University of California, Los Angeles, and Judy Zehr, Master EBT Trainer and attachment theory specialist, guided our way. The EBT 5-Point System was developed to achieve immediate switches from allostasis to homeostasis, but one additional discovery was needed to treat some of the more stubborn circuits that showed up in our brain due to random moments of stress overload: reconsolidation.

Discovery #5: Rewiring Stress Circuits – The gold standard of reconsolidation

The fifth discovery that made stress treatable was reconsolidation, not just building a healthy circuit on top of faulty ones, as that is what has produced the Band-Aid approach to healthcare. Many methods can work through external support – counseling, medications, procedures. However, without addressing the root cause of the problem, treatment must be ongoing or, if not, often results in a vicious cycle of treatment and relapse.

The 3 Rules of Reconsolidation
Rule #1. A Spark – Unlock the old circuit with a moment of stress.
Rule #2. Emotional Flow – Feel your feelings and encode a new circuit.
Rule #3. Spiral Up – Lock in the new circuit with a surge of dopamine.

Given the absence of an underlying cause of chronic diseases to target and treat throughout the 20th century, we have become accustomed to treatments not curing problems. That could change, as physiologic stress is an underlying cause of most health problems and curtails the effectiveness of interventions. Psychologist Roy Baumeister and behavioral economist Kathleen Vohs wrote, "every personal and social problem affecting large numbers of modern citizens involves some kind of failure of self-regulation." On a neural level, a failure of self-regulation is the encoding or activation of allostatic circuits. The only treatment for these circuits that has the potential to erase a wire for lasting results is reconsolidation.

The research of Elizabeth Phelps and colleagues in 2010 (see The Missing Link page 5) showed us more about how to accomplish reconsolidating a circuit. By briefly achieving the same level of stress in which the circuit was encoded, the synaptic connections between neurons unlock. By delivering a new experience to the unlocked circuit, the wire changes. Then, by sparking a dopamine surge with positive emotions, the new circuit can both erase the old wire and encode a new one. Although the hippocampus keeps the memory fragile for up to six hours, it then locks that new wire into long-term memory. Our personal storehouse of these new and improved wires that have erased others is our best defense against relapse, as well as the self-blame and discouragement that often follow. The Phelps research showed us that stress activation was the doorway to lasting change. However, if we wanted to rewire those circuits on our own, we needed to quickly ease stress enough to deliver a new message to the brain, then lock in that new circuit. In 2017, we developed the three rules of reconsolidation to make it easier for us to direct our own rewiring and to see if our "antibiotic" of neuroplasticity was beginning to kill the "germ" of a Stress Circuit.

The first of the three rules of reconsolidation is to use stress to unlock the synapses of the circuit. This rule is based on the Phelps study described above. The second rule is to follow that stress

Method	Follows the 3 Rules of Reconsolidation?
EBT	yes
Psychotherapy	sometimes
Relationships	sometimes
Group Support	sometimes
Spiritual experiences	sometimes
CBT*	no
Mindfulness*	no
Exercise	no
Relaxation	no
Medications	no

*Does not stress-activate the circuit. Relies on cognitive processing for stress reduction, which has been shown to be ineffective. Raio, CM, et. al. (2013). Cognitive emotion regulation fails the stress test. *Proceedings of the National Academy of Sciences* 110:15139-44

activation with a flow of emotions, which rapidly reduces stress, so the prefrontal cortex stays online as we rewire. This is based on the research of Candace Raio, Elizabeth Phelps, and colleagues that is described above, which showed that cognitive processing when we are in stress fails to improve stress and negative emotions. The third rule of reconsolidation is to lock in the new synaptic connections with a dopamine surge, which is based on Michael Merzenich's research. He showed that by stimulating the reward system, the ensuing release of dopamine increases brain plasticity. Feeling that glow of reward after the rewiring experience is a sign that we have locked in the new learning.

By identifying the three rules of neuroplasticity, the rise in stress-related diseases makes more sense. All conditions are multifactorial, but traditional therapies may not have adequately addressed the root cause of what ails us. The table above lists the most common treatments for stress-related problems. Most were developed 50 or more years ago, long before the age of neuroplasticity. As we focus on updating our treatments, how will rewiring circuits fit in? Stress circuits impact our physiology, and to the extent that we rewire them, the role of EBT may become foundational. With lowered physiologic stress, other treatments could become more effective and relief from allostasis could boost well-being in all domains of life.

The emergence of a new golden age

Neuroscience-based medicine is gaining ground – and it is all because of the important successes of the past. If germ theory had not made strides toward wiping out many infectious diseases, people would not have lived long enough to develop chronic diseases. If medical progress had not been so exceptional, we would have kept looking for a "silver bullet" medication. Yet with growing acceptance that the solution is not a pill, a cluster of discoveries have begun to offer a new paradigm in healthcare. The problem all along was stress, which we can now treat in a matter of fact way, as if it were a germ!

At the start of a golden age, once the modifiable root cause of a problem has been discovered, enthusiasm abounds. Scientists want to study it, clinicians want to explore using it, and people want to try it out. We may be seeing the beginnings of that enthusiasm now. Physicians are using "bedside EBT" in hospitals. Psychologists have asked about using EBT rewiring plans rather than diagnoses for emotional health issues. Expectant parents are using neuroplasticity to improve their own wiring so that they can pass along highly effective wires to their babies. Training to enhance mental sharpness has become mainstream, and couples are using brain-based techniques to reset their relationships. People are busting up their old addictive circuits and encoding new wires of optimal health and well-being.

Yet, just when neuroplasticity begins to sound concrete and practical to you, consider that there is another level to this story. The golden age of bacteriology saved us from infectious diseases, but this golden age is different, for the wires of stress are stored in the emotional brain, the center of connection and the seat of the soul. To transform those wires, we must connect to the deepest part of ourselves. In that state of connection, we automatically radiate our peace and joy to others. As we raise our own set point, and become healthier, we do our small but important part to raise the set point of the planet. That alone may be worthy of sparking the beginnings of a new golden age . . .

Rewiring Made Easy

Imagine that you have a wire in your brain that you do not like. You can choose to activate that wire, pour out its emotional contents, break apart that wire, and revamp it as a wire that you do like.

For example, I have a wire that I do not like, and it's reached the top of my list for rewiring. It's a priority in this moment.

Granted, I've had a lot more damaging wires than this one, but life always presents new opportunities to rewire! The wire that is bothering me now is my "I throw everything in my trunk and only clean it out when I cannot slam it shut anymore" wire.

In a matter of a few minutes, I can complain about that wire, protest how it makes me hoard things in my trunk, and find the unreasonable expectation (probably from childhood) that drives me to find safety, love, comfort, or pleasure in tossing things into my trunk until I can no longer slam it shut!

The synaptic connections between the neurons that drive my behavior will become fluid. By staying present to my emotions, I can encode a new wire. My drive to be a trunk pack rat will fade or disappear. I may have to repeat the message of the new wire ("grind it in") a few hundred times to break it, or it might break instantly. It doesn't matter. What matters is the process. It is a way for me to take charge of my life, and it is remarkably . . . easy.

Up until now, you may have thought rewiring was complicated. That makes sense because there are about 100 billion neurons in the brain, each with about 10,000 synaptic connections. How would I ever be able to find the precise neurons that fuel my trunk-stuffing habit? What about other wires that I have already transformed, which were far more challenging to fix? The one that seemed most elusive to me was my circuit that triggered my depression-with-self-pity-thrown-in wire. How could I find that one, let alone rewire it?

The brain makes it easy to rewire these circuits because the survival of the species depends on our being able to adapt to different environments. If our ancestors didn't have a terrific and automatic updating system for their fight-or-flight response, then none of us would be here. Evolutionary biology "gifts" us with this amazing capacity. All we are doing in using EBT is capitalizing on what comes naturally! Let's take a closer look at the universal power to rewire.

The brain seems to be a tangle of wires

The ultimate organizer: the brain

The brain organizes our wires for us – automatically and rapidly – based on stress level. This is due to state-specific memory. When we are at a particular stress level, all wires with instructions about how to respond that were encoded at that stress level are "hot" or "online."

This makes rewiring easy. When we are in high stress, the wires that are the problem are activated. If we use our neocortex to focus our attention on our body, where we experience our emotions, we can reprocess that memory. We'll not only feel great rapidly, but we'll begin to rewire that circuit! By using the tools to feel better, we train our brain to become stronger, sharper, and more resilient!

Our wiring automatically organizes itself by stress level

We number our stress levels based on a five-point system to make it easier to think about our wiring and to share our stress information with others. As you move through this course, you'll find that this system helps with everything from knowing what tool to use to rewire, to identifying where in the brain a specific circuit is stored.

We can number our stress levels for easy access to our wires

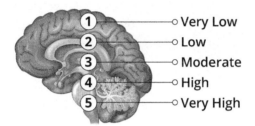

1	Very Low
2	Low
3	Moderate
4	High
5	Very High

At each stress level, a different brain area is in charge

You've probably noticed that your experience of life varies a lot. This is normal. At each level of stress, the brain automatically puts a different area in charge.

If we are in very low stress, at Brain State 1, the neocortex (our thinking brain and the seat of our consciousness) takes control. This higher functioning is ideal for that stress level, as with the neocortex in charge, we can analyze problems, think complex thoughts, and make good decisions. We are naturally kind.

On the other hand, if we are in very high stress, at Brain State 5, the reptilian brain, the brain area given to extremes, is in charge. This functioning is perfect for orchestrating a fight-or-flight response. We aren't kind at all. Kindness doesn't help us fight or flee!

It's normal to spend time in all five stress levels in any day. A short-term experience of very high stress is not bad for us. In fact, it's good for the brain, as it gives us an opportunity to unlock circuits of extreme disconnection. After unlocking, if we can experience a connection to the deepest part of ourselves, we wire into our brain a loving, humble, and secure connection. In high-stress states, stress levels 4 and 5, we can briefly "bottom out" and find ourselves desperate enough to surrender to acceptance and encode new wires that enable us to grow.

As a result, there are no bad stress levels. However, in high-stress states we can do damage, and as we are responsible for our actions, we must learn from them and make amends. The sooner we recover from a chemical surge of stress and access external support – human connection, the EBT app to guide us through the tools to spiral up, or, as needed, healthcare support – the sooner we raise our set point and experience optimal well-being. We are not our brain state, nor is anyone else! Brain states do pass!

This is helping me judge less. When my husband is obsessing about all the wrongs his ex-wife did to him, I know that his reptilian brain is controlling him. He is at stress level 5. I have a reptile within, too. Knowing this is not only humbling, but makes me a kinder person.

At each number, a different brain area is in charge

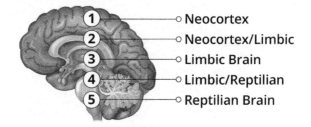

1. Neocortex
2. Neocortex/Limbic
3. Limbic Brain
4. Limbic/Reptilian
5. Reptilian Brain

We have different basic needs at each level of stress

The overall priority of the brain is to help us survive with a sense of well-being. Its job is to help us identify how we feel, determine what we need, and effectively meet that need.

At each level of stress, we have a different need. When we are in stress overload (Brain State 5), the brain is sure that we are going to die. We do not feel safe. The brain pulls out all the stops and unleashes a fight-or-flight drive to survive. Even if the stress is caused by a psychological hurt, such as someone rejecting us, the brain unleashes an overwhelming drive to find safety.

When we are at Brain State 4, we are definitely stressed. The survival of our species depends upon emotional connection, including the baby connecting to the parent and the formation of families and communities for protection. When we slip into a high-stress state, we are disconnected, and activate a natural drive for emotional connection. Our need in Brain State 4 is love.

What about Brain State 3? In Brain State 3 we are a little stressed. Perhaps we are anxious or thinking too much. We need to find some small ways to feel better. Our need in Brain State 3 is for comfort.

When we are at Brain State 2, we feel good, but not great. We are present and aware, but the brain's reward center is not activated. The brain demands that we not only ease our stress, but experience positive emotions. That dopamine surge and the glow of endorphins are just what we need to complete challenging tests with precision and grace. Our need in Brain State 2 is for pleasure.

And at Brain State 1, we feel great. The brain is integrated and our entire physiology is at its best. We have the self-regulatory strength to become aware of why we do what we do. The brain is so connected in that state that the thought travels from the neocortex to the amygdala, shuts off the stress response, and activates the brain's reward center. We feel a surge of well-being. Our need in Brain State 1 is to be aware of the meaning of our actions, our purpose. That is our power!

I thought of stress as teeth grinding, tension provoking, and putting me on edge. The softer side is that it's my brain's way of telling me that I have an unmet need. Growing up in my family, nobody spoke about needs. We were just told what to do. This is a new world for me, and I think it will be helpful.

At each number, we have a different basic need

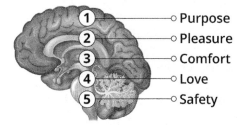

1 — Purpose
2 — Pleasure
3 — Comfort
4 — Love
5 — Safety

Understanding wires

During times of stress, when we did not have the support to meet a particular need, the brain moved from homeostasis to allostasis. This is normal and natural! However, the downside of stress is that the brain remembers those extreme responses. There are two types of wires that it can encode. One is a drive to escape from feeling stressed and unrewarded. That drive is encoded as a false association between an unmet need and whatever extreme response we happened to use at the time. It's a crossed wire, linking together two things that have nothing to do with one another.

These crossed wires are brain glitches. If they were encoded either during stress overload or when we happened to escape in a way that delivered an immediate and high-intensity reward, we call them survival circuits. For example, a wire is a brain glitch whether it is a craving for alcohol or an urge to eat sweets, but we reserve this special term of survival circuit for wires that are so strongly triggered that we sense we will not survive if we do not get that drink or those cookies now. When a survival circuit is activated, we fear annihilation, that without taking action we will cease to exist! These are particularly harmful wires, but also, the rewiring of them yields the most rewarding results.

The other type of circuit is a core circuit. It's a false belief, such as "I am not worthy," which the brain perceives as true when we are in stress overload. However, it generalizes that expectation, encoding that we are not worthy all the time and in any situation. These wires cause chronic stress, an uneasy inkling that something is wrong even though everything (objectively) might be very right. As we rewire them, anxiety, discouragement, irritability and other signs of chronic stress fade. We find that we don't catch colds as easily and those backaches can disappear. We are healthier and happier!

How do we make it easy to rewire these circuits? We take first things first. The brain glitches are fight-or-flight drives that usually cause immediate problems. We start rewiring them in this 30-day course. Later, in the advanced courses of EBT, we rewire core circuits, as by rewiring several of these glitches, brain stress is lower, so the thinking brain becomes more effective in rewiring these core expectations. Most of the core circuits were encoded early in life and transforming them often requires more intensive use of the tools.

Rewiring solves three problems

When one of our brain glitches is encoded, instantly we have three problems. These problems are really illogical, as they are caused by emotional wires that cannot be resolved by self-analysis. Once we appreciate that the issue is one of these illogical wires and rewire it, we solve the three problems caused by the circuit. It's so efficient!

We respond effectively – The first problem is that we have a drive that tells us to do something that is ineffective, for example, that we get our safety from hostility. That drives us in a reflexive way (think "knee-jerk") to be hostile. Our crossed wire falsely connecting safety and hostility activates such a strong stress response that our neocortical functioning is compromised. We have no internal "good parent" to soothe, comfort, and reassure us that we cannot get our safety from being hostile. In that moment, we are completely consumed by following those instructions and being really hostile. All external solutions that are extremes – behaviors, emotions, and thoughts – are drives to survive and access the fundamental safety that we need. By rewiring these circuits, we encode a good parent inside, and can soothe, comfort, and reassure ourselves. We can more easily discover ways to feel safe that are effective for us.

We learn to meet our deepest needs – The second problem is that these wires are intense! When activated, before we know it, we're doing what they tell us to do. If a homeostatic wire is activated, we have plenty of time to feel our feelings, identify our real need, and consider various ways to meet it. That's not the case with allostatic wires! For example, the hostility wire can cause us to be enraged, irritable, or furious in an instant! We are so consumed with this response that we do not have the time, attention, or motivation to learn how to get safety in effective ways. If a wire causes us to drink too much, take drugs, abuse pornography, overspend, sink into depression, distance in relationships, or something else we don't want to do, our underlying need continues to go unmet, causing us even more stress. Relieved of that gnarly wire, we find highly effective ways to meet our actual need.

Other problems fade or end – The third problem is that these wires cause secondary problems. Issues that seem impossible to resolve are usually natural outgrowths of one or more circuits. We don't know why we do what we do and can begin to believe that we will never overcome these behaviors. However, when we rewire their emotional root cause, they fade or disappear. For example, a hostility wire, when teamed up with a distancing circuit, can lead to relationship issues. We become furious and stomp off. Transforming just those two circuits can change relationships dramatically. We don't become furious, and even if we do, we do our best to continue communicating with the other person and working things out.

What is your stress style?

One of the most rewarding aspects of rewiring is that we learn why we do what we do. Some of us have circuits that arise out of one particular unmet need. Most of my circuits were my brain's

The 5 Stress Styles

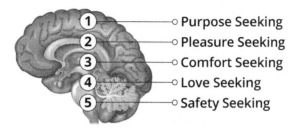

1 ○ Purpose Seeking
2 ○ Pleasure Seeking
3 ○ Comfort Seeking
4 ○ Love Seeking
5 ○ Safety Seeking

way of trying to deliver love. Most of my glitches were "crossed wires," equating some ineffective response, such as depression, overeating, or rescuing, with love. My stress style was love seeking.

For the four wires you will rewire in this challenge, you might find that each of them was your brain's way of meeting either one specific need, or different needs. Either way, that information is helpful, because we will know ourselves better and can become more effective in meeting our needs.

I'm excited about my rewiring revealing why I do what I do. Of the five basic needs, I think my unmet need is for safety. I feel really scared most of the time, however I won't know for sure until my unconscious mind reveals it.

Rewiring the brain for a solution

As you can see, rewiring is quite logical. When a faulty circuit encoded by some random life event tells us to get our comfort from procrastinating, being on guard, using drugs, over-exercising, or anything that doesn't work well for us, we can shut off that wire, and replace it with a new one that activates a drive to use healthy ways to comfort ourselves.

As you sort through your circuits and rewire them, you will find that you encode wires that meet your most fundamental needs for safety, love, comfort, pleasure, and purpose. EBT becomes a way to emotionally evolve and live your best life.

What's more, rewiring is so easy. All our circuits line up and are available to us based on state-specific memory. When we are in a particular state, we can use the emotional tool for that state and spiral up to a higher state. That shuts off a faulty wire, making it weaker, and activates an effective wire, making it stronger. Also, we are in control of which circuits we rewire. Nobody tells us which wires to select for rewiring, or what will be the message of the new wire we encode. Support can help, such as coaching from an EBT Provider, or inspiration from others in a small telegroup. However, ultimately each of us is the creator of our new wires, and the messages we encode are the ones we want to guide us as we move forward in life.

I didn't like my judgment wire. It bothered me, so I encoded a wire to give and receive love, rather than judging. It's buried in my unconscious mind now, so I don't have to try hard not to judge people. On a cellular level, my brain tells me to love, not judge.

The 5 Stress Solutions

1. Live for Higher Purpose
2. Feast on Natural Pleasures
3. Choose Healthy Comforts
4. Give and Receive Love
5. Create Safety from Within

My habit wire was smoking marijuana. The wire told me that I got my safety from weed. It sure gave me a lot of safety! Actually, it drained my bank account, made me lazy, and ruined my work ethic. Once I broke that circuit, my love affair with marijuana stopped. It doesn't "do it" for me anymore. I get my safety from inside me. My natural inclination changed.

All of our wires support us in decreasing stress and finding reward. The brain is reward-driven. Part of training the brain for optimal well-being is to focus on something positive – experiencing more of the natural pleasures of life. Let's take an inventory of the rewards you experience in daily life . . .

The Power of One Inventory

Your brain is learning how to filter out stress and create more natural pleasure in your daily life.

Track your progress in accessing the power to meet your needs, connect more effectively, and find pleasure throughout the day. Take this inventory now, again at Day 17 of the challenge, and on the last day of the challenge.

Be prepared to be surprised by your responses on this inventory. Just the way we do not talk about problems or issues, but about circuits and set points, the new language of the emotional brain is about the precision and effectiveness of our automatic wires to meet our needs, connect with ourselves and others, and be aware of the exact reason that we are doing what we are doing.

My needs score was high, with my two unmet needs being love and comfort. I scored almost no points on connection, but my purpose score was high.

All three of my scores were in the 3 to 4 range. No wonder I'm depressed. My reward center isn't getting natural pleasures. Nobody in my family uses natural pleasures, except my older brother who over-exercises, although I think his exercise is an addiction.

This was surprising. I scored high on purpose and connection, but on my basic needs, I scored low. I think I live for purpose and connection, and forget to meet my basic needs. That rings true.

 Track your progress.

The Power of One Inventory

Needs

In the last week, how often did you meet each of your basic needs?

Purpose
    1 = Rarely   2 = Sometimes   3 = Often   4 = Very Often

Pleasure
    1 = Rarely   2 = Sometimes   3 = Often   4 = Very Often

Comfort
    1 = Rarely   2 = Sometimes   3 = Often   4 = Very Often

Love
    1 = Rarely   2 = Sometimes   3 = Often   4 = Very Often

Safety
    1 = Rarely   2 = Sometimes   3 = Often   4 = Very Often

Total Baseline Needs Score _____

Rewards

In the last week, how often did you experience these rewards?

Sanctuary: Peace and power from within
    1 = Rarely   2 = Sometimes   3 = Often   4 = Very Often

Authenticity: Feeling whole and being genuine
    1 = Rarely   2 = Sometimes   3 = Often   4 = Very Often

Vibrancy: Healthy with a zest for life
    1 = Rarely   2 = Sometimes   3 = Often   4 = Very Often

Integrity: Doing the right thing
    1 = Rarely   2 = Sometimes   3 = Often   4 = Very Often

Intimacy: Giving and receiving love
    1 = Rarely   2 = Sometimes   3 = Often   4 = Very Often

Spirituality: Aware of the grace, beauty, and mystery of life
    1 = Rarely   2 = Sometimes   3 = Often   4 = Very Often

Freedom: Common excesses fade
    1 = Rarely   2 = Sometimes   3 = Often   4 = Very Often

Total Baseline Rewards Score _____

Connection

In the last week, how often did you connect in this way?

Being aware that I can create joy in my life
    1 = Rarely   2 = Sometimes   3 = Often   4 = Very Often

Choosing to create a moment of at One
    1 = Rarely   2 = Sometimes   3 = Often   4 = Very Often

Spiraling up from stress to One
    1 = Rarely   2 = Sometimes   3 = Often   4 = Very Often

Enjoying sensory pleasures
    1 = Rarely   2 = Sometimes   3 = Often   4 = Very Often

Eating healthy food
    1 = Rarely   2 = Sometimes   3 = Often   4 = Very Often

Exercising in ways that are fun
    1 = Rarely   2 = Sometimes   3 = Often   4 = Very Often

Feeling love for myself
    1 = Rarely   2 = Sometimes   3 = Often   4 = Very Often

Feeling love for others
    1 = Rarely   2 = Sometimes   3 = Often   4 = Very Often

Feeling love for all living beings
    1 = Rarely   2 = Sometimes   3 = Often   4 = Very Often

Total Baseline Connection Score _____

The Power of One Inventory Summary

Category	Baseline	Power of One Range
Needs	_____	15 to 20
Rewards	_____	21 to 28
Connection	_____	27 to 36
Power of One Total	_____	63 to 84

What is your amazing learning about your needs?

_____

What is your amazing learning about your rewards?

_____

What is your amazing learning about your connection?

_____

Setting Up Your EBT Practice

The purpose of this chapter is to help you set up a personal EBT practice. You are training your brain to process life in a highly effective way, which takes learning something new each day, practicing the tools, and for best results, using the tools with another person.

Learning: 10 Minutes Daily

Take 10 minutes per day to learn something new. The reptilian brain would be happy if you did not use the tools well, as it does not like change. However, by using the tools well, you raise your set point more rapidly and see better results faster. Determine when you will do your 10 minutes of learning daily, and make it a habit. What if you want to take two days to do one day's activities or need a day off now and then? Take that time. This is your book and please personalize the pace to meet your needs.

I do my 10 minutes of learning when I wake up in the morning. My mind is fresh and I use the new ideas all day.

Check Ins: 10 Per Day

The Check In Tool gives you the power to give yourself small bursts of feel-good chemicals throughout the day. It interrupts the spontaneous firing of faulty circuits that cause us stress and

Your EBT Daily Practice

- 10 minutes of learning
- 10 Check Ins
- 1 Connection

activates highly effective circuits that promote well-being. Each check in improves your wiring and gives you control over your biochemistry and your health. The Check In Tool is the master tool of EBT.

The EBT Practice includes checking in 10 times daily. Checking in takes 30 seconds to four minutes, depending on our stress level. These emotional tools are very quick in comparison to relaxation or cognitive tools, which take 20 or 30 minutes to accomplish the same relief.

When I check in a lot, my brain starts staying "checked in" automatically. Highly recommended!

Connections: One Per Day

You will experience better results faster if you use EBT with others by making connections, listening to others use the tools, and asking them to listen to you use the tools. The emotional brain is the social brain and allows the tools to go deeper into the brain when it is stabilized by another person listening to us.

Some people form their own EBT group through book clubs, neighborhood groups, or corporate study groups. Consider doing that.

Many others want more privacy, and an "instant" circle of support and join EBT telegroups at ebt.org. Telegroups are facilitated by Certified EBT Providers or Mentors and give you access to connections with five to seven other people. Our research has shown that these connections, along with weekly group sessions, or even more frequent sessions, spark more rewiring and better health outcomes than using this method on your own.

I have a 30-minute weekly telegroup with six people to connect with and my sister who lives in Connecticut to be another connection. She's doing the Joy Challenge, too. I have plenty of connections right now.

Connections are brief periods of practicing the tools between two people. In a telephone call that lasts one to five minutes, someone uses a tool or does a Check In. The reptilian brain calms down, and the tools become even more effective.

Connections are quick and effective. There is no chit-chat. While you may see these people as your friends, they are functioning as connection buddies, which can be even more important than friends. If you are a member of an EBT telegroup, your connection buddies have no idea who you are – no contact information is shared. All calls are made through our private EBT telephone system. No advice is given, and either party can conclude the connection at any time. Also, they have the same mission that you do – to conquer stress overload and raise their set point. Afterwards, both people go on with their day, radiating positive energy.

Now that you've set up your EBT Practice, let's look at the technology that can make it easy to integrate EBT into your daily life.

Using Tech to Connect

This book can be used without any technology. However, if you choose to use the EBT technology, then this chapter will help you use it more effectively. To access this technology, visit ebt.org and use the coupon code stressoverload to receive a discount on the Online Plus membership. Questions? Email support@ebt.org.

EBT Technology
• The EBT App (iOS and Android) • The EBT Website • The EBT Phone System

The EBT App (iOS and Android)

The EBT App ("Connect by EBT") is designed to give you immediate access to the tools, anytime and anywhere. When we are stressed, the brain "forgets" to check in, and even if we have memorized the tool lead-ins, the brain cannot access those memories. The brain perceives the app as a separate entity, an outside source of support in tracking and using the tools. Develop a close relationship with the app, and your results from the Power of One Challenge will be far better. It will soon become a habit to keep your EBT app with you and reach for it hourly, plus whenever you are stressed.

The EBT app includes relaxing audios, so you have stress relief in your pocket. If you join a telegroup, your app will give you one-touch access to your group members by telephone and messaging, and direct messaging with your Certified EBT Provider or Mentor.

The EBT Website

The EBT Website delivers all the features of the app, as well as many more. We recommend logging in daily to view the video demonstration that accompanies this book's content for each day. Also, take a minute or two to read a posting on the forum boards and leave a connecting message in response. Also, post your own comments, Cycles, and learnings.

The EBT Online Community is designed to give you a variety of ways to learn EBT. Check out the weekly live call-in workshops, listen to recordings of past sessions in which other participants do Cycles on just the challenge you are facing now. Want small group support and private community connections? Join a telegroup. If you have a particular circuit that is difficult to rewire or are dealing with a situation that is hard to resolve, schedule a 25-minute coaching session with the Certified EBT Provider of your choice. With their support, you can spiral up quickly!

The EBT Phone System

EBT has a private phone system. The emotional brain is extraordinarily sensitive to the sound of the human voice, so telephone communication is extremely powerful. You can use the EBT line for groups, coaching, workshops, and mentor sessions. The vocal experience is pure, as other people on the call cannot see you. Each person maintains privacy, yet verbal exchanges convey the range of tender, warm, and powerful human experience.

The EBT Phone System includes a special feature for using the tools when you do not have privacy. You just call in on your EBT phone line, select "1" and you will hear me guide you through a Check In. Select your brain state on your phone's keypad, and I will walk you through the appropriate tool. Spiral up to One rapidly and privately.

EBT Technology Support

Our EBT Support Team can help you set up and become comfortable with the technology. Our goal is to continuously improve our services and make EBT an even more life-changing experience for you. Please share your feelings and needs with us. We hope you enjoy this high-tech way to connect with yourself and others, and to raise your emotional set point.

Community Connections

- Two people meet by telephone for one to five minutes.
- Ask, "Is this a good time?"
- Plan the activity (use a tool, share an amazing learning or a Joy Point).
- One person speaks, the other listens.
- The person who listens gives a connecting message.
- The connection ends . . . Goodbye.
- If you have time left within the five minutes? Share another Joy Point and connecting message.

How do connections fit in?

You connect with people who you intend to know over time. If they are members of your telegroup, you can get to know them slowly, being with them in the weekly or daily group, and connecting with them as you feel comfortable doing so. The weekly or daily telegroup session serves as an anchor for the group, with structure, inspiration, and shared experiences.

All connections are by voice, as the brain craves the sound of the human voice, and the sound of the voice activates legions of feel-good emotional wires. Oddly enough, when you listen to a voicemail from a connection buddy, your brain processes it as if that person were connecting with you in real time. Although the EBT electronic message system can be very convenient, we also make it very easy to make voice connections for one reason: the brain changes far more rapidly when we make them!

Innovative Ways to Connect

- Call and leave a Joy Point.
- Record a quick Cycle on their voicemail.
- Say 10 Grind Ins on their voicemail.
- Share your amazing learning on their voicemail.
- Do the Damage Control Tool on their voicemail.
- Call your buddy back and leave a connecting message.
- Call and speak with them in real time for Grind Ins.
- Read a written Cycle to them.
- Use the Flow Tool (3 Tool) with them.
- Do coursework together ("Kit Buddies") – call to coordinate, hang up, you both take 10 minutes to work, then call back to share your amazing learnings.
- Practice A+ Anger, so your Cycles go deeper.
- Do Cycles and give connecting messages.
- Call during a work break and say, "I have three minutes. What do you want to do?"
- Guide each other through a Check In.

What is a connecting message?

Have you noticed that right after you open up to someone, you feel a bit stressed? We noticed that, too, and to move through that stress, we invented connecting messages.

The person that listens to you use the tools is a warm presence and does not give advice. They give you the ultimate gift of listening to you without judgment, then saying a few kind words to you that they think will be nurturing for you to hear and they feel safe saying. We use "lead-ins" to guide your way in making these exchanges brief, safe, and rewarding.

Examples of Community Connections

Ring. Ring.

Denny: Hi Carla. Is this a good time?

Carla: *Yes, I have about two minutes.*

Denny: Great. That's perfect.

Carla: *What about sharing a Joy Point or doing a Check In together?*

Denny: Sure, I'd like to listen to you share a Joy Point, if you're up for it.

Carla: *Okay. I had a big Joy Point today when my dog had puppies – four of them!*

Denny: When you did your work, the feeling and sensations in my body were . . . a big smile. The way your work was a gift to me was . . . I have been stalled on my project, and now I feel like doing it.

Carla: *Bye. "See" you in group tomorrow.*

Denny: Great. See you then. Bye.

Ring. Ring.

Theresa: Hi Miguel. Is this a good time?

Miguel: *Yes, I'm glad you called. I can't find my Mood Circuit.*

Theresa: Do you want to work on it?

Miguel: *Yes, I want to do a quick Cycle.*

Theresa: Great.

Miguel: *The situation is that I am always in a bad mood. I fly off the handle and don't think about what I'm saying. I know I scare people and my wife hates it when I'm that way. What I'm most stressed about is . . . I fly off the handle. I feel angry that I fly off the handle. I can't stand it that I fly off the handle. I HATE it that I fly off the handle. I HATE IT!!! . . . My mind just went blank. I must have unlocked the circuit. I feel sad that . . . I lose it sometimes. I feel afraid that I am hurting my marriage. I feel guilty that I keep on flying off the handle. I feel guilty that I go on acting hostile. Of course I do that, because my unreasonable expectation is . . . I get my . . . safety from . . . being hostile. Hmmmmm. That rings true. That feels right. I discovered my Mood Circuit!*

Theresa: When you did your work, the feeling and sensations in my body were . . . fear and guilt, because I fly off the handle too, but also, security, that I am not alone. The way your work was a gift to me was . . . I realized that I judge myself for flying off the handle. I am going to stop judging myself. Thank you for helping me see that.

Miguel: *Thanks.*

Theresa: I feel better. Thanks for the connection.

Miguel: *Bye.*

Theresa: Bye.

Connecting Messages

- Be supportive but do not analyze, praise, or in any way be "parental." Instead, be open and intimate, just what the emotional brain needs most!

- Share the feelings and sensations you had while listening. The other person has been vulnerable. You are vulnerable back – it's a two-way street.

- This is a highly effective message: "The way your work was a gift to me was that your expressing anger inspired me to try. Expressing anger has been hard for me. Thank you!" This is less effective: "The way your work was a gift to me was that I learned a lot."

- Use these lead-ins to guide your way:

  When you did your work, the feelings and sensations in my body were . . . (e.g., I felt worried, then I smiled and felt happy.)

  The way your work was a gift to me was . . . (e.g., that I learned a lot about how to express joy because that is hard for me.)

Community Guidelines

Safety is our first priority. It is the responsibility of each member to take care of their own safety, and to create safety right away if for any reason an EBT experience does not feel comfortable. The community guidelines help create a safe, warm environment.

The EBT Community Guidelines

- Make no judgments.
- Offer no unasked-for advice.
- Do not interrupt.
- Be a warm presence for others.
- Do not mention other programs or products.
- Support privacy and confidentiality.

Great work – and on to the next step

You have completed the introduction to The Power of One Challenge. You are now prepared to have a wonderful time learning the EBT method. Start with Day 1: Personalize One. Enjoy seeing how rapidly you can change and savor your unique journey through the Power of One Challenge!

Spiral Up
to One

Day 1. Personalize One

Bring to mind your favorite moments in life. Perhaps you were curled up in bed, warm all over, with soft sheets touching your skin. Or, maybe you saw the sky light up with pinks and oranges, and you were in awe. Whatever makes you feel *that* good is great for you. The goal of our work today is to start organizing our lives around one thing: the Power of One.

The Many Signs of One

Joyful	In Awe	Aware	Grateful	Anchored
Glowing	Hopeful	Open	Secure	Connected
Warmed	Loving	Present	Amused	Comforted
Peaceful	Forgiving	Happy	Safe	Compassionate
Playful	Energized	Inspired	Creative	Expansive

The signs of One vary widely, and you have your own "thumbprint" of signs of that state. When you are feeling at your best, which of the signs above best reflect your experience? All the signs of Brain State 1 are grounded in our body, anchored in our awareness of our sensations, and sensitive to our emotions. In that state of connection, we experience safety from within. Moving through stress to be at One is a skill, involving using our brain's capacities to their best effects.

Brain State 1 is beyond happiness

The neuroscientist Antonio Damasio referred to the state of neural integration, or optimal physiology, as a joyous state. We use the term Power of One to signify that state of optimal functioning. Brain State 1 is more than a happy state. We can feel happy when we eat ice cream, play video games, or drink beer. These artificial pleasures tend to "wear out" the brain's reward center and hijack its ability to feel rewarded by natural pleasures.

Training our reward center to light up in response to natural pleasures is a big part of raising our set point. Through the reward center, dopamine is released that regulates our urges, motivations, and desires. Extreme highs and lows from reliance on artificial rewards hijack this pathway. We can lose our sensitivity to natural rewards and become dependent upon artificial ones. The homeostatic, balanced chemical surges stop. What is our goal? To take back our reward pathways – regaining that balanced get-up-and-go of dopamine followed by that natural glow of endorphins – and to enjoy an abundance of the natural pleasures of life.

The strong emphasis on joy and natural rewards in EBT is based on science. The neurons in the brain's reward center (nucleus accumbens) are fragile, and artificial rewards, especially chemicals or behaviors that drive a particularly strong and immediate wallop of reward, can quickly careen dopamine levels to abnormal highs. Dopamine highs are destructive to neurons, so evolution supplied us with chemicals that "down-regulate" dopamine receptors on these cells for protection. With fewer receptors, we have less chance of killing off neurons, however, down-regulation of receptors causes tolerance. Then we need more of that excess to feel good, or just to feel normal.

How much tolerance we have built up varies, but research from the National Institutes of Health is encouraging. We can train our brain not only to be more resilient to stress, but also to up-regulate our dopamine receptors. Research suggests that this recovery takes at least 12 months, but even small, sustained changes in lifestyle bring about significant improvements. At first, this might be challenging because the brain responds to boosts in natural pleasures as a source of threat. For reward centers that have adapted to relying on artificial rewards, the more subtle natural pleasures are unfamiliar, and therefore, stressful to encounter. However, in EBT, we treat our reward center comprehensively, including eating healthy food, engaging in regular exercise, and accessing small bursts of natural pleasure. We are establishing the joy habit, as the brain's habit center, the basal ganglia, can "reboot" our dopamine receptors, waking them up. As always, maintaining a sense of humor is helpful!

It's a beautiful day outside, so I went for a walk that should have boosted my mood. I felt so great at first, which is new for me, so it triggered stress. I didn't let it stop me. My brain has to learn how to feel good again slowly!

Why endorphins matter!

A natural morphine that surges after dopamine motivates us to take action, endorphins bring euphoria and a sense of optimal well-being.

"My euphoria is non-addictive. I use Joy Points."

The effectiveness of natural pleasures is based on two of their qualities. One is that they offer a multi-layered experience, compared to the flatness of artificial rewards. Compare standing in the moonlight with your arm around a friend to numbing out with video games! The other quality of natural pleasures is that the resulting emotions are intense but grounded in reality. Each pleasure leads to a small but essential deepening of our wisdom. We see a tree covered in pink blossoms and our heart sings. Then we notice a tinge of sadness, from knowing that the flowers will soon disappear. We delight in our child's hug, knowing that they will soon grow up and have a life of their own. The effect of a natural rise in neurotransmitters followed by a tinge of the awareness of the essential pain of life keeps us grounded in reality. Oddly, much like adding a squeeze of lemon to sugar water, this awareness of the realities of life elevates our experience. It ushers in love, compassion, gratitude, hope, forgiveness, awe, and . . . joy.

When I see my puppy, I feel so much love, but also a slight awareness that she will not always be with us. That makes me cherish the moment even more.

I watch the blazing sunset and am in rapture, but part of me knows that the colors will fade. That reality grounds me in the preciousness of life and brings me intense joy, even with the slight grieving I do.

The reptile is not happy about our being at One

As each Brain State 1 moment fades, we sense that another force aches to rise within it. We are not always securely connected to our joy. There is a rabble-rouser inside us, a reptilian brain. It likes the status quo, and if our set point is in stress, joy threatens it.

The reptile isn't that smart. If we start encouraging the brain to feast on natural pleasures, the reptilian brain will resist our efforts. It will want alcohol, technology, sugar, spending, and other artificial highs. Think of the reptilian brain as a toddler who is going through the terrible twos. It throws a bit of a fit! If we can keep our sense of humor and a certain affection for the reptile within, and keep feeding the brain natural pleasures, the reptile will come around.

After enough experiences with natural pleasure, the reptilian brain will surrender and even prefer them, particularly when we are not stressed! Eventually, the reptilian brain will accept that our new "go to" of daily life is natural pleasure – and the Power of One. It will allow us to raise our set point.

Why dopamine matters!

Dopamine is our "get up and go" reward chemical.
Natural pleasures promote healthy dopamine levels,
whereas artificial pleasures trigger extremes.

"I feast on natural pleasure to balance my dopamine."

My reward center was affected by drinking too much and over-using technology. Other people talked about going for hikes and enjoying sunsets. I needed a stronger hit of dopamine than that. I'm changing. I took a hike the other day, and I thought, "I live in paradise, and I didn't even know it."

Why

The more moments we spend at Brain State 1, the more we overpower the reptile and train our brain for joy. The emotional brain only learns by experience. Knowledge, insight, planning, and deciding do not reach the emotional brain. We can feed our brain experiences of resiliency, moving from stress to joy. The more often we deliver those experiences to the brain, the sooner it changes.

In this course, you will learn a myriad of ways to accomplish this. We will start off recognizing that we create our own stress or joy in life. Our power is based on how we respond – what circuits we activate – to each situation.

Two people can walk together through the same canyon on a sunny day. Depending on their circuits, one will experience the sun as harsh, the canyon threatening, and the company dreary. They have no joy. The other will experience that sun as uplifting, the canyon as magnificent, and the company exciting. They see joy everywhere, scads of it! Which person do you want to be? You can train your brain to see joy everywhere, and without changing your circumstances, experience surges of neurotransmitters by merely updating your mindset and seeing "joy accumulation" as a skill.

Morning Check In:
- State, "I am creating joy in my life."

Throughout the Day:
- Create 10 Joy Points.

Evening Check In:
- State, "I am creating joy in my life."
- Bring to mind three moments of joy from your day.

How

Start your day by saying, "I am creating JOY in my life." This statement activates every major circuit in the brain. It's a revolutionary statement, implying: I exist. I have the power to create. Joy is not just for other people, but for me, and my life is important.

Declare your choice to create joy

By declaring that you are creating joy in your life, your unconscious mind cooperates! You will feel chemical surges of joy throughout the day. We call them Joy Points. Each Joy Point bathes your body and brain in optimal chemicals. Score 10 Joy Points today.

Before you go to sleep, state again, "I am creating joy in my life." Bring three Joy Points that you created today to mind – this delivers three new Joy Points! Last night, I brought to mind having talked to my son on the phone about a piece of music I liked, going for a walk with Walt, and the special joy of discovering that I do not have to have surgery for my painful hip! Wha-hoo!

Don't wait for joy – Create it!

When we began using Joy Points as a way to quash stress, many people waited for them to happen. Do not wait for joy to happen to you. Instead, create it in one or more of these ways:

Bring up a happy memory

Bring to mind a loving moment, a happy reunion, or an experience of intense natural pleasure. Notice that you feel a wave a relaxation and a glow. Remind yourself, "Joy Point."

Enjoy a sensory pleasure

Any natural pleasure that our hunter-gatherer ancestors used to reward themselves can instantly activate a relaxation response and a joy response. Whether it is watching a sunset, slipping into a warm bath, stroking your own body, or hugging a loved one, you can use sensory pleasure to score a Joy Point!

Engage in a kind act

Weave into your day random kind acts. Even if it is just smiling at someone, adding some warm words to an email or text, or checking with a loved one about how they feel and what they need, you'll experience a warm glow. Be aware of that glow. Feel it! You've just scored another Joy Point.

Create a Joy Point
• Bring up a happy memory. • Enjoy a sensory pleasure. • Engage in a kind act.

Use your brain's capacity to create joy today and every day going forward. Use the amazing power of neuroplasticity to live your best life.

The Success Check

This course is based on learning one small but essential skill daily for 30 days. Master one skill each day. If you like, take an extra day, but after that, move on! The daily Success Check will help you track your progress. Each day, check off what you have accomplished.

Also, record your biggest accomplishment in EBT (what you are most proud of having done) and your biggest challenge (what you want to focus on during the next day in EBT to experience the best results). Last, reflect on one thing you learned that fascinated you. Record it. By the conclusion of this course, you will have reset your brain – and will have far more mastery over the quality of your life.

Success Check Day 1

- **Daily Success**

☐ In the morning, I declared, "I am creating joy in my life."

☐ I created 10 Joy Points.

☐ In the evening, I celebrated, saying, "I am creating joy in my life," and brought to mind three moments of joy from my day.

☐ I made one or more community connections to share Joy Points.

- **Did I pass the Success Check? YES NO**

If you did not, stay with this activity for one more day, then move on.

- **My Amazing Learning:**

_____

- **My Biggest Accomplishment:**

_____

- **My Biggest Challenge:**

_____

Congratulations!

**You have completed Day 1 of The Power of One Challenge.
Your next step is Day 2. The 30-Second Check In.**

Day 2. The 30-Second Check In

Keep looking for joy everywhere. The brain in the stress habit tells us that we get our safety from being anxious, depressed, addicted, exhausted, and overwhelmed.

That's not true! The brain is fully equipped to give us bursts of feel-good chemicals that can put us in a state of rapture. The missing element? Some simple techniques that you will be learning in this course.

Even by using the 30-Second Check In, which involves only three small steps, we can experience these immensely healing chemical surges. When you use the tools, imagine what is going on inside you – a Stress Circuit with its harmful chemical cascade is shutting off, and a Joy Circuit with its spigot of healing chemicals is opening up. All this is happening because you are using tools that enable you to emotionally connect within. You become your own chemist, exerting a new level of control over your body chemistry!

The 30-Second Check In

- Connect your neocortex and emotional brain.
- Tap into your inner strength and wisdom.
- Choose to experience joy and the goodness of life.

Today, continue with your Power of One Practice. Start your day by declaring, "I am creating joy in my life!" During the day, collect 10 Joy Points. Add to your practice the Check In Tool that is the gateway technique. After adolescence, the brain tends to switch off feelings and relies excessively on thinking. This tool penetrates that thinking-brain barrier and that changes everything!

Why

We need to stay emotionally connected, if we are to have optimal well-being. That's not easy to do, so we use our conscious mind and the Check In Tool to establish the habit of staying emotionally connected to ourselves.

By using the emotional tools of EBT, we can step through the portal of the emotional brain and begin to rewire that connection to ourselves, so it is more secure, loving, and powerful. It's with repeated contact with the tools that we upgrade our connection to ourselves. That's why the Check In Tool is so important. It opens the door to using all the other emotional tools.

Emotional connection is the pathway

Starting today, you will be accessing your emotions in a more robust and powerful way. Most of us process life by thinking. That's changing! Now we access our emotions 10 or more times per day. By surrendering our thoughts to the more vivid world of emotions, we relinquish control over which feelings we feel. That's not a problem. Sure, negative ones arise first as the brain's way of alerting us to a real or perceived threat. Only by feeling our negative emotions does the brain relax and deliver to us the authentic, robust, and gritty positive emotions. It rewards us for turning on the spigot of negative emotions with a burst of positive ones.

In the grand benevolence of the emotional brain, negative emotions are our pathway to emotional growth. Each time we stay present to our emotions, we automatically update our unreasonable expectations that guide our drives, behaviors, and rewards. Effectiveness in feeling our negative emotions is the solution!

The elevated emotions make us unstoppable

The multi-layered elevated emotions – love, compassion, gratitude, hope, forgiveness, awe, and joy – make us exceedingly strong, able to fulfill our unique mission in life. These elevated emotions are not like the false highs from artificial rewards (alcohol, technology, drugs, and the thousands of "go-tos" enshrined in our Stress Circuits). They are grounded in reality, which enables our prefrontal cortex to open up to new ideas, challenges, and possibilities that we could not fathom only moments before.

This the adventure of EBT! All you need do is stay the course. Do not quit. Appreciate that you are learning how to work with your emotional brain. It will take time, but each use of the tools – no matter how seemingly successful or unsuccessful it is – makes a productive mark on your unconscious mind. You will feel the difference and so will those around you.

When I check in, I feel a slight fear. I am accustomed to overthinking everything and I am not sure I want to connect with my emotions. I don't know what I'll find there, but I don't like the idea of being checked out. I will give it a try.

I can feel my emotions already and feel pretty connected to myself. I am eager to find ways that are more efficient in connecting and taking me to some more profound emotions. I am IN!

How

Just follow the simple steps below. If you are using the EBT app, it will guide you through three evidence-based techniques to rapidly reduce stress and will record your stats based on your combined Check Ins from both the app and website. Begin by clicking on the Check In icon on your app or following the instructions below:

Step 1: Take a deep breath

Begin by turning your attention to your body and your breathing. Take a deep breath and focus on breathing in so that your stomach rises up, and then exhale – a long, complete outbreath.

This is **diaphragmatic breathing**. It's unnatural, and unnatural activities require that we turn our attention away from the buzzing thoughts in our thinking brain. The long exhale eases stress and activates the brain's reward center.

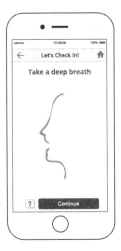

Step 2: Gently assume "Body at 1"

Next, change your posture and facial expression to the universal power positions. This gives your brain the message that you are in a state of well-being – even when you are not!

Sit up or stand up tall, then put your shoulders back and your chest out. Next, lift up your chin slightly, then stretch the corners of your mouth back toward your ears in a slight smile, and either warm your eyes with a loving expression or crinkle them as if you are laughing. This singular act sustained for two minutes reduces the stress hormone cortisol by 25 percent. This posture change also raises testosterone, so you are chemically supported in feeling powerful and safe. It is called **proprioceptive posturing**.

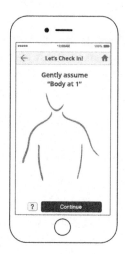

Step 3: Warmly observe yourself

Last, warmly observe yourself in the present moment, just as you are and without judgment. See yourself in this situation and notice a connection. You are connecting with yourself. This is important. Your thinking brain, the overseer of your emotional brain, is seeing you, hearing you, and feeling your feelings. That amounts to what we all need: a secure connection within.

This connection is your relationship with yourself. You might notice yourself using a nurturing inner voice. You may feel compassion for yourself. Your unconditional love for yourself – even a slight amount of it – makes a huge difference in your brain functioning and every aspect of your life in that moment.

When you complete Step 3, notice that your body is more relaxed, and you are aware of a slight glow. You have checked in!

Choose your Check In plan

There are two plans for checking in. One plan is the basic plan, checking in hourly, that is, 10 times per day. Set your alarm or notification hourly to remind yourself to check in. The advantage of this plan is that you only have to check in 10 times.

The other plan is the easy plan, checking in every 30 minutes. The advantage of the easy plan is that you stay connected all day. Rather than giving stress time to activate a Stress Circuit, sustain stress overload, and block your joy, you prevent that circuit from taking hold.

I liked the 30-minute Check In better right away. It was so much easier to stay checked in and have that glow in my body much of the day.

30-Second Check In

- **Take a deep breath.**

    Turn your attention to your belly and your breathing, pushing out your stomach as you inhale, followed by a long release.

- **Gently assume "Body at 1."**

    Shoulders back, chest out, chin up a little, a slight smile, and the expression of happiness or love in your eyes.

- **Warmly observe yourself.**

    Observe yourself, liking the person you see, and feeling a wave of compassion for yourself.

This easy, frequent Check In helps the brain learn to check in automatically. With enough practice (much like going to the emotional gym), the brain begins to stay "checked in" spontaneously more of the time.

Enjoy the 30-Second Check In and notice that you feel present and connected to your body – just what evolutionary biology designed.

Success Check Day 2

- **Daily Success**

☐ I continued my Power of One Practice, declaring, "I am creating joy in my life," morning and evening and scoring 10 Joy Points.

☐ I used the 30-Second Check In every 30 or 60 minutes.

☐ I made one or more community connections for support with the 30-Second Check In.

- **Did I pass the Success Check?   YES   NO**

If you did not, stay with this activity for one more day, then move on.

- **My Amazing Learning:**

_____

- **My Biggest Accomplishment:**

_____

- **My Biggest Challenge:**

_____

Congratulations!

**You have completed Day 2 of The Power of One Challenge.
Your next step is Day 3. Lifestyle Reset #1 Exercise.**

Day 3. Lifestyle Reset #1 Exercise

This is our first of six lifestyle resets to give us easier access to the Power of One. The EBT exercise recommendations are based on reducing stress and facilitating your brain's capacity to change. Exercise strengthens not just your muscles and lungs, but your brain!

As you use the EBT tools, chances are you will feel like exercising. You will want to get moving and enjoy your body. Like our hunter-gatherer ancestors, the plan in EBT is to move rather than to sit. Being sedentary is as big of a health risk as smoking! Likewise, over-exercising increases stress and may be a sign that other elements of life, such as intimacy, are not as fulfilling as they might be.

The goal of this lifestyle reset is for you to feel powerful, enjoy your body, and improve neuroplasticity. That means being active in daily life and exercising for 30 minutes per day. This exercise must be fun. If it is not fun, it doesn't count.

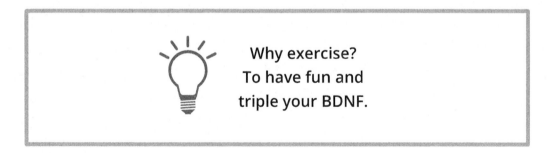

**Why exercise?
To have fun and
triple your BDNF.**

Why

You know all the reasons to exercise, and those reasons do not prompt most people to move. Stress promotes inactivity or overactivity because the brain is disconnected. It's hard to "motivate" ourselves to move. As usual, when the reptile is in charge, it's really hard to find a middle ground.

Although exercise is a recommended treatment for stress and depression, it activates emotions. Updating our emotional processing is the first step toward enjoying physical activity and being excited about finding creative ways to make it fun. With your Power of One Practice and Check Ins, you will process more emotions, so exercise will become far more appealing.

> ## Why BDNF matters!
> Brain-derived neurotrophic factor is "miracle grow" for neurons.
> Thirty minutes per day of exercise using major muscle groups
> (legs and arms) increases BDNF synthesis by 300%.
> ### "I exercise for optimal brain health."

How

Exercise for 30 minutes per day, engaging in some activity that uses the major muscle groups. This will boost the power of your Check Ins and Power of One Practice. Endurance activities increase BDNF (brain-derived neurotrophic factor). This chemical is delivered by major muscle groups and passes through the blood-brain barrier. In the brain, it stimulates and controls both neurogenesis (new neurons forming) and locking those new neurons into existing neural circuits, rather than letting them be sloughed off.

This "BDNF" factor is important to long-term memory and aging. Thirty minutes of aerobic exercise daily can boost BDNF synthesis in the brain three-fold and has been associated with improved cognitive functioning, behavior change, neuron growth, and memory.

The Move In Joy Prescription

- Instead of sitting, STAND.
- Instead of standing, MOVE.
- Always make it FUN!

The best exercise prescription is to do endurance activities that you enjoy. Research has shown that if exercise is too stressful, it does not improve neuroplasticity. A great way to avoid stress overload when exercising is to make it fun. If it is fun, you'll do it regularly.

What if you over-exercise?

That's a wire! As you become comfortable with processing your emotions, the chances are that your need for over-exercising will fade, and, if it doesn't, consider choosing it as the habit you rewire later in the Power of One Challenge. How do you know if your exercise is a Stress Circuit? If it gets in the way of your experiencing the seven rewards of purpose.

I use exercise as a healthy addiction. If I don't get one hour in a day at the gym or a good bike ride of an hour or two, I'm explosive. I get agitated and fly off the handle. I throw my keys or sulk. Which reward does that block? Intimacy. That might be the habit I rewire in the course. We'll see.

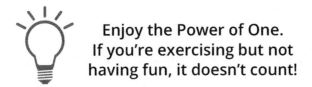

**Enjoy the Power of One.
If you're exercising but not
having fun, it doesn't count!**

What if you haven't been exercising recently?

You can still get your BDNF dose of exercise in. Just take it slowly. Instead of powering up a hillside, walk somewhere flat. Slow your pace. Definitely avoid movements that tax your joints that could cause injuries. Exhaustion and injuries do not boost your Power of One!

If you haven't been exercising recently, be sure to move carefully and more slowly than you otherwise would. Keep it fun and yet still devote 30 minutes daily to moving your major muscle groups. Walking is always an option, but check the exercise list for more ideas.

Our emphasis is on moving the major muscle groups. This includes walking, dancing, hiking, or playing sports. Overall conditioning, including flexibility and strength, matter. However, this core lifestyle reset of engaging in endurance activities that boost BDNF is essential to building a better brain. Let's do it!

My depression stops me from moving. I like sleeping 10 hours a day, staying in bed late, and reading fantasy novels. Exercise is the last thing I want to do! I'll have to paddle in the high school pool near me. I think stretching or yoga could work, too.

I've become a brain junkie. I'll do anything to triple my BDNF. Lift weights, clean out the basement, run around the block – I can do that!

If you are stressed, you will not want to exercise. Exercise will activate emotions and that may not feel safe to you. How to combat exercise shutdowns? Have fun!

Be at One Exercise Checklist

- ☑ Turn on your favorite music and rock out at home.
- ☐ Does a co-worker want to meet? Suggest a walk and talk!
- ☑ Try solo stretching, relaxation, or yoga.
- ☑ Take a walk at lunchtime and listen to music.
- ☐ Play a sport: tennis, golf, baseball, volleyball . . .
- ☐ Locate a basketball court and shoot hoops.
- ☐ Play hide and seek with kids (or adults).
- ☐ Take the stairs.
- ☐ Find a happy gym with many ways to be playful.
- ☐ Give your partner or spouse a vigorous massage.
- ☑ Enjoy walking meditation or prayer.
- ☐ Sign up for classes in your favorite martial art.
- ☐ Take the dog for a walk, play Frisbee or fetch.
- ☐ Go outside in the morning: walk and watch the sunrise.
- ☐ Invite your romantic partner to exercise with you – be creative!
- ☑ Take a five-minute stretch break at work.
- ☐ Bike to and from work or the store.
- ☑ Get going with projects: cleaning, painting, gardening, building . . .
- ☐ Dance with your children, spouse, partner, or friend.
- ☐ Use a standing desk and isolate muscle groups as you write.
- ☐ Join a roller derby league or soccer team.
- ☐ Play a musical instrument like a violin or guitar standing up.
- ☐ Go for a morning swim at the local pool.
- ☐ Take a walk at twilight and enjoy the night air and magical light.
- ☐ Invite a friend to walk or run with you.

Success Check Day 3

- **Daily Success**

☐ I continued my Power of One Practice with 10 Check Ins and 10 Joy Points.

☐ I reset my lifestyle to exercise for 30 minutes per day.

☐ I made one or more community connections for support with this lifestyle reset.

- **Did I pass the Success Check?　YES　NO**

If you did not, stay with this activity for one more day, then move on.

- **My Amazing Learning:**

_____

- **My Biggest Accomplishment:**

_____

- **My Biggest Challenge:**

_____

Great Progress!

**You have completed Day 3 of The Power of One Challenge.
Your next step is Day 4. What Number Am I?**

Day 4. What Number Am I?

You are already connecting to your emotional core just by using the 30-Second Check In. There will be times that you check in that way and feel complete. You instantly connect to the deepest part of yourself and feel secure and rewarded. However, often you need more clarity to know precisely what brain state you're in. That way, if you want to actively change your state, you can spiral up to One more easily. You need to become comfortable with brain states.

Today we will boost the power of the Check In Tool by identifying stress levels or "brain states."

Why
If it's not fun, it's not EBT. One purpose of understanding brain states is to help you keep your sense of humor. After using the 30-Second Check In for the last two days, you may have noticed that your stress level varies a lot.

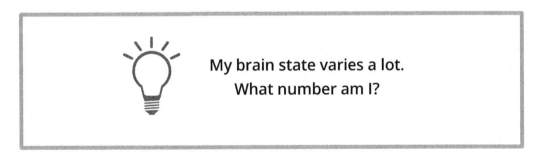

This is normal. The automatic emotional brain is ceaselessly checking to see if your needs are met for safety, love, comfort, pleasure, and purpose. If your needs are not met, it perceives that you are being threatened, and it shifts gears to a more stressed state. This is a silent, ongoing process that everyone experiences. We are not "stable" people. Our brain is always making moves that we do not know are happening!

Your wiring is making these decisions for you all the time without your permission or awareness. What's more, most of the wires were encoded early in life, so they send messages to you that are not of your choosing! Keep your sense of humor about your brain state and also, use that information to create more joy in your life.

I wasn't stressed, but then I started worrying about my pregnancy (I am 20 weeks along). That gave me a slight headache, and I ate a piece of chocolate cake. I thought I was at Brain State 3, but I was really at Brain State 5. The stress from different sources all added up.

My boss called a meeting. There have been threats of layoffs. I checked in and determined that I was numb, overwhelmed, and terrified – all at once. I realized that I was at Brain State 5, so I'd better not voice my list of complaints. I kept quiet, and it turned out that the meeting was about a new customer that signed on with us! Afterward, I checked in at One.

Understanding Brain States

1. We experience ourselves differently in all five levels
Celebrate that you are five different people – and so is everyone else! Again, our moods, behaviors, thinking, perceptions, and sensations vary widely depending on our brain state. It makes sense that the person we are when the reptilian brain is in charge is different than who we are when we are at One, and the neocortex is running the show. Amazing!

2. We activate different wires or memories in each state
In each brain state, our memories from past experiences in that state are "hot" or "online."

Most of our responses are replays of the past. Each replay impacts how we feel, what we expect, and what we do. These wires have no source attribution. When a conscious memory is triggered, we have a body feel that we are remembering something. But the unconscious mind is completely stealthy. It gives us no sign that our current experience is a replay of the past!

The brain stores circuits in five drawers, one for each stress level

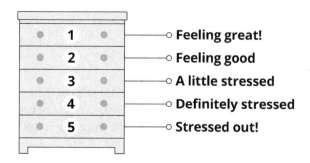

1 — Feeling great!
2 — Feeling good
3 — A little stressed
4 — Definitely stressed
5 — Stressed out!

3. There is a different brain pathway to joy for each brain state

To return to the Power of One, we must process our emotions effectively. At each stress level, effective emotional processing differs. We have **five brain states** and **five corresponding tools**, so by knowing our brain state, we can use the most effective pathway back to One.

4. If you know your brain state, you can understand yourself better

By being aware of your brain state, your self-concept will begin to change. You can keep your sense of humor about some of the strong messages that come from being in the "5th Drawer" of the brain! We are not wrong or bad. We are responsible for our actions, but judgment can stop! Let's take a closer look at brain states.

In the following table, you can see the five brain states on the left column. Across the top are four areas of life. Most of us think of each area of life as separate, but with each decrease in stress level, the more balanced and effective our thoughts, emotions, relationships, and behaviors. In other words, the brain is not vertical, but horizontal. When we spiral up, life gets better.

State	Thoughts	Feelings	Relationships	Behavior
1	Abstract	Joyous	Intimate	Optimal
2	Concrete	Balanced	Companionable	Healthy
3	Rigid	Mixed	Social	Moderate
4	Reactive	Unbalanced	Needy/Distancing	Unhealthy
5	Irrational	Overwhelmed	Merged/Disengaged	Destructive

Understanding brain states helps me in two ways. One is to see my anxiety not as anxiety but as a State 4 issue. The other way is to see that every aspect of my life is out of balance to the same extent. When I'm anxious, I merge with my two children and I am so mean to my husband. It's reassuring to know the problem is my brain state.

5. Brain states control our stress styles

Our drives change in each brain state. At a high brain state, the neocortex maintains control, so seeking purpose or pleasure has low to moderate drives. In lower brain states, the drive to feel comforted, loved, or safe becomes far stronger. The Brain State 4 drives are strong, and the Brain State 5 drives are the strongest – definitely fight-or-flight drives!

When I'm at Brain State 1, I have no interest in gambling. When I'm at Brain State 3, I can usually stop myself from gambling. However, when I'm in Brain State 5, nothing will stop me! I want what I want when I want it. I don't care how it impacts anyone else or how it will impact me the next day. I'm seeking safety, some way to hide.

The Check In Tool

- Take a deep breath.
- Assume "Body at 1."
- Warmly observe yourself.
- What number am I?
  - 1 = Feeling Great!
  - 2 = Feeling Good
  - 3 = A Little Stressed
  - 4 = Definitely Stressed
  - 5 = Stressed Out!

How

Use the 30-Second Check In Tool 10 to 20 times today, adding one more step. Ask yourself, "What number am I?" There is an important part to doing this – you guess.

Why is guessing so important? We are far more intuitive than we know. To access our inherent strength, goodness, and wisdom, we need to keep our thinking brain from interfering!

Effective Check Ins

- Guess your brain state. *Do not overthink it!*
- No judgments. Each brain state has advantages.
- Be curious. Your state can change quickly!

When you check in, do not think. Ask, "What number am I?" and trust your initial answer to that question. Then, after you guess your brain state, feel a surge of relaxation and pleasure in your body for one reason – you chose a number! At that moment, *the activity for today is complete.*

The challenge now is to have fun with these ideas. Be curious about your brain state and notice how it changes throughout the day. Find ways to feel more compassion for yourself!

Success Check Day 4

- **Daily Success**

☐ I continued my Power of One Practice with 10 Check Ins and 10 Joy Points.

☐ I checked in 10 or more times and guessed my brain state.

☐ I made one or more community connections for support with guessing my brain state.

- **Did I pass the Success Check?   YES   NO**

If you did not pass, take another day to complete it, then move on.

- **My Amazing Learning:**

_____

- **My Biggest Accomplishment:**

_____

- **My Biggest Challenge:**

_____

Well Done!

**You have completed Day 4 of The Power of One Challenge.
Your next step is Day 5. The Tipping Point.**

Day 5. The Tipping Point

Today's tool is the 3 Tool – or the Flow Tool. It gives you the power to flow through the negative emotions and activate authentic, robust, positive emotions. It takes only a minute or two to use, and it can change your entire day.

I was watching the news and starting to feel anxious. I realized I was at the tipping point, Brain State 3, and reached for my app. I used the 3 Tool and I spiraled up to Brain State 1. I thought, "What am I doing to myself? I don't have to watch this anymore." I turned off the TV and went for a walk. It was a beautiful day!

Why

When we are at Brain State 3, we're at the tipping point. The brain could trigger a Stress Circuit and spiral us down to Brain State 4 or 5. Or, it could activate a Joy Circuit and spiral us up to Brain State 1 or 2.

In this wobbly state of feeling a little stressed, the 3 Tool prevents the activation of Stress Circuits leading to compulsions and addictions. Instead, it ushers us rapidly back to a state in which we have peace and power from within. Stress? Somehow, it has vanished. This is why the 3 Tool is a trusted standby in the EBT Toolkit.

Going to the emotional gym

This is the tool that could be your emotional mainstay. Use it five or more times per day if you like, to momentarily clear your mind. What could be better than accessing your power to turn negative emotions into positive ones and stop overthinking!

When I'm at Brain State 3, I start overthinking and I can feel stress getting a grip on me. My body gets tense and that negative inner voice starts talking to me. I use the 3 Tool and all of that vanishes.

I have a history of depression, and this tool is working for me, making me happier, with more zest for life.

Even though it feels good to use, one of the most important benefits of using the 3 Tool is a long-term one. Imagine an emotional resiliency pathway in your brain. It's like a one-lane road. The more you use this tool to spiral up to the Power of One, the more that highway broadens. What do we need? A four-lane highway so that when we're in a moderately-stressed state, we can begin to spontaneously spiral up to One.

When I started EBT, I was so resistant to emotions. I had the habit of shutting off my mind with various excesses – videos, science fiction books, crossword puzzles. They distracted me but left me feeling even more disconnected. Now I use the 3 Tool preventively. I have planted a garden and started bike riding. I'm switching from artificial rewards to natural pleasures effortlessly. It must be the Power of One.

The days that I use the Flow Tool at work – usually about five times – I don't tire out in the late afternoon. After work, I feel like stopping off at the gym and then having a relaxing evening. My pre-EBT norm was taking a dive into drinking at night. That's less appealing to me now.

The reason this tool works so well is that if you are a little stressed (Brain State 3), you are neither activating an allostatic circuit that keeps you stuck in some form of stress response nor are you activating a homeostatic circuit that spirals you up to One.

The brain is giving you a lot of power here. If you take that power and move through your gently negative emotions, it will reward you with some gently positive ones. What's more, you'll be in a high brain state, running Joy Circuits that keep you out of stress territory.

My issues are overworking and procrastinating. Both are 5 Circuits, my ways of seeking safety. Instead of trying to control my issues, I control my brain state. I spiral up from Brain State 3 to Brain State 1, and I feel pretty good. Even if that only lasts a few minutes, it's a huge relief.

The Tipping Point

Need Comfort?

Use the 3 Tool to spiral up to One.

Instantly improve your stress style.

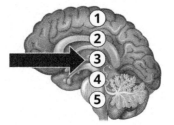

How

This is an easy tool. If you use it with excellent technique, it can almost always land you in Brain State 1. The entire world looks different when you are at One. The stress styles of seeking comfort, love, or safety calm down. Carefully follow the techniques below, and this tool can light up an important part of your brain. It's the area behind the left side of your forehead, the left prefrontal cortex. When we are flooded with positive emotions, brain scans show that this area lights up!

Pause between lead-ins

To use the 3 Tool, state the first lead-in, or phrase. Then pause and wait for words to appear in your mind to complete the sentence. Pause again. Feel that feeling until it fades. Feeling the feeling is what heals us and brightens our mood.

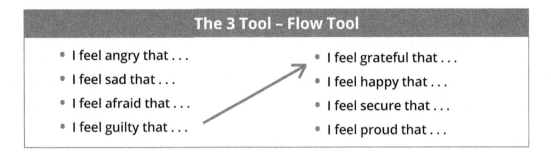

The 3 Tool – Flow Tool

- I feel angry that . . .
- I feel sad that . . .
- I feel afraid that . . .
- I feel guilty that . . .

- I feel grateful that . . .
- I feel happy that . . .
- I feel secure that . . .
- I feel proud that . . .

Next, state another lead-in . . . pause . . . and once again, feel the feeling until it fades. Continue this process for all eight feelings. **The pause makes all the difference**, as it prompts the thinking brain to connect with the emotional brain. That emotional connection between the two brains is the source of our safety and power. Imagine that! Our safety comes from a brain connection that we can achieve in real-time throughout the day!

What if no words appear in your mind?

What if no words bubble up to complete the sentence? Just go on to the next lead-in. What if a couple of these lead-ins do not prompt your brain to express a feeling? Chances are you are not in Brain State 3. We'll learn tools for the other states starting tomorrow.

How do I know if I am too stressed to use this tool?

The words that appear in your mind for the first four lead-ins will all be on the same subject. That's a sign that you are at Brain State 4 and may need the 4 Tool (the "Cycle Tool"). We'll learn it soon.

How do I know if I am not stressed enough to use this tool?

If you feel present and aware but no words appear in your mind when you state the first four lead-ins, you could be in any of the states! Sometimes the brain does that. However, it's quite common that when we are in Brain State 2, feelings do not flow. You can state one feeling, but a flow of feelings? Most strong emotions come from stress. They are the "steam" that comes off a circuit. You may not be stressed enough to use this tool. You may be better off with the Brain State 2 Tool. We'll learn that tool soon.

The order of the feelings in the 3 Tool matters

The order of the feelings mirrors the brain's natural emotional processing. Use the lead-ins exactly as shown. For best results, do not change the order.

A brief expression of anger can profoundly reduce stress. Expressing anger alone rather than as part of the natural flow of feelings is not always effective. In fact, it can be harmful. The anger can become stuck and turn into an allostatic emotion, such as hostility or rage. However, expressing anger within the natural flow of feelings predictably ushers us forward, taking us to sadness. The sadness can be tender and we can heal from expressing it. Once we have expressed our sadness, we will naturally become aware of our fear.

When we state what we are most afraid of, the fear fades! Just by stating the fear, it loses its power over us! Next, state, "I feel guilty that . . ." and notice something bubbling up that you regret, or would have liked to have done better. This is not shame, but an opportunity to identify what you could do differently next time. When we discover what we could have done differently, the stress switch in the brain (hypothalamus) flips. Positive emotions begin to flow! This is emotional healing in action!

Enjoy knowing the contents of your unconscious mind
The words that appear in your mind come from pouring out the contents of circuits that were encoded long ago. They do not have to make sense. Enjoy this always fascinating, deeper knowledge of yourself.

I used the Flow Tool and said, "I feel angry that . . ." and the words that appeared in my mind were: my sister is so critical of me. I had no idea I was stressed about that. I felt compassion for myself and compassion for my sister. We grew up in a household in which being critical of each other was considered a loving act. We were "helping" each other with self-improvement. I like this tool!

It's surprising – the 3 Tool takes us to One!
As you move through each of the eight lead-ins, notice the changing sensations in your body. If you started out at Brain State 3, more often than not you will find yourself at Brain State 1.

Once you are aware of sensations and emotions associated with the Power of One, do not distract yourself from them. Savor them. Prolong them. Enjoy them! The longer they last, the more resilient you become. You are "treating" your brain with a chemical wash of positive emotions.

Do you have a missing feeling?
Most of us have one of the eight core emotions that is challenging to express. That's your missing feeling. Make it easier to feel that feeling by adding the words "a little" to the lead-in. For example, "I feel *a little* secure that . . ." Adding them to the tool will train your brain that it's safe to feel that missing feeling, and soon you will be quite effective at expressing it.

My missing feeling is happiness. I know how to binge on videos, zone out in front of the TV, or get high. All these ways of keeping myself going help. But feeling happy? I'm not sure exactly what that means. I will try the tool and see if it works.

The special power of guilt
Guilt is the most common missing feeling. Perhaps we were raised in a stressed environment in which we had to be perfect to feel loved. Expressing guilt seems rather foolish, or even dangerous. Guilt is not shame. Shame is "I am a bad person." Guilt is "Next time I would do this differently

. . ." Do you prefer a different lead-in? Try: "I have some power here. In the best of all worlds I wish I had . . .", "My part of this was . . .", or "I regret that I . . ."

Anger is hard to find . . . and so liberating!

Anyone who has been harmed has anger. Our hunter-gatherer brain uses anger to quickly and powerfully reduce stress. We need our anger, and by using these tools, our anger becomes both safe and productive. Suppressing anger can cause anxiety or depression. As you use EBT and find anger liberating and safe, your brain will begin to like anger. It just takes practice!

I feel secure. Is that possible?

With so much stress overload, the thinking brain and emotional brain connection begins to wobble! Since this connection is the source of our security, we become anxious or tense. However, this tool reconnects the brain, and notice that you can pause for a moment and feel a slight sense of security. Your brain is connected!

Am I emotionally lopsided?

I hope so. We all are. The brain's processing starts with negative emotions because its primary role is keeping us from danger, so it is lopsided. Naturally, it goes right to the negative emotions. Only when the negative emotions have been felt and expressed does it enable you to access the positive emotions.

Positive emotions? They make me uncomfortable!

The reptilian brain favors negative emotions. That will change with practice. Using this tool often – about five times per day – is one of the most effective ways to feel comfortable with positive emotions.

I think I'm numb. Can this tool work for me?

Yes! Most of us are numb for good reason. If we do not have a full set of emotional tools, when we start to feel our feelings they will become stuck. They won't tell us what we need, only what we want. Now that you are learning these tools, your brain will become comfortable with emotions, and numbness will fade.

Enjoy using this tool and be aware that it will work sometimes and at other times feel rather flat. We're back where we started. The only way to make EBT really work for you is to keep laughing about the elusive and magical emotional brain. It's by experimenting with these tools that your brain changes!

Success Check Day 5

- **Daily Success**

☐ I continued my Power of One Practice with 10 Check Ins and 10 Joy Points.

☐ I tried the 3 Tool at least five times.

☐ I made one or more community connections for support with practicing the 3 Tool.

- **Did I pass the Success Check?   YES   NO**

If you did not, stay with this activity for one more day, then move on.

- **My Amazing Learning:**

_____

- **My Biggest Accomplishment:**

_____

- **My Biggest Challenge:**

_____

Congratulations!

**You have completed Day 5 of The Power of One Challenge.
Your next step is Day 6. Clear Those Blocks!**

Day 6. Clear Those Blocks!

So far, you've scored Joy Points, checked in with yourself, and turned negative emotions into positive ones. Today we'll go head to head with the fight-or-flight response. When the overall stress in the brain exceeds the brain's capacity to process it, the stress switch flips and we trigger a stress response. It can happen in a nanosecond!

I was talking with my co-worker and she mentioned that she was taking over my project. Instantly, I felt rage, then numbness, and finally, overwhelmed. I was at Brain State 5.

Why

What is the stress response? A wire activates the Stress Triangle, which involves three centers in the emotional brain – the amygdala (stress center), the nucleus accumbens (reward center), and the hypothalamus (control center) – that orchestrate changes in the entire brain and body. The Stress Circuits are stored in the amygdala, and when activated, they start the cortisol (stress hormone) cascade and impact the reward center, causing extreme highs and lows in dopamine. The hypothalamus activates the fight-or-flight response and chronic stress. That fight-or-fight response triggers us, making us reactive and driving us to repeat old patterns. The chronic stress causes harm to every organ system and increases inflammation. Together, stress reactivity, chronic stress, and inflammation cause, exacerbate, or prolong nearly all health problems.

Basically, if you want the Power of One, it is essential to take charge of managing the stress response. Learning tools that calm down or stop the stress response can give you the freedom to do things that you might otherwise choose to avoid.

For example, during a leadership group meeting of EBT, one researcher was talking about attending the wedding of her ex-husband to the new-found love of his life. Another member questioned if that was a good idea. The researcher's response was, "He hurt me. Going to his wedding is not worth my triggering a cortisol cascade, but I can use Damage Control, and be fine."

The Power of One is based on physiology. It gives us more control over the Stress Triangle and the chemical cascades that the brain activates.

> ### Why cortisol matters!
> Cortisol is the main stress hormone
> and "public health enemy #1,"
> as it switches on the Stress Triangle.
> **"I use the EBT tools to rapidly shut off cortisol."**

How

When we're confused, lost, overwhelmed, or feel impervious, we are often at Brain State 5. Safety is the first priority in EBT. If you worry that you could harm yourself or others, then call 911 and immediately access support. If this is not an issue, start by assuming you're at Brain State 5 PLUS. You are not just highly stressed or stressed out but in a full-blown stress response. Your brain is signaling that a lion is about to eat you!

Begin by using the Full-Blown Damage Control Tool. Simple, rhythmic activities work well to stop stress overload. Belly breathing is evidence-based for reducing physiologic stress. Just turn your attention to your body and focus on your breathing. Watch your belly move up and down and be sure to use a long, slow exhale. When you have released all the air from your lungs, your reward center will activate slightly. You might even notice a glow. Do something rhythmic that you would do to calm an infant, such as rocking in your chair, stroking your arm, or rubbing your neck.

The 5 Tools
The 5 PLUS Tool – (Full Blown Damage Control)   • Rocking back and forth   • Belly breathing   • Stroking the body   **The 5 Tool – (Damage Control)**   • Do not judge   • Minimize harm   • Know it will pass

When you feel a bit better, use the regular Damage Control Tool on your own or by using the app. Repeat the statements: Do not judge. Minimize harm. Know it will pass. Do this in whatever style works for you – slow or fast. Don't hold back with repeating the words. Sometimes it takes 10 to 30 repetitions of this tool to calm a circuit.

What do the words of Damage Control mean?
The first phrase of the Damage Control Tool is *Do not judge*. It is normal for our brain to judge ourselves or others when we are in stress overload. This is the natural expression of cortisol release. You might notice that you tend to do one or the other. A person who distances tends to judge others. People who merge tend to judge themselves. You can revise the words to say either of these statements or both, such as to say, "Do not judge. I will NOT judge myself!" or "Do not judge. I will not judge others. I will NOT judge myself!" Feel free to personalize this tool.

What does *Minimize harm* mean? Don't we mean do no harm? The neurophysiology of stress ensures that there will be harm. The stress overload alone impacts every organ system in significant and deleterious ways. In addition, in the 5 State, our thinking brain is offline, and we lose our good judgment, flexible thinking, and impulse control.

Let's make the reptile a bit happier: The Damage Control Tool

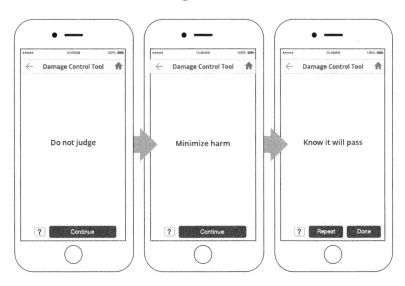

The minimize harm statement means that we accept that this is a harmful state, but we are going to do our best to control the damage. Perhaps we will go on a small spending spree, take half a pill, or drink one glass of beer. Depending upon the circuit and how strong and addictive our response, even a small activation of a 5 Circuit can be very harmful. If abstinence is your goal, you may want to personalize your Damage Control statement and choose words, so that instead of saying minimize harm, you say something like "Do not drink" or "Do not use drugs." Many people prefer to tell themselves to minimize harm, honoring that they will do the best they can, and that reducing harm is a reasonable goal. Always personalize the tools to meet your needs!

What about the phrase *Know it will pass?* The statement is general, because depending on the strength and dominance of the circuit, a Brain State 5 can persist for quite a while. The allostatic circuits are positive feedback loops, which means they have no shut-off valves. If they are triggered, they can trigger other circuits that were encoded at the same level of stress. However, the state – sooner or later – does pass! We use this statement to remind ourselves that it won't last forever!

Completely faulty messages ring true!
Why is the 5 State so challenging? Imagine that the brain is a big chest of drawers and when the fight-or-flight drive is activated, we land in the lowest drawer of the brain, the 5th Drawer. This is the drawer that contains the memories from experiences of stress overload. During those times the prefrontal cortex and hippocampus (our only conscious filters of which memories are reasonable and worth keeping) are offline.

When we are at 5, faulty messages ring true

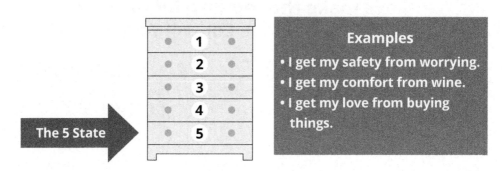

The 5 State

Examples
- I get my safety from worrying.
- I get my comfort from wine.
- I get my love from buying things.

Circuits that are essentially emotional trash are encoded and treated as if they are the holy grail. When one faulty circuit is activated, based on some random life experience that tells us something ridiculous (such as I get my love from alcohol or I get my safety from making everyone happy all the time no matter what) it causes mayhem. It activates stress that causes other 5 Circuits to be activated at the same time. This cacophony of damaging messages amplifies our stress.

Worst of all, because this is the "survival circuit" drawer, these messages are extremely convincing. The survival of the species is based on our believing and obeying the messages in the 5th Drawer reflexively. We believe these messages, and each one stresses us out even more. The result? We can be stuck in Brain State 5 for hours, days, or even weeks! In that state, impulse control vanishes and reflexive (knee-jerk) responses rule us.

Most people have no idea how to short-circuit a 5 State. This is why using the 5 PLUS Tool as your first defense and the 5 Tool right after that are core life skills. Everyone goes to 5 and everyone needs a personalized process for calming the reptile within!

Protect Yourself from Brain State 5

- Use the 5 PLUS Tool as your first defense.
- The prefrontal cortex is offline – be careful!
- Stress causes a time warp – know it will pass!

Going to 5 then spiraling up to 1 is core to the human experience

Brain State 5 never feels good! However, our repeated dips into Brain State 5, and the rise to Brain State 1 that follows, are core to human development. The 5 State is woven into our lives as a way of helping us evolve and update our brain's emotional architecture. Every moment at Brain State 5 triggers the reptile. It activates the family of circuits in our 5th Drawer and if we use the tools, those circuits quiet down and we update our brain and can even spiral up to Brain State 1.

My daughter came home from college and even before she arrived, I had an "anticipatory 5 State." The thought of facing all the drama and depression from her high school years again really got to me. I tried to stay connected to myself, to use the tools, to pray, to hum, to do whatever I needed to do to get to Brain State 4.9. That worked pretty well. After I got to 4.9, I felt better.

The light side of Brain State 5

What follows a moment at Brain State 5 is often a natural high one can experience in no other way. The astonishing spiral ups after stress overload can bring about a very strong and healing Brain State 1 PLUS!

The "joy" of Brain State 5 can happen in two ways. Sometimes Brain State 5 seemingly miraculously turns into a Brain State 1. If we stay present to our feelings when we feel horrible, something good can happen. Perhaps we surrender to the greater good or discover some kernel of wisdom. At other times we use the tools to spiral up, and we are back to One.

I don't know what caused it, but the other night I was at a 5 PLUS, and I felt bone-chillingly alone. So I curled up in bed and shut off the light, and I tried to connect with my body and keep my mind from racing. I surrendered to my emotions and connected to the deepest part of myself. The next morning, several things that had been troubling me seemed to take care of themselves. I think the 5 State had something to do with it.

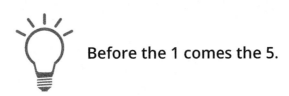

Before the 1 comes the 5.

The Perfection of Brain State 5

- A moment of opportunity
- A prelude to Brain State 1
- A time for profound connection

The other joy of Brain State 5 is that stress offers a moment of opportunity to rewire faulty circuits. Only when we are in highly stressed states are our wires unlocked so that we can transform them.

I am going through a divorce and adjusting to the fact that I've lost many of my friends. The circumstances of the breakup were so egregious and full of betrayal and back-biting that my life will never be the same. I was sinking into a 5 PLUS state and started rocking back and forth and really listening to my desperate, negative inner voice. I realized that maybe my life needed a shake-up. Maybe this is the best thing that could have happened to me. I spiraled up to Brain State 1!

When in the emotional crisis of a 5 State, we are in the middle of a fight-or-flight response that tells us that there is no hope, and all is lost. It is not. Instead, if we can find a shred of compassion for ourselves, any semblance of loving connection, we can change our brain for the better.

Experiment with this tool and personalize it. That way you can minimize the harm of Brain State 5 and reap the rewards of this important state.

Success Check Day 6

- **Daily Success**

☐ I continued my Power of One Practice with 10 Check Ins and 10 Joy Points.

☐ I used the 5 Tool and the 5 PLUS Tool three times each (even if I was not actually at Brain State 5).

☐ I made one or more community connections for support with these tools.

- **Did I pass the Success Check?   YES   NO**

If you did not, stay with this activity for one more day, then move on.

- **My Amazing Learning:**

_____

- **My Biggest Accomplishment:**

_____

- **My Biggest Challenge:**

_____

Congratulations!

**You have completed Day 6 of The Power of One Challenge.
Your next step is Day 7. Zap a Glitch.**

Day 7. Zap a Glitch

Today we will learn how to use the Cycle Tool. We'll focus on learning the Zap a Glitch Cycle that deactivates drives to repeat old patterns.

Using this tool is great fun. It gives you a way to unlock your unconscious mind. Words bubble up into your conscious mind and sometimes they make no sense at all. Perfect! This is the nature of breaking open wires in the unconscious memory system and pouring their contents into the conscious mind. We have both amazing awakenings and rapid stress reduction.

There are three types of Cycle Tools. They are all used at Brain State 4, when we are definitely stressed. This technique, the Zap a Glitch Cycle, short-circuits our drive to escape from being present by repeating an old way of coping, even if it did not work very well. When that wire is activated, we lose our access to the Power of One and become so stressed that the thinking brain does not function well. We're at the mercy of the circuit and do whatever it tells us to do! The Zap a Glitch Cycle fights back, shutting down that wire!

These wires are the bullies in the world of neural circuits. They are extreme, quick, and stealthy, so when they are triggered, we have no idea what happened to us! They hijack our brain! Having a simple tool to deactivate this wire makes for a better day and a better life!

The circuit is triggered so quickly that I go from feeling a little stressed to going numb and merging with my children, trying to be sure that nobody ever hurts them the way I was hurt. The problem is my glitches.

The Zap a Glitch Cycle

- Stop cravings, overreactions, and feeling triggered.
- Rapidly spiral up and enjoy the Power of One.

Why

We focus much of our attention in this challenge on the Zap a Glitch Cycle because when we rewire these escapes, a cascade of positive changes follows. Our behavior changes. Stress-fueled patterns quiet down and we can raise our set point more easily.

The Zap a Glitch Cycle rapidly reduces stress. In one to four minutes, we can radically change our mindset. If we are triggered, that strong activation stops. What if we have a craving? We can short-circuit it with this tool and access the Power of One. It will become a mainstay for you for dealing effectively with the daily stresses of life.

My stress style is to get safety by procrastinating on a project. Today I was stalled and procrastinating about something and checked in at Brain State 4. I did a quick Cycle and spiraled up. I got started on the project right away.

This tool works well because it switches off a faulty allostatic circuit and replaces it with an effective homeostatic circuit. These stress-overload wires activate inaccurate, often extreme emotions, and make unreasonable expectations sound completely reasonable! They tell us to do something that is totally ineffective, but it not only sounds reasonable, we feel compelled to do it! We spiral down into a stressed state and have a bad feeling in our body – an afterburn from stress overload.

By using the Cycle Tool, we can switch off this circuit and switch on a homeostatic circuit. This is not possible when using cognitive tools only. One can't "think" their way out of a spending spree or be "mindfully aware" enough to process emotions effectively when they are this intense. The stress of an allostatic circuit (brain glitch or Stress Circuit) takes emotional tools to process effectively. By becoming proficient in the Cycle Tool, you can switch from spiraling down to spiraling up!

Once you switch gears in the brain's circuitry, the effective circuit takes charge. Our emotions are balanced and accurate and point us to what we need. It's easier to meet those needs and return to the Power of One. We get a spurt of dopamine and an afterglow of well-being.

How

To use this tool, just follow the lead-ins, stating the phrases word for word. They are the pathway to making this tool perform optimally. State the lead-in, then pause and wait for something to bubble up into your mind. Don't judge the words and feelings that appear. Just feel them and then go on to the next lead-In.

Neuroscience-based Resiliency
• Shut off that Stress Circuit!
• Switch on a Joy Circuit.
• Collect a Joy Point.

I think of doing Cycles throughout the day as my way of being an emotional warrior. It's a personal policy of mine to charge forward into my stressed feelings and clear away that emotional clutter. Who knows what profound insights could come from doing a Cycle!

You will become very good at cycling sooner than you might think. In time, you'll notice that you can cycle through almost anything – and come out the other side feeling connected to your body with a smile on your face. Once you establish that you are not passive about your emotions, but instead, cycle through them, life becomes far more manageable. You don't have to worry about getting triggered or shutting down. You have tools – and you know how to use them!

Whenever you check in at Brain State 4, definitely stressed, use this tool. Once you start, DO NOT THINK! If you are stressed enough to use the Cycle Tool, the thoughts coming from your thinking brain are not very helpful. They will be soon, though, once you spiral up!

Use the lead-ins for Zap a Glitch. What if it does not spiral you upward? That's not a problem. Just circle back around and try a different tool. The reptile will want you to quit, but we just laugh off the lizard's negativity and keep using the tools!

The Zap a Glitch Cycle Tool

- **Focus on what is bothering you.**
  The situation is . . .
  (COMPLAIN, STATE FACTS, NOT FEELINGS.)
  What I'm most stressed about is . . .
  (ONE SIMPLE STATEMENT ABOUT ONE TOPIC.)
- **Express anger (A+ Anger) to unlock the circuit.**
  I feel angry that . . .
  I can't stand it that . . .
  I hate it that . . .
  (plus more anger until your mind shuts off for a moment – you've unlocked the circuit!)
- **Feel your feelings (pause before and after each one).**
  I feel sad that . . .
  I feel afraid that . . .
  I feel guilty that . . .
- **Discover the glitch so that you can deactivate it.**
  OF COURSE I would do that, because my unreasonable expectation is . . .
- **Switch to a new circuit and lock it in.**
  SLOW – Negate the unreasonable expectation 3 times.
  RAMP UP – Ridicule the unreasonable expectation 3 times.
  JOY – State the reasonable expectation 3 times.

The situation is . . . I have way too much work to do and I don't know how I am going to get it done. I keep working and it is never good enough. It takes me so long to get anything done. What I'm most stressed about is . . . Whatever I do never works out. I feel angry that . . . nothing ever works out. I can't stand it that . . . I am bad at everything I do . . . I hate it that . . . I am such a failure. I HATE IT! I HATE IT! I HATE IT! I feel sad that . . . I can't get it right. I feel afraid that . . . no matter what I do it is wrong. I feel guilty that . . . I give up so easily. Of course I would give up easily, because my unreasonable expectation is . . . I get my safety from . . . being perfect. If I am not perfect, I quit! I . . . can . . . NOT . . . get my . . . safety from being perfect. I . . . can . . . NOT . . . get my . . . safety . . . from being . . . perfect. I can NOT get . . . my . . . safety . . . from being perfect. That's ridiculous! I can NOT get safety from being perfect. Being perfect just makes me stressed. It makes me quit. That's ridiculous! I get my safety from . . . connecting with myself and doing the best I can. I get my safety from connecting to myself and doing the best I can. That's it! I get my safety from connecting to myself and doing the best I can! Hey, I'm at ONE!

Why should I complain?
When you complain about something, the circuits that are causing you to feel bad become activated. When they are activated, you can change them!

I spent my entire life trying not to be negative. I was taught not to complain. I have lots of complaints that I've been suppressing. Finally, I can let off steam about things that have bothered me for decades. Maybe that will help stop me from stressing out.

I was raised with shame, I don't want to express guilt
How do we discover wires? By stating what we believe we could have done differently. We complete the phrase: I feel guilty that . . . And if we state what we truly believe we could have done differently, we discover that we did that because of a wire. That guilt draws us right to the wire (the unreasonable expectation) that is the problem, so we can rewire it. There is no shame here.

We are not bad. It's a matter of learning from our mistakes. If you have lived in a shaming environment, consider using a lead-in that makes it absolutely clear there are no judgments involved such as: In the best of all worlds, I wish that I had . . . I do have some power here. Why didn't I just . . . or I regret that I . . . Personalize this lead-in so that it is supportive and powerful for you!

I don't like to be angry
The anger we use in the Cycle Tool is not the kind of anger people express when they yell at someone or go into a rage. It is a protest against being hurt. As soon as you activate the reptilian brain and express enough anger to unlock the circuit, the anger goes away. It flows into feelings that heal. Anger has a unique role in activating circuits so that we can rewire them. It is the only negative emotion associated with power. Start slowly and practice safe, effective anger. Go at your own pace. In time you will have a great A+ Anger skill, and you'll be crushing circuits right and left!

How do I figure out the unreasonable expectation?
This is easy. The key is that you do not figure it out. You let your unconscious mind do the work. It's all in the power of using the lead-ins, then pausing, tolerating irresolution for a moment, and watching what bubbles up into your mind.

Move through the lead-ins for Zap a Glitch until the prompt turns your focus to guilt. This is where you exercise your power to identify the wire and to change it so that you will respond differently in the future.

Say what you feel guilty about. Be sure it is authentic. It's not what other people tell you that you should feel guilty about, but what you believe is your part of what happened. It must be something that you have the power to change. Feel free to change the lead-in for guilt if you would like. Make it work for you!

The reason you did what you did or responded the way you responded is because a wire in your unconscious mind told you to do it. The problem is the wire, and by stating what you wished you had done differently, you can then find the wire, or unreasonable expectation, that made it perfectly reasonable that you would do it. Use the next lead-in with a strong, supportive vocal tone. Even though you may be saying it to yourself, vocal tone has a powerful impact on the brain. Be kind to yourself. The problem was not you. It was a wire!

Of course I did that . . .
Say to yourself, "Of course I did that, because my unreasonable expectation is . . . " This is where you pause. Turn your attention to your body and wait for something to bubble up into your mind. That is your unreasonable expectation.

What if no words appear in your mind? Repeat the lead-in. Perhaps words will bubble up into your conscious mind when you repeat it. If you are using the EBT app, click on "Select an option" to review some of the most common first words for the unreasonable expectation. Regardless, repeat this process until the words that bubble up ring true for you.

. . . because my unreasonable expectation is . . .
Tolerate not thinking! Pause and allow words to appear in your mind. Let the activation of the emotional circuit inform you of its contents. What if no words appear? Return to the "I feel guilty that . . . " and run through the lead-ins again. Stay relaxed, and keep circling around through the lead-ins. Sometimes you never find words that ring true and sometimes you do. There are NO judgments. Just have fun with it!

When the words of the unreasonable expectation ring true, the message in your emotional circuit and the words in your conscious mind match! You have discovered your unreasonable expectation. Once you have identified it, follow the prompts to complete the Cycle. In other words, spiral up. Enjoy the Power of One.

Now let's change the circuit: the Grind In
Once you have discovered the unreasonable expectation stored in that wire, you can deactivate that circuit with a series of statements. This is your Grind In. Repeating these words that are personalized will weaken and transform your circuit. That grinding in – first slowly, then ramped up (ridiculing the wire), and finally transforming it – brings on two benefits.

The Grind In

The first benefit of grinding it in is that it often short-circuits the wire, helping you switch off stress and activate Brain State 1. The second benefit is that each time you do a Cycle can make a small but important change in your wiring. If you activate enough A+ Anger to experience "the unlocking moment," the six hours following your Cycle are an optimal time to use your Grind In to maximize progress rewiring the circuit. During that time, the synaptic connections between the neurons are still fluid, so by continuing to repeat the Grind In, the wire can continue to change.

Within that six-hour rewiring window, the effectiveness of repeating the Grind In decreases over time. Repeating your Grind In during the 30 minutes after your Cycle can have the greatest impact on that wire. Up until two hours after your Cycle has a lesser effect and after six hours, the impact of repeating it becomes minimal at best.

Some people take the 30 minutes after doing a deep Cycle (the Cycles that include A+ Anger and the unlocking moment) to repeat their Grind In. As strong emotions amplify rewiring, some people even dance, sing, shout, or yell the words, which is not only effective, but also a lot of fun!

I was devastated when I found out that my fiancé was happy to sleep with me but was dating another woman that "he liked better." As soon as he left my apartment, I did a rip-roaring Cycle, then shouted and sang my Grind In for half an hour. I said I can NOT get my love from him. That's ridiculous! I can NOT get love from that man. How ridiculous! I can absolutely NOT get my love from HIM. I get my love from inside me. I GET MY LOVE from inside ME. I get my love from inside ME!!!! WHA-HOOOOO! For the first time after a major breakup, I did not go into depression, drink, or overspend. I left and went for a long walk. It was an absolutely beautiful day! I had one of the best walks of my life. The colors were so beautiful, and the air was cool and fresh on my cheeks. I was so happy to be FULLY alive!!!

The 3 rules: Rewiring success!

Be sure to check after doing each Cycle if you followed the three rules of reconsolidating: 1) you used a spark of emotions to unlock the circuit; 2) you felt your feelings to begin to discover and change the wire, and 3) you locked in that improvement in your wiring with a surge of dopamine. Do a rewiring success check, then collect a Joy Point for being part of the new golden age of emotional plasticity.

Have fun with it. Overthinking is not allowed!

Much like the Check In Tool, when using the Cycle Tool, do not overthink it! These are natural brain processes, and each use of the tool is perfect in its own way. If a tool does not alleviate stress, how perfect! Both your conscious and unconscious mind learn from that. Just try another tool! Be devoted to the process, and trust that by continuing to stay connected to your emotions and using the tools, sooner or later you will feel MUCH better, and will have rewired your brain in a small but important way. Experiment and explore!

Day 7 is a fun day. Just play with zapping a glitch. Take it slowly and do exactly what the reptilian brain dislikes the most – Have Fun!

Success Check Day 7

- **Daily Success**

☐ I continued my Power of One Practice with 10 Check Ins and 10 Joy Points.

☐ I played with the Zap a Glitch Cycle Tool – and did at least five Cycles.

☐ I made one or more community connections for support doing Cycles.

- **Did I pass the Success Check?   YES   NO**

If you did not, stay with this activity for one more day, then move on.

- **My Amazing Learning:**

_____

- **My Biggest Accomplishment:**

_____

- **My Biggest Challenge:**

_____

Congratulations!

**You have completed Day 7 of The Power of One Challenge.
Your next step is Day 8. Lifestyle Reset #2 Play.**

Day 8. Lifestyle Reset #2 Play

Congratulations on completing Spiral Up to One. It's time to play with the reptilian brain in a new way. You are coaxing the brain to get out of the stress habit. That requires asking it to respond differently to daily life.

The exceedingly serious reptile within becomes completely disoriented when you ask it to do one thing: play. It simply cannot stay serious and stressed when you play. The activity for today is to take time to play.

Even one minute of play can befuddle the reptile enough to change your entire day. Tease, goof off, or be a little mischievous, even a bit bad. Oh, how the excessively serious reptilian brain can't stand that!

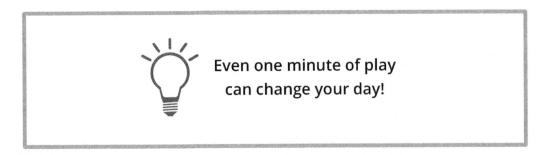

Even one minute of play
can change your day!

Why

Each moment of play delivers a new kind of Joy Point. That joy keeps a twinkle in our eye, a bounce to our step, and a sense of lightness about us. We can't help but like ourselves more because we are having fun. That playfulness is catching and people around us lighten up, too. You've already loosened up the reptilian brain's attachment to stress by scoring Joy Points. Today you'll build on that success by being playful – for even one minute.

> Instead of being serious, TEASE.
>
> Instead of being productive, GOOF OFF.
>
> Instead of being good, BE MISCHIEVOUS!

My teenage son Keith has a lot of hormones raging and he is so prickly. I can't do anything right! I looked him straight in the eye and said, "Keith, want to play gin rummy?" He looked at me as if I were crazy, then said, "Okay!" We had so much fun.

I am an accountant and have been accused of being too serious, so this reset of play irritated my reptilian brain. I almost didn't do it. Then when I was driving home from work, instead of listening to the news on the radio, I switched to the Beatles Channel and started singing and rocking out in the car. What fun!

How

Much like it's hard to know what is a funny joke until you notice yourself laughing, it's impossible to know what is fun for you until you expand your repertoire of things to do that could feel playful.

Notice your emotions and sensations. Which activities are fun and activate the sense of freedom that you had as a child? Reject thinking too much and all that silly perfectionism. Life is to be enjoyed. Play!

Play Checklist

- ☐ Get into a tug of war with your dog!
- ☐ Toss basketballs from your desk into a hoop.
- ☑ Turn on your favorite music and rock out at home.
- ☐ Throw a Frisbee with a friend.
- ☐ Play "cat and mouse" with your cat.
- ☐ Watch a movie you love for the hundredth time.
- ☐ Buy finger paints or a coloring book and create.
- ☐ Find a bug and love it – watch it for two minutes and feel the glow.
- ☐ Sing off key intentionally and remark, "That's creative!"
- ☐ Play a musical instrument in ways that are fun.
- ☐ Poke your teenager and say, "Poke me back!"
- ☐ Soak in a bubble bath and play with the bubbles.
- ☐ Splash in the pool instead of swimming.
- ☑ Wear a bright color or a fun hat.
- ☐ Tickle a loved one when they least expect it.
- ☐ Find and read your favorite book from childhood.
- ☐ Gently tease your loved one until they throw a pillow at you.
- ☐ Dance silly until you fall onto the sofa exhausted and laughing.
- ☐ Gaze at the night sky and choose a star that is yours and yours alone.
- ☐ Ask your family member or roommate to dance.
- ☐ Dress up as your favorite character in a movie – be them for a night.
- ☐ Play a game you haven't played since childhood.
- ☐ Stomp your feet while sitting down and get a rhythm going.
- ☐ Imagine that you are a superhero and bask in your glory.
- ☑ Go to a playground and swing on the swings.
- ☑ Write a short story in which you make your dreams come true.

Success Check Day 8

- **Daily Success**

☐ I continued my Power of One Practice with 10 Check Ins and 10 Joy Points.

☐ I reset my lifestyle in these two ways: Exercise and Play.

☐ I made one or more community connections for support with this lifestyle reset.

- **Did I pass the Success Check?   YES   NO**

If you did not, stay with this activity for one more day, then move on.

- **My Amazing Learning:**

_____

- **My Biggest Accomplishment:**

_____

- **My Biggest Challenge:**

_____

Congratulations!

**You have completed Day 8 of The Power of One Challenge.
Your next step is Day 9. Expand You Power.**

Day 9. Expand Your Power

Today you'll expand your power to be at Brain State 1. There are four more EBT tools that will complete your set for spiraling up. After this, you'll focus on drilling down into the circuits that block the Power of One, the Stress Circuits.

Right now, your attention should turn to one thing: How do I get to One 10 times per day? Becoming highly proficient at getting to One is important. Each time you spiral up, the "grooves" in your brain to get to One become deeper, and it's all so much easier.

My daughter just threw up on our new couch, my sister is divorcing her husband, and my boss has been glowering at me, expecting me to be perfect. Hmmmm, I can stay depressed or I can experience all this at Brain State 1. What's my choice?

Why
To expand your power, you'll use the tools for Brain States 1 and 2 and the remaining two Cycle Tools. Although the Zap a Glitch Cycle is the powerhouse of this challenge, the other two Cycle Tools are also amazingly effective. Personalize the tools to your brain, using any of them you like and noticing what occurs. Use them flexibly. Try out a tool and see if it works!

I was at a deep Brain State 5 and used the 5 PLUS Tool, then had the intuition to use the 1 Tool. IT WORKED! I was radiating joy for the next hour! Who would have thought that would happen?

My first guess was that I was at Brain State 4. On a lark, I tried the 2 Tool and shot right to One. My brain state had been higher than I thought!

I use all three of the Cycles. I start with Zap a Glitch, then Feel Better, and finish with Take Action. If I am bordering on Brain State 5, that works really well. I know I had a lot of trauma growing up, and the bottom of my brain is a hotbed of circuits of hurt. It takes me a little longer to move through stress, but that's fine. It's a good use of my time!

The Most Important Habit of All

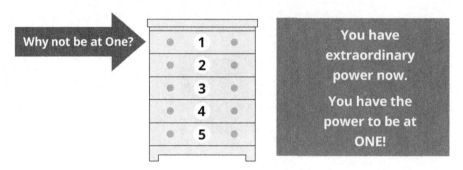

Why not be at One?

1
2
3
4
5

You have extraordinary power now.

You have the power to be at ONE!

How

Use the lead-ins and your brain will warm up to using these tools. State each word of each lead-in carefully. The tools are very precise. Each one is based on neuroscience. You use specific phrases in order, stating them to yourself or aloud. PAUSE. Wait for your unconscious mind to complete the sentence. Without that PAUSE, the tools will not be effective. Then move on to the next lead-in. Learn these tools by using them in your daily life!

The 1 Tool (the "Compassion Tool")

This tool sustains Brain State 1. The 1 Tool activates the brain's reward center with sustainable surges of neurotransmitters. Our reward center lights up. In this state of connection, our motivations are based on purpose, that is, moving forward in our own evolution and making the world a better place. We have all the energy in the world. Not only are our needs for safety, love, comfort, pleasure, and purpose met, but we are aware of the elevated emotions of love, compassion, gratitude, hope, forgiveness, awe, and joy.

Access a natural high throughout your day

Use the 1 Tool to prolong and deepen an elevated emotion. Most people vastly underestimate how often they are at One. Try using this tool at least once a day, and surprise yourself by how well it works. Each of the three lead-ins is a "command" to yourself to feel the elevated emotion of compassion. First, you instruct yourself to feel compassion for yourself.

The 1 Tool – Compassion Tool
• Feel compassion for myself.
• Feel compassion for others.
• Feel compassion for all living beings.

Then you pause for a moment and notice a wave of compassion in your body. That body sensation confirms that you are at Brain State 1 and encourages you to continue using the tool to experience an even stronger natural high.

Next, you tell yourself to feel compassion for others. Once you feel that wave of compassion for others in your body, you are ready for the last command of the tool. You tell yourself to extend your compassion to all living beings. When you do that, you feel a glow.

Where did my compassion go?

Do not hold back from using this tool! Often you will surprise yourself that you can access compassion. When you are connected, it is easy to feel compassion for yourself and others! However, when you are in stress, compassion vanishes.

The problem is not you. It's a wire that triggered a stressed brain state. Cortisol blocks our capacity to feel compassion. This is true for all people. When you have no compassion, fantastic! You have valuable information. You are at a lower brain state. Perfect! The most fundamental rule of the emotional brain: DO NOT JUDGE!

I follow the lead-ins with my thinking brain and I feel a wave of compassion, then another one. I am controlling my chemical reality.

The Compassion Tool Lead-Ins

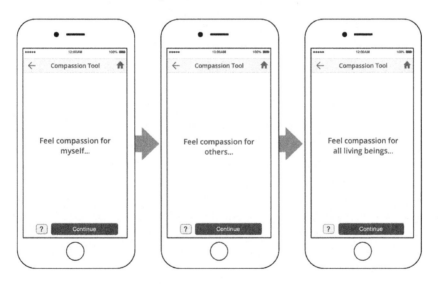

The 2 Tool (the "Feelings Tool")

Use the 2 Tool when you feel present and aware, but lack that certain glow of feeling rewarded. When we are at Brain State 1, our emotions accurately signal us to meet our true needs. When we are at Brain State 2, this tool guides our way back to Brain State 1.

The 2 Tool – Feelings Tool
• How do I feel?
• What do I need?
• Do I need support?

This tool is miraculous. By the time I ask the first two questions, I'm connected, present, and in the flow. I tingle with warmth and excitement about . . . being alive and having a chance to try to figure out what my dreams are, and how to make them come true!

How do I feel?

The trick to making this tool effective is to ask yourself, "How do I feel?" and then pause. Several emotions will compete for dominance. Let them fight it out!

After about 10 to 20 seconds, one emotion will be strongest. Based on evolutionary biology, the dominant feeling points to the most important need. Knowing what we need is so important to our survival that we experience a surge of dopamine from being aware of our need! We are at Brain State 1 before taking any action to meet our identified need.

Basic Feelings				
Negative				
angry	sad	afraid	guilty	tired
tense	hungry	full	lonely	sick
Positive				
grateful	happy	secure	proud	rested
relaxed	satisfied	loved	loving	healthy

To identify your need, ask, "What do I need?" In other words, given that feeling, what is the corresponding need? Pause until some words appear in your mind, then ask yourself, "Do I need support?" to check whether you need support from others to meet that need. Sometimes you will and sometimes you will not.

I wish I had known about this tool before. I think my set point may be 2 because I can use this tool as part of my Check In. I get to Brain State 1 about 70 percent of the time. I was on vacation this week, so that may explain it!

The Feelings Tool Lead-Ins

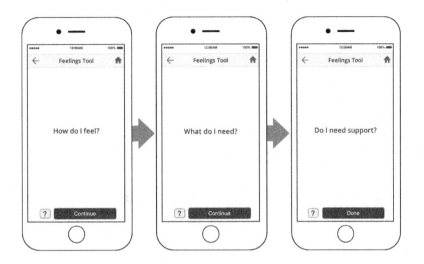

What do I need? The logical need vs. the intuitive need

Sometimes our need is very logical. I am tired. I need to rest. However, most of the time it is not logical. It is intuitive, reflecting our deeper knowing of what we need. Instead of trying to figure out what you need, it's best to wait for the intuitive need – the product of the wisdom of your emotional brain – to bubble up.

When you ask the question, "What do I need?" and pause for long enough (usually about 10 to 20 seconds), words that convey the accurate need will arrive in your mind.

Do I need support from others?

The last question of this tool checks whether or not we need support from others. We have added that question because all humans need emotional connection and interdependence. It's the unifying experiences of giving and receiving support that add so much meaning to our lives. When in doubt, ask for support from others!

I asked, "How do I feel?" I wasn't sure, but after a bit, the word "lonely" appeared in my mind. I pondered that for a few moments. That surprised me. I didn't think I was lonely. Then I asked myself, "What do I need?" The answer appeared in my mind: to open up and talk about my feelings. Do I need support to do that? Yes! I need to talk with my partner and not be so closed down!

The 4 Tools (the "Feel Better Cycle" and the "Take Action Cycle")

When you are at Brain State 4, any of the Cycle Tools will help you move toward Brain State 1. When the 4th Drawer of the brain is activated, an array of circuits take charge. The Zap a Glitch Cycle deactivates cravings, overreactions, and shutdowns. The other two Cycles are extremely helpful when you have chronic stress and feel bad or when you need the motivation to take action. Try out these tools and see how they work for you!

The Feel Better Cycle Tool

When you feel a steady bad feeling, rather than a sense of being triggered, often this tool will work wonders. Like the Zap a Glitch Cycle Tool, it deactivates unreasonable expectations and activates reasonable expectations, but the "body feel" of using this tool is quite different. With the Zap a Glitch Cycle, the craving or drive ceases. We have more freedom to control our responses. With the Feel Better Cycle Tool, the chronic sense of discomfort, uneasiness, or disconnection ends and is replaced by a sense of comfort, ease, and connection.

For example, if we felt powerless in a moment of extreme stress, the brain encoded a circuit that activates the general message: I have no power. That causes the chronic activation of stress chemicals. We feel bad! The Feel Better Cycle discovers that message and turns it into a positive message that makes us feel good.

The 4 Tool – Try Out the Feel Better and Take Action Cycles

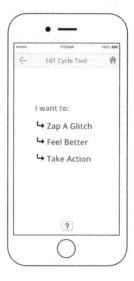

The situation is . . . I am alone, and it's a holiday. Everyone has family but me. What I'm most stressed about is . . . I am alone. I feel angry that . . . I am alone. I can't stand it that . . . nobody cares about me. I HATE it that . . . everyone else has family, and I don't. I feel sad that . . . I am alone . . . I feel afraid that . . . there is something wrong with me . . . I feel guilty that . . . I don't put more effort into making friends. OF COURSE I don't put more effort into making friends, because my unreasonable expectation is . . . I have no power. That rings true. I'm going to negate it . . . I . . . DO . . . have . . . power . . . I . . . DO . . . have . . . power . . . I . . . DO have power. Of course, I have power. I do have power. In fact, I do have power, and I'm going to use it!

The Take Action Cycle Tool

The Take Action Cycle can almost always bring us to Brain State 1 because it helps us construct a pathway forward that leads to a higher-order purpose. Use it after another tool when that tool does not bring you to One or use it on its own.

This tool begins with the same lead-ins as the other Cycle Tools but finishes by encoding an expectation of how you will follow through. This tool involves more steps than the other Cycle tools but can reliably bring us to One. When we find our pathway forward our brain rewards us with a burst of dopamine. You will use this tool frequently when you are wired at One. However, use it now anytime you have no idea what you should do. This tool will guide your way. It can be a lifesaver!

The situation is . . . I want to put more effort into friendships, but with my work being so demanding, I do not know how I will do that. What I'm most stressed about is . . . I do not know how to make time for friends. I feel angry that . . . I don't know how to have a work life and a personal life. I can't stand it that . . . I don't know what I'm doing. I HATE it that . . . it's so complicated . . . I feel sad that . . . I have not made this a priority. I feel afraid . . . I will never make it a priority. I feel guilty that . . . I do not know how to organize this. I expect myself to do the best I can to go out socially once per week. Positive powerful thought? I can do that. The essential pain? It takes work. The earned reward? Integrity, doing the right thing. I do not want to live an isolated life. What do I need? To put it on my calendar and call someone I like. Do I need support? No, I can do this.

The situation is . . . everyone around me is anxious, focusing on how terribly things are going, and is perpetually at Brain State 4 to 5. What I'm most stressed about is . . . I am different from them. I feel angry that . . . I am different. I can't stand it that . . . I can get to One and they don't even believe that One exists. I feel sad that . . . I am alone. I feel afraid that . . . I will make them feel bad if I am as happy as I can be. I feel guilty that . . . I am diminishing my life because of them. I expect myself to connect with myself and get to One. Positive, powerful thought? I can do that. The essential pain? They may not like me. I may be threatening to them. They could reject me. The earned reward? Even if they reject me, I will not reject myself! My reward? Authenticity. What do I need? To check in and get to One. Do I need support? Yes, lots of community connections.

You have a full toolkit of emotional tools. Well done! The reptile may be pushing back, not wanting you to be as powerful and connected as you can be. Also, if others around you have a lower set point, you might be afraid to be at One. Keep in mind why you are doing this work, your earned reward, because the world needs you to be at One. Nobody can do it for you, but now that you have the tools, you can do it for yourself!

Success Check Day 9

- **Daily Success**

☐ I continued my Power of One Practice with 10 Check Ins and 10 Joy Points.

☐ I used each of the four tools at least once.

☐ I made one or more community connections for support with practicing the tools.

- **Did I pass the Success Check?   YES   NO**

If you did not, stay with this activity for one more day, then move on.

- **My Amazing Learning:**

_____

- **My Biggest Accomplishment:**

_____

- **My Biggest Challenge:**

_____

Congratulations!

**You have completed Day 9 of The Power of One Challenge.
Your next step is Day 10. Discover Your Mood Circuit.**

Create Connection

Day 10. Discover Your Mood Circuit

Let's start rewiring! This is the most exciting part of this course. You will unlock and update a fight-or-flight drive that triggers an unwanted mood. You'll create a Power Grind In to use in daily life to deactivate the circuit and transform it into a circuit that brings you to Brain State 1. You will target four circuits in this course and use the same process to deactivate each wire and transform it into a circuit that gets you unstuck from stress. Once you are unstuck, the brain's resiliency drive will take you up and over to your joy.

The Four Circuits
• The Mood Circuit • The Love Circuit • The Work Circuit • The Habit Circuit

I didn't realize that something inside me was striving to feel good about myself and have peace inside. All I needed to do was dislodge myself from that clog of stress in my brain. The rest became so much easier.

What is a Mood Circuit?

A Mood Circuit activates a fight-or-flight drive for a particular mood. Each circuit was encoded by random life experiences when we were in stress overload. We rewire this circuit first because Mood Circuits are co-activated with all other circuits. By weakening this circuit first, all the other wires you choose in this course will be easier to revise.

As Mood Circuits are activated so often, they become strong and familiar. It does not feel good to be depressed, lost, or anxious, but the reptile within will activate a familiar circuit, even if it doesn't seem objectively rewarding. According to the work of neuroscientist Candace Pert, an addiction to

The Mood Circuit

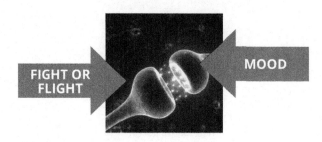

an emotional state may be stronger than other excesses and, ultimately, we may be more addicted to a mood than to whatever we do in that mood state.

My mood circuit is anxiety. I have been anxious since my dog died and my parents divorced in the same year. I don't like anxiety, but I have no idea what I would do without it. Anxiety is so familiar. It's like a best friend.

I can't say that depression feels good, but it is familiar and when I trigger my depression circuit, it keeps me from being present to my balanced emotions. I do not want to feel those feelings, and my depression circuit takes me on an escape to all the other times I was depressed. In a way, it brings me home to a world that is familiar to me.

My wife tells me I have a rage problem. I am feeling calm and fine, then something shifts in my mind like a switch going off, and suddenly I'm furious. I have a lot of stuffed outrage from my years in the service, including three deployments, so it makes sense that it is a Mood Circuit.

If you told me I was addicted to shame, I would have laughed. Yet I feel an ongoing sense that there is something wrong with me most of the time. My Mood Circuit could be shame, or it could be numbness, as my shame is so painful that it triggers a numbness wire. That's when I use drinking, drugs, or another escape like video games.

All mood types can be Mood Circuits

The most confusing aspect of Mood Circuits is that they can appear in such diverse forms – we can feel very high, very low, or numb. What these wires have in common is that they take us away from being present to our balanced feelings. Whatever emotional escape the brain chooses, it can be stuck on for so long that the brain begins to believe that it is normal. Then, the reptilian brain forgets how great we can feel and becomes stuck in that mood.

These moods vary a lot. Some are quite weak and don't bother us much. But others are so strong that they significantly block our Power of One. For example, with anxiety, a weak mood circuit might cause us to be unsettled and a little anxious, but a strong one could cause us to have a full-blown panic attack. What determines the strength of a wire? Both the brain state we were in when it was encoded, and all the activations of that circuit since then, that either strengthened or weakened it.

Stressed Moods

Mood Type	Examples
False Highs	rebellious, all-powerful, manic, arrogant, frenzied, reckless, righteous, bullet-proof, chaotic, high
Unnecessary Lows	anxious, depressed, hostile, irritable, powerless, self-pitying, panicked, worried, discouraged, lost, ashamed, overwhelmed, disgusted, annoyed
Numbness	no feelings, shut down, numb, empty, detached, disconnected, zoned out, empty, blanked out

Why

We rewire these circuits because they trigger, co-activate, and prolong every other circuit we have that causes us to respond to life in a way we don't like. There is an economy to rewiring them, which is why we launch our rewiring campaign by creating a Power Grind In for Mood. The goal of this course is to create four personalized Power Grind Ins, which you will use to rewire these four circuits and raise your set point during the Second 30 Days Program.

How

For each of the four major wires, one in each domain of life, you will use the same rewiring process. There are three steps: discover, negate, and transform. Take one step per day. If you need more time for a step, it is important to take that time!

The EBT Rewiring Plan

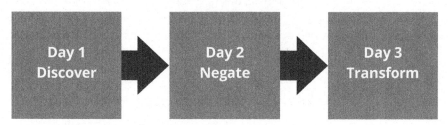

Mood Circuits vary in intensity

Like all of our circuits, the habit of being in a particular mood can be encoded in any brain state. It can be our stress style as a way to get safety, love, comfort, or pleasure. However, the strongest drives and the most disruptive are those encoded when we are in high-stress states: Brain States 4 or 5.

In Brain State 5, an especially strong wire (a survival circuit), can be linked to an unbalanced mood, such as anxiety, depression, shame, or hostility. These survival circuits, or 5 Circuits, have a special role in EBT because they are evolutionarily based. They originated from a fight-or-flight drive for us to survive that inadvertently bonded to a response that did not help us survive. The new response became easily activated. These circuits are that touchy! Even small stresses, like an annoying comment someone makes or a slightly aggravating situation, can trigger that wire. Then the brain's stress switch, the hypothalamus, triggers biochemical mayhem throughout the brain and body. Every aspect of life, including our mood, becomes more extreme. What has caused it? That 5 Circuit! And because allostatic circuits are sticky and become stuck on, that 5 State can last for hours, days, or weeks!

Day 1. Discover your Circuit

Begin by discovering the specific circuit you want to rewire. You'll do that today for your Mood Circuit. It involves using the Zap a Glitch Cycle Tool to complain about the mood that bothers you the most. The result is that you activate and unlock the circuit so that you can update it. The first day is primarily an emotional experience, as once you discover the circuit, you'll focus on being aware of it. Six hours after you discover the circuit, strong emotions will begin to subside, and your attention will turn to analyzing your circuit, such as when it might have been encoded and whether or not it is an intergenerational circuit.

Day 2. Negate your Circuit

Next, weaken the circuit. Just the way that one must make a left turn in a car before continuing the arc to make a U-turn, changing a circuit requires steps. A quick hairpin turn of expectations triggers the reptilian brain, and in stress overload, the rewiring process shuts down. You'll negate the circuit, that is, add the word "NOT" to the unreasonable expectation. For example, if the unreasonable expectation is, "I get my safety from overworking," the negated statement is, "I can NOT get my safety from overworking."

You might wonder if the brain can hear that "NOT" or might instead take in the message "I get my safety from overworking." That concern is valid for circuits stored in the top two drawers of the brain! However, to rewire a 3, 4, or 5 Circuit, the fundamental laws of neuroplasticity require that we first negate it. The word "NOT" is stated with strong emotion, as the brain preferentially listens to the word that is expressed with the strongest emotion. You'll learn more about this tomorrow.

 **Take three days to create a Power Grind In,
then use it to clear away that wire!**

Day 3. Transform your Circuit

During the last day, you'll create a new circuit, one that tells you to connect with yourself, use a new approach to this stressor, and bring to mind a higher-order reward. This completes your Power Grind In and you can start using it four times daily to short-circuit this wire that triggers and sustains an unwanted mood and to transform the wire into any automatic response to stress of your choosing.

How do I discover my circuit? Use the Zap a Glitch Cycle lead-ins

To find your circuit, move through the Zap a Glitch Cycle lead-ins. Keep your sense of humor! The reptile would be happy to keep you from expressing A+ Anger until your mind goes blank. Here is step-by-step guidance for discovering your first wire.

Discover the Circuit!
Use the Zap a Glitch Lead-Ins

- The situation is . . .
- What I'm most stressed about is . . .
- I feel angry that . . .
- I can't stand it that . . .
- I hate it that . . .
- I feel sad that . . .
- I feel afraid that . . .
- I feel guilty that . . .
- OF COURSE I would do that, because
  my unreasonable expectation is . . .

---

1) Say What Is Bothering You
The situation is . . . What I'm most stressed about is . . .

In describing the situation, complain about your mood – Bring to mind your range of moods over the last week. Which mood would you most like to experience less often? State the facts, rather than expressing feelings. Complain about the mood in two to five sentences, then pause, and your emotional brain will look for the part of your complaint that is the most stressful to you. Then use the second lead-in, to find a simple, short statement of what you are most stressed about. This is the topic of your Cycle. Stay with this topic for the remainder of the Cycle.

EXAMPLE: *The situation is . . . I am completely out of control of my anxiety. I am on edge all the time and it's horrible. I don't know what to do about it. I get stuck feeling anxious and then I start overthinking and I can't stop! What I'm most stressed about is . . . I'm so anxious!*

2) Unlock the Circuit
I feel angry that . . . I can't stand it that . . . I hate it that . . .

Roust out that wire with A+ Anger – Express anger effectively by using the first lead-in, which is: I feel angry that . . . and complete the sentence by stating your topic. This is important. Staying on that topic will bring the best results! If your topic was: I am so hostile! Then state: I feel angry that I am so hostile. Continue with the next two lead-ins (I can't stand it that and I hate it that). Then continue expressing anger that is stronger, deeper, and grittier until you experience the unlocking moment.

What is the unlocking moment?

It's the experience of your mind going blank for a moment. You might even feel dumbstruck. It's your reward for reaching the circuits at the bottom of the brain and unlocking the synaptic connections of the neurons. This is a precondition for rewiring an allostatic circuit. You may find this difficult to do at first, but before long, it will be easy, satisfying, and, even enjoyable!

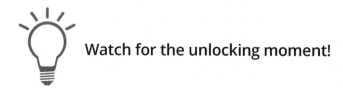 **Watch for the unlocking moment!**

Once your mind shuts off, pause. Take three deep breaths to connect with your body. You have just unlocked a major wire that is stored at the very bottom of your unconscious mind. Perfect!

EXAMPLE: *I feel angry that . . . I can't stop being so anxious. I can't stand it that . . . my anxiety controls my life. I HATE it that . . . I am so on edge . . . I hate it that I can't relax. I am furious that I am so afraid of everything and everyone. I HATE THAT! I hate that I can't stop worrying. I hate it that I am on pins and needles. I hate it that I have no peace inside. I HATE IT, I HATE IT . . . I HATE IT!!!* (The mind turns off for a moment and sadness flows. The circuit is now unlocked.)

3) Discover the Hidden Message
I feel sad that . . . I feel afraid that . . . I feel guilty that . . .
OF COURSE I did that, because my unreasonable expectation is . . .

State one feeling, then pause and feel It – You've cracked open that circuit and now it's time to release the pressure of its emotional contents. After pausing for long enough to feel connected to your body again, state each of the next three lead-ins. Instead of expressing emotions rapidly, feel the feelings deeply and avoid using more words. Once you say the lead-in, stay present to the emotions it stirs up until they fade. It is feeling the feeling, not simply expressing it, that begins to change the circuit. Do this for each of the three feelings, following the order of the lead-ins.

Start with "I feel sad that . . ." and pause. Wait for words to bubble up into your conscious mind to complete the sentence. Stay on the topic, which is your complaint about mood. Feel the sadness until it fades, about 10 to 20 seconds. Do not talk. Just feel your feeling until it fades. Then say, "I feel afraid that . . ." and do the same.

How do you discover the circuit?

- Use your thoughts about what is bothering you to activate the circuit that is the problem. Complain!

- Try to activate a high-stress state, such as Brain State 4 or 5. By using the lead-ins to express A+ anger, your brain will find and unlock the circuit that is driving your unwanted mood.

- Continue expressing anger until you have the "unlocking moment," the sign that your circuit is open, and you can change it!

- Pause and relax for long enough to return to Brain State 3, so that you can slowly and deeply feel your feelings.

- Complete the Cycle Tool and spiral up to Brain State 1 to lock in the new learning.

- What if it does not work? It always works because each time you do a Cycle, your brain becomes better at using this tool. With practice, you will become highly effective at rewiring circuits – sooner than you think!

Only when they cause problems, such as an unwanted mood, do we do the work to excavate these wires and update them. It is by finding your part in it – what you could have done differently – that your brain can direct you to the wire that is the problem. There are no judgments in this process. That wire made it perfectly reasonable for you to do what you did. We automatically obey our unconscious, primitive circuits as a survival strategy. The problem is not us. It's that old wire!

EXAMPLE: (After taking several deep breaths to ease stress so you can feel your deepest feelings) *"I feel sad that . . . I am always so anxious . . . I feel afraid that . . . I will always be anxious . . . I feel guilty that . . . I am so anxious!"*

Once you have identified your part in it (guilt), nurture yourself. A Stress Circuit made you do that! With an understanding and loving voice, say, "OF COURSE I did that, because my unreasonable expectation is . . ." and wait for words to bubble up. Once they appear in your mind, do not analyze the words. Trust them. Do not question the meaning of these words.

This is not a logical process. The test of whether these words "match" the wordless message stored in your unconscious mind is if you have a "body feel" that they ring true. If the words do not ring true, circle back to the I feel guilty lead-in and repeat the process until they do.

When the words match the emotional circuit's message, you will have nailed your cycle. When you state the words, your body will relax, and you will feel a slight glow. You may even be at Brain State 1, experiencing a surge of dopamine from finding your circuit.

Use the structure: I get my _____ from ____. These allostatic Stress Circuits are false associations between an unmet need and whatever we did to achieve a false sense that we were meeting our need. The most common unreasonable expectation used in EBT for Mood Circuits is: I get my safety from (a mood). However, listen to your body! Use the words that ring true for you! What if it's hard to find words that give you that body feel of "Yes! That's it!"? Repeat the lead-in and try again. Repeat it as many times as needed until you find the words that sound right to you. These words will match the emotional message in that circuit.

Discover Your Mood Circuit
I get my __(need)__ from __(mood)__ .

EXAMPLE: *"OF COURSE I would be anxious all the time, because my unreasonable expectation is . . . I get my safety from being anxious. I'm going to try that again. That doesn't ring true. OF COURSE I would be anxious all the time, because my unreasonable expectation is . . . I get my love from . . . being on edge. That's better, but it still doesn't ring true. OF COURSE I would be anxious all the time, because my unreasonable expectation is . . . I get my love from . . . being anxious. That feels right. That's my circuit. I get love and attention when I am slightly anxious, and a bit tense. I get my love from being anxious! That rings true."*

For the rest of the day, feel your feelings, and be aware of your circuit – Seeing that circuit just as it is – an extraneous wire that a random life event encoded in your brain – is often quite an emotional experience. For the first 30 minutes after you do your Cycle, the synaptic connections in the wire are very fluid, and by being aware of that wire, you can have the most impact on changing it. Between 30 minutes and two hours after discovery, the synapses are open, so focusing your attention on the emotions that were generated by the circuit is particularly helpful. Six hours after your Cycle the rewiring window closes, and although you can still impact the circuit, the synapses between the neurons have solidified and the hippocampus has stored them in long-term memory – for now! We can reactivate them later, but the rewiring window has shut. This is why the first day of the three-day rewiring plan is so powerful!

When I discovered my Mood Circuit, I was shocked. I was completely dumbstruck as the unconscious message my brain had been giving me is that I get my love from feeling depressed. My stomach turns over when I say that even now. It makes so much sense that I would be triggered to feel depressed, then wallow in it. I've done that since I was about nine years old. I sat in the feelings, and even though I was at work, I brought to mind this vision of a wire in my brain telling me that. I was filled with emotion all day. After the six-hour rewiring window, my mind turned to analyzing my circuit. It is my mother's circuit. Maybe there is a genetic component to this too, but she transferred it to me. So it was intergenerational. I think my grandfather had it too. I started feeling grateful for that circuit, as I had no emotional processing skills and must have been scared out of my mind, given what was going on at school and at home, and this circuit gave me an emotional escape.

Travel back on your circuit – As you become more comfortable with executing these "Discovery Cycles," you will learn how to reliably activate the A+ Anger that brings you an unlocking moment. Your EBT work will deepen. Sometimes, right after doing a Cycle that includes an unlocking moment, your mind will "travel back" on that circuit. Think of it as a trip through the past to a moment when the circuit was encoded or strengthened. This travel back is only possible when you happen to reach a very deep circuit, but you can always give it a try! Just focus on the place in your body where you feel stress, then say to yourself, "I have felt that sensation before!" Turn your attention to wondering about the past and notice any images that arise. If an image arises, you might even see yourself in a situation in which you turned to an unbalanced mood for comfort. You needed comfort from others, not from that mood! You can imagine yourself stepping into the image and comforting your past self. This can be a very loving and powerful experience. You are wiring in reconnecting to yourself, rather than to an unbalanced mood!

Ask questions about your circuit and do Cycles to grieve the losses – Six or more hours after your Discovery Cycle, when the rewiring window has closed, you might want to ask yourself questions, such as: Is it an intergenerational circuit? Did your mother or father or someone else who was close to you have that circuit? If you have a sense of when it was encoded, what changes, losses, or upsets occurred around one year from that time? Help fill in the pieces of the puzzle about your story. Write notes about your circuit. Include the words that rang true for you, how your body felt, when the wire could have been encoded, and any additional information that helps you see yourself and your life more accurately.

What if this discovery day stops being fun? If you do not find this to be fascinating, exciting, or illuminating, chances are that you are stressed. Do five Cycles to clear the stress. Cycle about anything, such as, the experience that encoded the wire, the fact that you did not know it was there, or the reality that the circuit has been harmful to you. Or the worry that you will miss having that wire. Cycle through your feelings.

If at any time you do not feel safe doing this work, stop doing it and consult a health professional. If you are a member of the EBT community, then consider scheduling a coaching session. One-on-one coaching with a Certified EBT Provider can help you discover your circuit and process its emotions more easily and efficiently.

Use the checklist at the end of this chapter to guide your way in discovering your Mood Circuit. Identify a mood that you want to change. Use the lead-ins to do a rousing Zap a Glitch Cycle, complaining about that mood. The words of the unreasonable expectation of circuits generally follow the formula "I get my (need) from (mood)."

There are two columns at the bottom of the checklist.

The *"I get my . . ."* checklist includes the five basic needs that the brain seeks: safety, love, comfort, pleasure, and purpose. This list includes additional words that may more accurately convey safety needs: survival, existence, protection, security, power, and nurturing.

The "*. . . from feeling*" checklist includes a range of specific moods, that is, how the wire tells you to feel in order to meet that need. It's likely to be the mood you complained about in your Discovery Cycle.

Discover the hidden message in that wire, so that you can rewire it!

This is your first circuit. Be gentle with yourself. You do not have to do this perfectly. Once you learn this skill, you will have it for life!

Before using the Rewiring Checklist, see page 297 for a list of ways to enhance your EBT experience. Join the EBT community, print out the companion forms for this book, or if you have questions, call in and chat with me. Congratulations on launching the discovery of your Mood Circuit!

The Rewiring Checklist
Day 1. Discover Your Mood Circuit

Say What Is Bothering You

- The situation is . . . (Complain about the mood that bothers you most.)
- What I'm most stressed about is . . . (Say what bothers you the most about that mood.)

Unlock the Circuit

- I feel angry that . . .
- I can't stand it that . . .
- I hate it that . . .

Discover the Hidden Message

- I feel sad that . . .
- I feel afraid that . . .
- I feel guilty that . . .
- OF COURSE I would do that, because my unreasonable expectation is . . .

I get my: **from feeling:**

I get my:	from feeling:	
☐ Safety	☐ Anxious	☐ Rebellious
☐ Love	☐ Depressed	☐ All-powerful
☐ Comfort	☐ Hostile	☐ Manic
☐ Pleasure	☐ Irritable	☐ Arrogant
☐ Purpose	☐ Powerless	☐ Righteous
☐ Survival	☐ Self-pity	☐ Bullet-proof
☐ Existence	☐ Panicked	☐ No feelings
☐ Protection	☐ Ashamed	☐ Numb
☐ Security	☐ Abandoned	☐ High
☐ Power	☐ Overwhelmed	☐ Zoned out
☐ Nurturing	☐ Worried	☐ Disconnected
☐ Other _____	☐ Lost	☐ Other _____

Success Check Day 10

- **Daily Success**

☐ I continued my Power of One Practice with 10 Check Ins and 10 Joy Points.

☐ I discovered my Mood Circuit.

☐ I made one or more community connections for support with discovering my circuit.

- **Did I pass the Success Check?   YES   NO**

If you did not, stay with this activity for one more day, then move on.

- **My Amazing Learning:**

_____

- **My Biggest Accomplishment:**

_____

- **My Biggest Challenge:**

_____

Congratulations!

**You have completed Day 10 of The Power of One Challenge.
Your next step is Day 11. Negate Your Mood Circuit.**

Day 11. Negate Your Mood Circuit

You've discovered your Mood Circuit! Now it is time to move to the second step of the EBT 3-Day Rewiring Plan. Let's negate it.

You're going to confront that unreasonable expectation with a strong statement that you can NOT get your safety, love, comfort, or pleasure from becoming stuck in that unwanted mood.

This will be a particularly fun day because you can use Power Boosters to enhance your results, such as using scented oils and doing some nocturnal rewiring!

Weaken that Mood Circuit

- Do not ask yourself to snap out of your mood.
- Instead, change the circuit that drives it.
- As the circuit changes, your mood will change!

Why

Before transforming the circuit into a message that sounds reasonable, we negate it. We need to take this intermediate step of weakening the old unreasonable expectation to follow the rules of neuroscience.

Neuroplasticity is based on Hebb's Law: Neurons that fire together wire together and become stronger. Neurons that fire apart wire apart and become weaker. Circuits only change through experience, and only the most emotionally-charged experiences are strongly remembered by the brain. The combination of discovering the circuit and repeatedly and intensively negating it with the opposite (mutually exclusive or orthogonal) message is just what we need.

Why is a very precise technique needed?

Why don't we simply say something that is more sensible than our circuit? Instead of saying, "I get my safety from being anxious," why not say I get my safety from being happy or from my feelings?

When we're going after the strong circuits at the bottom of the brain that activate the inner reptile, a completely different intervention is needed. There are several reasons for this:

Fight-or-flight circuits do not change easily

When we're at Brain State 1 or 2 and dealing with circuits that are not fueled by fight-or-flight drives, we can switch to a new expectation easily. However, to protect us, the brain holds onto the circuits that control our health and happiness the most strongly, so we have to use methods that conform to the science of how these emotional wires change. Simple awareness and rational thought are not enough!

Touching those circuits activates a stress response

These circuits can only be updated when we are in the same level of stress as we were in when they were encoded. Most really faulty wires were encoded when we were at Brain State 4 or 5, and to rewire them, we must go to those stress levels, but somehow manage to then rapidly reduce our stress so that the neocortex stays online and enables us to be present to our thoughts and emotions. That is not easy, which is why we use the Cycle Tool!

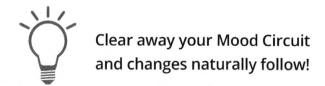

**Clear away your Mood Circuit
and changes naturally follow!**

Weakening the circuit is an essential step

We take time to weaken the circuit because if we change the expectation too rapidly and without taking away some of its strength, the reptile will reject the message. It will become highly stressed and trigger a Brain State 5. We need to keep the brain in the Brain State 3 range so that the thinking brain will be functional enough to access the feelings.

Is it true that you should NOT use the word NOT?

A commonly-discussed rule of changing circuits is to NOT use the word NOT in a corrective message. This rule applies when we are clearing out the top drawers of the brain. However, the circuits in the bottom drawers function differently. The unreasonable expectation must be confronted with the experience that it is not true. The negation accomplishes that and weakens the circuit. The brain can hear the word NOT because we state it very strongly, making it stand out like neon! The rest of the statement is very monotonal and the NOT is loud, emotional, vibrant, and strong so that the brain cannot miss it!

With those ideas in mind, let's look at what you actually do to weaken that Mood Circuit and begin to break free of its hold over you.

How

To negate your Mood Circuit, keep it simple. For the expectation, **"I get safety from making people happy all the time,"** say **"I can NOT get safety from making people happy all the time."** Again, state it very slowly at first, then ramp it up and ridicule the circuit. If you like, sing or stomp when you are negating it. The more emotionally-charged the experience, the better the results.

2 Stages of Negating a Mood Circuit	
SLOW	I . . . can . . . NOT . . . get . . . my . . . safety . . . from . . . anxiety. I . . . can . . . NOT . . . get . . . my . . . safety . . . from . . . anxiety. I . . . can . . . NOT . . . get . . . my . . . safety . . . from . . . anxiety.
RAMP UP	I can NOT get safety from feeling anxious. I can NOT get safety from feeling anxious. That's ridiculous! I can NOT get safety from feeling anxious. That's impossible!

SLOW – State it slowly the first three to six times

State the negated expectation very slowly. Don't scare the reptile. Say it so slowly that it almost hurts. The more slowly you state it, the deeper in the brain it will go. If you state it quickly at first, the brain stress will be so high that the prefrontal cortex cannot stay flexibly aware of your feelings. We disconnect from feeling our feelings in our body, and that connection is essential for self-directing our emotional plasticity. Start with stating the negation one word at a time. Pause between each word so that the reptile can let off steam.

RAMP UP – Ridicule that circuit three to six times

After stating the negation three to six times, you'll notice that your feelings start shutting down. The emotional vividness of the statement dulls. We need strong emotions in order to strengthen the new memory. Over the years, we have noticed that participants who were seeing better results actually made fun of their circuit. They used a ramped-up negation of the wire – saying, "That's ridiculous!" By making fun of the circuit, we "externalize" the wire, so we experience more power and pleasure while short-circuiting any latent shame that could arise.

Keep it fun – Sing or dance or scream it!

To lock in the incremental change in the wire, we need a burst of dopamine which we can get with this simple technique. As you negate the circuit, be sure to add a dose of dopamine in a way that works for you. Some people use an enthusiastic voice, others say it standing up, even while they are dancing. This celebration that you really cannot get your need met by that response is exhilarating. That ridiculous hidden message that has caused you so much absolutely unnecessary, unproductive stress is on its way OUT of your brain!

I negated this circuit 200 times. The first time I did it, I went 30 minutes straight. I started slowly, but before long I was singing it, and then yelling it. I did another 50 after that, but I think I busted that circuit with the first 150 because I was so passionate. It was a celebration of my freedom from that stupid wire!

Example (All Grind In Clusters count as 10 Grind Ins)

SLOW

- I . . . can . . . NOT . . . get . . . SAFETY . . . from . . . being numb . . . (pause)
- I . . . can . . . NOT . . . get . . . SAFETY . . . from . . . being numb . . . (pause)
- I . . . can . . . NOT . . . get . . . SAFETY . . . from . . . numbing out . . . (pause)
- I . . . can . . . NOT . . . get . . . SAFETY . . . from . . . NUMBING . . . (pause)
- I . . . can . . . NOT . . . get . . . SAFETY . . . from . . . NUMBING OUT . . . (pause)

RAMP UP

- That's ridiculous! I can NOT get safety from numbing out.
- Numbing out does NOT give me safety.
- Unplugging from my feelings does NOT make me safe.
- How could numbness make me SAFE?! Totally RIDICULOUS!
- Numbness is NOT my safety blanket. No Way!
- HOW RIDICULOUS!!!!

How many times do you repeat your Grind In?
The goal is to weaken the circuit enough so that the reptilian brain will happily accept a new expectation. When the circuit is weakened, it's easier for the brain to override the message.

The stronger your Mood Circuit, the more repetitions will be required. It takes as many repetitions as it takes, however, a general guideline is based on where that circuit is stored in the brain. If your Mood Circuit is a weak one, meeting a need for pleasure or comfort, you may only need 50 repetitions. What if your Mood Circuit is strong, say in the 4th or 5th Drawer? Then it will require a lot more of repetitions and every bit of passion, enthusiasm, and power you can express through your words, vocal tone, and body! It's just a wire. You can weaken it!

How much negating do we need to do?

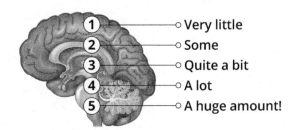

1. Very little
2. Some
3. Quite a bit
4. A lot
5. A huge amount!

How do you keep it fun?

There is a very simple way. First, notice if it is not fun. When you aren't excited to zap that wire, do not do it! It will be a waste of your time to negate that wire until you have processed your emotions about it. That lack of enthusiasm is your brain's way of telling you that there are emotions to process prior to dismantling your circuit. Heed that message. Our saying "If it's not fun, it's not EBT" is based on neuroplasticity research. When the brain is ready to rewire a circuit, you may feel slightly scared, but a big part of you will say, "Let's have at it. I want to smash that wire!"

This is part of the process of rewiring emotional circuits. Again, when it is NOT fun, stop and do five Cycles. Then check to see if it sounds like fun to negate your circuit. If it doesn't, do another five Cycles. It takes as long as it takes. The reptile is watching us and fuming! Do as many Cycles as you need to do, then **negate that circuit with enthusiasm and joy!**

If it's not fun, then do 5 Cycles.
Grieve the loss, so that it's fun again.

Depression with a tinge of powerlessness has been my circuit since I was nine years old and my parents divorced. I hid from my feelings in the way that worked best for me, which was depression. After doing Cycles about it, I feel emotionally lighter and ready to make fun of that circuit!

I did five Cycles on my Anxiety Circuit, first on the fact that it was encoded, another on all the pain it caused me, and the rest on that it didn't give me safety. I could be anxious all day and all night, and that wire could not give me the safety that I need.

Let's add some Power Boosters to zap that Mood Circuit

As always, the best time to negate your Mood Circuit is when it is activated. Is your Mood Circuit activated when you communicate with a particular person? What about when you are in a specific work or home situation? Consider choosing one challenging situation today and using your Grind In before, during, or after it.

Challenge your beliefs about "stuck" moods. When you think that your mood is controlling you, use your Grind In. See if you can dislodge that mood, even a little. It's so empowering to shift to a better mood and a higher brain state! The added benefit of rewiring Mood Circuits is that they are under MANY other circuits. When I busted up my depression circuit, my eating, my overspending, and my procrastination all eased up. You'll love being free of this wire!

Power Boosters for your Mood Circuit

- Use your Grind In right when your circuit is triggered.
- Choose one challenging situation today and use your Grind In.
- State your Grind In before going to bed.
- Repeat your Grind In when you awaken in the night.
- Add essential oils with a scent to deepen your rewiring.

Also, take advantage of how easily the brain changes during sleep. The hippocampus consolidates the learning of the day into long-term memory when we are asleep. By doing Grind Ins right before going to sleep, or whenever you awaken during the night, you'll see better results. Some people drink water before retiring, to ensure they awaken in the night, so they can do Nocturnal Grind Ins.

Essential Oils Can Help!

Chamomile	Sandalwood	Lemon
Ginger	Rose	Bergamot
Lavender	Peppermint	Sage

The mechanism for improving neuroplasticity by using scents is based on the observation that scents go straight to the emotional brain. Creating an association between a scent and your Grind In is thought to intensify the experience of this new message and thus, promote more change in the circuit. If you want to try this, do Grinds Ins with a dab of scented oil under your nose or on your chest. Massage it into your skin or put a drop on your pillow at bedtime. The scent will continue to help grind in your message as you sleep.

Let's crush your first circuit – the Mood Circuit – then we'll move on to transforming it into a new message of your choosing!

The Rewiring Checklist
Day 2. Negate Your Mood Circuit

I negated my Mood Circuit:

- **SLOW**

  I can NOT get my _____ from _____.

- **RAMP UP**

  That's ridiculous! I can NOT get my _____ from _____.

  I did it: 50 75 100 125 150 200 _____ times.

I boosted the power of my Grind In (one or more ways):

- ☐ Using my Grind In right when my circuit is triggered
- ☐ Choosing one challenging situation and using my Grind In
- ☐ Stating my Grind In before going to bed
- ☐ Repeating my Grind In when I awaken in the night
- ☐ Adding essential oils with a scent to deepen my rewiring

Success Check Day 11

- **Daily Success**

☐ I continued my Power of One Practice with 10 Check Ins and 10 Joy Points.

☐ I negated my Mood Circuit.

☐ I made one or more community connections for support with negating my circuit.

- **Did I pass the Success Check?   YES   NO**

If you did not, stay with this activity for one more day, then move on.

- **My Amazing Learning:**

_____

- **My Biggest Accomplishment:**

_____

- **My Biggest Challenge:**

_____

Great Work!

**You have completed Day 11 of The Power of One Challenge.
Your next step is Day 12. Transform Your Mood Circuit.**

Day 12. Transform Your Mood Circuit

Let's transform your Mood Circuit. You will create a Power Grind In that will shut off the old message in that wire and activate a new message of your choosing.

You'll decide on a new message that tells you what to do, that is, to connect with yourself, to approach emotions in a new way, and to be aware of how rewarded you feel for doing that.

This is your "transformation statement." It replaces the old message and gives the reptilian brain a road map so it has something to do other than replay the old message. Wiping the old message out is not enough. The brain needs a new instruction, something even more rewarding than that unwanted mood.

To deliver that new instruction, you will use your prefrontal cortex and make a personal decision what message you want encoded in your unconscious mind. Then you will state that message to yourself throughout the day or whenever that circuit begins to be activated.

That will accomplish two things. It will deactivate the circuit on the spot so you feel better faster. Also, it will make a change in that wire, so it is less likely to be triggered again. By using this Power Grind In over time, you not only feel better, but the circuit can stop bothering you. You can use your energy to move forward in life and fulfill your purpose rather than solving problems that are created by old wires.

**We can transform!
Just replace the old message
with a new one.**

A New Wire Replaces the Old One

	Connect	Mood Approach	Reward
OLD WIRE	Disconnect	Ignore Emotions	Unhealthy
NEW WIRE	Connect Within	Process Emotions	Healthy

Why

The purpose of the Power Grind In is to deactivate the Stress Circuit in real time, switching it to a Joy Circuit that reduces stress and activates a surge of neurotransmitters, which feels great! Basically, we give the brain a more effective response.

To accomplish this, the new statements need to directly confront the old statements on three counts. One is to check in or connect within rather than checking out or disconnecting. Without being checked in and connected, we have little or no power over the reptile!

Next, we add a new emotional approach, since the brain will continue its old mood response until we encode a new and better one. Last, we absolutely must install a natural reward (earned rewards of purpose are the best) which will deliver a dopamine spurt that makes using this new circuit sound like a great idea.

Once you've created this new statement, it's essential to learn to express it in an effective and handy way. The best method is to first remind the brain of your negation once, ridicule it with a hearty ramp up twice, and then grind in the new expectation three times.

Be sure to use the three-pronged approach to the new statement (connect – approach – reward). Consider that the deeper circuits are controlled by the reptile within. It's our job to fight back! Use the three-pronged approach to punch the reptile in the nose, and take back your power!

The new instruction has three parts

- Connect – connect to yourself
- Approach – use a new approach
- Reward – savor your reward

How

There are three parts to the new instruction. Keep the message brief, clear, and sensitive to the reptile's strong urge to replay a familiar mood. Let's look more closely at how to construct your transformation statement for your Power Grind In:

Connect: Tell yourself to connect to your body, to the deepest part of yourself. You are instructing your prefrontal cortex (thinking brain) to turn its attention to your unconscious mind (emotional brain). It is that connection that makes us feel safe, loved, comforted, pleasured, and purposeful.

Approach: State what you're going to do when your Mood Circuit has been activated. We'll look at a range of approaches, then do a brief visualization called an Imagine to finalize your plan. This is your opportunity to create a statement based on seeing and knowing yourself and then develop a plan that will do one thing: shut off that old wire because you have a far better one to replace it!

Reward: Which of the earned rewards will light up your brain with surges of powerful neurotransmitters so you joyfully unplug from that unwanted mood? Bring to mind your higher-order reward: Sanctuary, Authenticity, Vibrancy, Integrity, Intimacy, Spirituality, or Freedom.

Connect Statement Examples
• Connect with myself.
• Check In.
• Connect to the love inside me.
• Connect to my body.
• Take a deep breath.
• Connect to the spiritual.
• Honor my feelings.
• Connect inside.
• Be aware of my body.
• Know my number.

Say how you will connect with yourself

Use a connect statement that is brief and clear to instruct your brain to connect within as your first defense against the activation of that Mood Circuit.

What is your new approach to mood?

The next statement is a general approach to this area of life. It's not a specific plan but a general new way of operating. We won't always act in a specific way and perfection is not the goal. Here are some ideas for constructing your new approach to mood.

The Know Your Number Approach

You can keep it straightforward and brain-based, and simply check your number and use the tools. This works well for all Mood Circuits.

My moods are so mixed, some anxiety, some powerlessness, and false highs, too. I am better off checking my number. If I am at 4, I know what to do. Use the lead-ins for Brain State 4 and do one of the Cycles – Feel Better, Zap a Glitch, or Take Action.

Know Your Number Approach Examples
• Check my brain state.
• Use the tools.
• Spiral up to Brain State 1.

The Words I Need to Hear Approach

The thinking brain is our internal overseer, the good parent within. The circuits in the emotional brain are the kids. If a parent states the words a child most needs to hear in that moment, stress vanishes. This works best with circuits that are stored in the 3rd Drawer, as our thinking brain function is good enough to come up with those words!

My Mood Circuit is mild, stored in the 3rd Drawer, so if I gently tell myself that I am loved, and I am not in danger, that helps. I use a nurturing inner voice. I am cultivating that as part of my EBT practice.

Words I Need to Hear Approach Examples
• Say the words that I need to hear.
• Tell myself, "I am creating joy in my life!"
• Talk to myself with a nurturing inner voice.

The Listen to My Body Approach

When a Mood Circuit is activated, our thinking brain cannot connect to the emotional brain. What do we most need? To reconnect! This approach of grounding ourselves with body awareness can be highly effective.

When my anxiety circuit is activated, I go right to Brain State 5. I use the 5 PLUS Tool which is really about rocking, breathing, and stroking. I was raised by a mother who was perpetually at Brain State 5. I acquired her set point. I like being grounded in my body to start the process. I can use the tools after that, if I want.

- Rock gently back and forth.
- Focus on my breathing.
- Stroke my body and soothe myself.

The Meet My Need Approach

The last approach is to wire into our brain the drive to meet the original unmet need for safety, love, comfort, or pleasure. It's a simple approach because you bypass any plan for processing emotions and zero in on the underlying need.

That's the ticket! I tell myself to meet my basic need. If my need is comfort, I'll comfort myself. If my need is safety, I'll connect to the safe place inside me.

Meet My Need Approach Examples

- Meet my true need, rather than worrying about everything.
- Get my safety from inside me, not from a bad mood.
- Get my love from life, not from feeling on edge.
- Comfort myself in ways other than self-pity.
- Access natural pleasures, rather than savoring misery.
- Bring to mind my purpose in life.

Where is your circuit stored?

The precise words you will use for your approach statement depend upon the drawer in which your Mood Circuit is stored. The lower the drawer, the more specific and the stronger your approach statement must be.

For example, if your mood comes on gradually and keeps you in the 3 range, then it's probably in the 3rd Drawer and a gentle reminder to feel your feelings may be enough to deactivate your Mood Circuit. **If your circuit is in the 4th Drawer**, being more directive is key. **If it is in the 5th Drawer**, be outright commanding. The 5th Drawer houses our compulsion and addiction circuits. And your drive to stay stuck in that mood may be that powerful. If it is, be blunt with your approach statement. Tell your brain to stop it!

Where is my circuit stored?

LOCATION	NEED	STRENGTH OF DRIVE
The 1st Drawer	Purpose	Very Low
The 2nd Drawer	Pleasure	Low
The 3rd Drawer	Comfort	Moderate
The 4th Drawer	Love	Strong
The 5th Drawer	Safety	Overwhelming

Which reward matters most to you?

Finish off your transformation statement by choosing the reward that motivates you to short-circuit that mood wire. All seven of the rewards are important, but when it comes to this specific circuit and your Power Grind In that zaps that wire, which is the one that is most powerful for you?

The 7 Rewards

• Sanctuary	Peace and power from within
• Authenticity	Feeling whole and being genuine
• Vibrancy	Healthy with a zest for life
• Integrity	Doing the right thing
• Intimacy	Giving and receiving love
• Spirituality	The grace, beauty, and mystery of life
• Freedom	Common excesses fade

The Mood Circuit Imagine

One of the most rewarding ways to construct your transformation statement is by using the brain's astonishing capacity to imagine. This visualization will give you insights into just the instructions your brain needs to short-circuit that Mood Circuit. Give it a try! We use this Imagine activity extensively in Advanced EBT because it reaches into the unconscious memory systems and changes them.

Relax: Set whatever limits are necessary to create privacy for yourself. Settle into a comfortable spot and begin to relax. Focus your attention on your body and your breathing. Breathe in through your nose and out through your mouth or in any way that is comfortable and comforting to you. Then when you are ready, begin to imagine.

Imagine: See yourself walking through your day, naturally moving through the whole range of brain states and living your life in a way that works for you at the time. Know that it is all perfect, no matter what, because your emotional brain is firing just the circuits that are there. Every good feeling you have is the firing of a circuit, and a reminder of how rewarding that wire feels. And every painful moment is the firing of a circuit that is reminding you, through the language of stress, hurtful sensations, and negative emotions, that a wire is activated and primed for rewiring. This is the nature of the always-perfect emotional brain. Take a deep breath and continue to see yourself move through your day.

Now bring to mind a moment when your Mood Circuit has been activated. See that wire firing and your brain triggering that mood. Take a few moments and be aware of where you are . . . who is around you . . . how your body feels . . . and the thoughts that appear in your mind. Notice what you do . . .

Last, imagine words appearing in your mind, clear instructions to connect with yourself . . . what would those words be? Take a few deep breaths . . . and after telling yourself to reconnect with yourself, what would you most need? How would you approach this Mood Circuit? What actions would you need to take? What approach would be just what you need in that moment?

Notice that if you stay focused on your body, imagining that scene, the words will bubble up into your mind. Finally, what would motivate you to follow through and connect with yourself and use that approach? Would it be Sanctuary, Authenticity, Vibrancy, Integrity, Intimacy, Spirituality, or Freedom?

The Power Grind In for Mood: Example
(Counts as 10 Grind Ins)

Stage	Statements
1 SLOW	I can NOT get my safety from worrying.
2 RAMP UP	*That's ridiculous!* I can NOT get safety from worrying. How absurd. Worrying will NOT make me safe. *That's ridiculous!* NO WAY will worrying make me safe!
3 JOY	I get my safety from connecting inside, using the tools, and getting to One. My reward? Vibrancy. I get my safety from connecting inside, using the tools, and getting to One. My reward? *Vibrancy!* I get my safety from connecting inside, using the tools, and getting to ONE! My reward? VIBRANCY!

Please take all the time you need and when you feel complete, use the upcoming checklist to record the transformation statement that feels right to you.

Sometimes your Power Grind In will change as you use it. If it does, update it, but then lock it in again, as repeating the same words, rather than varying them, is more effective in encoding and strengthening a new circuit.

I can . . . NOT . . . get . . . my . . . protection . . . from . . . hostility . . . That's ridiculous! I can NOT get my protection from hostility. Being hostile is not going to work. I can NOT get protection from hostility. I get protection from checking in and connecting to the love inside me. My reward: Integrity. I get protection from checking in and connecting to the love inside me. My reward: Integrity. I get REAL protection from checking in and connecting to the love inside me. My reward: Integrity!

This Power Grind In comes in very handy as a stress reduction tool in daily life. Use it preventively, during a stressful experience, and/or afterwards to further shift that old wire. Stressful moments speed up the process of breaking free from that circuit.

I'm going to use my Power Grind In for Mood when I go to visit my mother. I know it will come up because she has a self-pity wire and so do I. It is, "I get my safety from feeling sorry for myself for everything that goes wrong." That's ridiculous! I cannot get my safety from feeling sorry for myself. That is absurd. No way is that true. I get my safety from checking in and using the tools to get to Brain State 1. My rewards? Sanctuary and Vibrancy.

Use the checklist on the next page to record your Power Grind In for Mood. Grind this in 100 or more times today. Want better results faster? Grind it in 200 times today. Each cluster counts as 10. Your brain will become comfortable with it. Then use this Power Grind In daily.

Watch for moments of opportunity to use your Power Grind In

Once you have created your new Power Grind In, be in joyful anticipation of a bad mood. When one appears, seize the moment. Use your Power Grind In. Do not try to memorize your Power Grind In. These circuits are activated so quickly and so strongly that you will forget the words. It's essential to write your Power Grind In on a piece of paper or on your phone. Have your Power Grind In with you at all times. Who knows when the lizard brain could strike? In addition, use it four times daily, particularly during high-stress times.

This is your first Power Grind In, and the most challenging one. Congratulations!

The Rewiring Checklist
Day 3. Transform Your Mood Circuit

I transformed my Mood Circuit:

- **SLOW**

    I can NOT get my _____ from _____.

- **RAMP UP**

    That's ridiculous! I can NOT get my _____ from _____.

- **JOY**

I get my _____ **from:**

CONNECT	APPROACH	REWARD
☐ Connecting with myself	☐ Checking my brain state	☐ Sanctuary
☐ Checking in	☐ Using the tools	☐ Authenticity
☐ Connecting to my body	☐ Spiraling up to One	☐ Vibrancy
☐ Taking a deep breath	☐ Meeting my true need	☐ Integrity
☐ Staying connected	☐ Using my nurturing inner voice	☐ Intimacy
☐ Honoring my feelings	☐ Focusing on my breathing	☐ Spirituality
☐ Connecting inside	☐ Rocking gently back and forth	☐ Freedom
☐ Being aware of my body	☐ Stroking my body to soothe myself	
☐ Knowing my number	☐ Saying the words that I need to hear	
☐ The deepest part of me	☐ Comforting myself in healthy ways	
☐ Being present	☐ Telling myself, "I am creating joy in my life!"	
☐ Other _____	☐ Other _____	

I did it: 50 75 100 125 150 200 _____ times.

Success Check Day 12

- **Daily Success**

☐ I continued my Power of One Practice with 10 Check Ins and 10 Joy Points.

☐ I transformed my Mood Circuit and created my Power Grind In.

☐ I made one or more community connections for support with transforming my circuit.

- **Did I pass the Success Check?   YES   NO**

If you did not, stay with this activity for one more day, then move on.

- **My Amazing Learning:**

_____

- **My Biggest Accomplishment:**

_____

- **My Biggest Challenge:**

_____

Great Work!

You have completed Day 12 of The Power of One Challenge.
Your next step is Day 13. Lifestyle Reset #3
Joy Breakfast and Sanctuary Time.

Day 13. Lifestyle Reset #3
Joy Breakfast and Sanctuary Time

As you settle into using your Power Grind In for Mood, notice that you are more present, aware, and connected. Your interest might turn to lifestyle, upgrading how you live to be in alignment with the Power of One.

Today we'll add two small but important resets of the brain for natural pleasures. One reset is the Joy Breakfast and the second is solo time devoted to the more rewarding work of EBT – Sanctuary Time.

Why

Not surprisingly, nutrition has a huge impact on both stress and neuroplasticity. Eating healthy not only reduces the physiologic stress caused by those blood sugar lows triggered by eating too much sugar, but has been associated with improved long-term memory (increased plasticity of neurons). What's more, excessive intake of sugary, processed foods can encourage hijacking of the brain's reward center to favor artificial pleasures.

All in all, with our goal of raising the brain's set point, shifting toward eating healthy makes perfect sense.

The Power of Eating Healthy
• Reduces brain stress
• Improves neuroplasticity
• Trains reward center to favor healthy pleasures

Healthy eating is a lot like healthy emotions. It begins with connection – connect with your body, eat only when hungry, and stop when satisfied, not full. Within 20 minutes, you'll feel full, and avoid a food hangover from having overeaten. Our hunter-gatherer ancestors had it right when they ate during the day and took a food rest for a long period at night. Giving yourself a food rest for 12 hours per day allows your body to clear excess glucose (sugar) and glycogen (body starch) and start burning up extra triglycerides (body fat).

What about the foods you choose? An easy way is to separate food into two categories: Joy and Stress. Joy Foods are whole foods and Stress Foods are processed foods. Think of foods based on evolutionary biology. Joy Foods include hunter-gatherer foods (fiber foods, healthy fats, and lean proteins). We emphasize including all three of these groups in a meal as that combination of foods is likely to keep hunger at bay for four to six hours. The protein-fat combination has staying power for glycemic control and fiber foods increase peptide YY ("PYY"), a chemical in the intestines that hastens satiety. There are also agrarian foods (other whole foods) if you prefer a plant-based diet.

The other food category is Stress Foods. Instead of reducing your stress, in the long term they increase it. They are not "bad" foods, but they have multiple disadvantages for brain health and raising our set point. Stress Foods are lower in nutrient density (nutrition per calorie), can tip the scales toward the reward center thereby promoting addiction, and can cause metabolic stress (the stress from blood sugar lows). Belly fat is often caused by the toxic combination of psychological stress and the metabolic stress amplified by processed foods.

Let's get back to basics and keep it simple! Eat only when hungry. Eat healthy foods (Joy Foods), and only eat highly processed foods (Stress Foods) when you need them. When you eat them, do not feel guilty. Avoid guilt as it causes stress! Take a food rest for 12 or so hours per day (research is ongoing as to whether or not 14 hours is better) and allow your body to clear away extra glucose, glycogen, and fat. We call that the EBT 3-Point Food Plan.

We launch the healthy eating part of EBT with breakfast because breakfast sets the stress tone of your day. The stress hormone cortisol is high in the morning, to help us awaken, and the combination of high cortisol and consumption of Stress Foods can cause self-created hunger and the related ups and downs of your brain function and energy.

How

Next are some suggested breakfasts. Consider giving several of them a try and noticing your brain state for the next six hours. When you choose breakfasts that sustain your glucose level for longer, it will be easier for you to stay present, connected, and at One!

Select something to eat for breakfast that is healthy. You may not like this at first, but the reptilian brain likes whatever foods are familiar. After eating it 12 times, the reptilian brain will see it as familiar and you'll start to like it!

Check off ideas that appeal to you on the following pages. Or, create your own meals based on selecting primarily Joy Foods from the EBT Food List on page 144. Eat a Joy Breakfast going forward.

Joy Breakfast Ideas

☐ **Eggs and Fruit**
2 eggs and 2 egg whites cooked in healthy fat, ½ grapefruit with cinnamon.

☐ **Avocado Eggs**
2 scrambled eggs cooked in healthy fat, topped with avocado and salsa.

☐ **Sausage Breakfast**
2 chicken or low-fat sausages and 1 egg cooked in healthy fat, 1 sliced orange.

☐ **Protein, Spinach, and Onions**
4 oz. salmon, chicken, or sardines sautéed in healthy fat with sliced onions and fresh spinach.

☐ **Eggs and Toast**
2 eggs cooked in healthy fat, 1 slice high-protein whole grain bread with healthy fat.

☐ **Eggs and Stuffed Celery or Apple**
2 eggs and 2 egg whites cooked in healthy fat, served with apple slices or a celery stick with pecan or almond butter.

☐ **Green Smoothie**
Blend 1 handful spinach, 1 c. almond milk, 1 banana, pear, apple, or orange with 1 scoop protein powder.

☐ **Power Smoothie**
Blend 1 scoop protein powder, 1 banana, 2 T. almond butter, 1 T. ground flaxseed, 1 c. frozen blueberries, and water to cover.

☐ **Strawberry Banana Smoothie**
Blend 1 scoop protein powder, 1 banana, and 1 c. strawberries plus almond milk to cover. Serve with a handful of pecans.

☐ **Eggs, Chorizo, and Berries**
2 scrambled eggs cooked with a few slices of chorizo sausage and fresh basil. Serve with fresh berries.

☐ **Sausage Patty Breakfast**
2 low-fat sausage patties and 1 sliced green apple sautéed in healthy fat. Sprinkle apple slices with cinnamon as they cook.

☐ **Breakfast Bowl**
1 c. berries sprinkled with 2 T. nuts, with 1 c. almond milk with 1 scoop protein powder.

☐ **Leftover Protein and Fresh Tomatoes**
Chicken or other lean protein reheated in healthy fat then tossed with sliced tomatoes and fresh basil.

☐ **Salad Breakfast**
A large plate of fresh greens with reheated lean protein (fish, poultry, or meat) and topped with olive oil and balsamic vinaigrette.

☐ **Hawaiian Special**
2 eggs and 2 egg whites cooked in healthy oil, served with 1 sliced papaya topped with a squeeze of lime.

☐ **Chia Seed Smoothie***
Blend ½ c. cashews, 1 T. chia seeds, ½ t. vanilla extract, 1 c. ice cubes, and 1 banana with water to cover.

☐ **Beet and Raspberry Smoothie***
Blend ¾ c. cooked beets, ¾ c. frozen raspberries, 1 c. almond milk, and 1 T. ground flaxseed with water to cover. Top with slivered almonds.

☐ **Wheat Germ Smoothie**
Blend ¾ c. Greek yogurt, ½ c. almond milk, 1 c. frozen blueberries, 1 T. wheat germ, and a few ice cubes with water to cover.

☐ **Whole Grain Toast and Nut Butter***
Toast any whole grain bread that you like and top with any nut butter that appeals to you.

☐ **Vegan Salad Breakfast***
A large plate of fresh greens tossed with ¼ c. nuts and ½ avocado cubed and topped with olive oil and balsamic vinaigrette.

☐ **Quick Cottage Breakfast**
¾ c. cottage cheese with ½ banana sliced and 1 T. toasted wheat germ.

☐ **Yogurt and Fruit Breakfast**
1 c. Greek yogurt with ½ c. fruit of your choice and 2 T. nuts of your choice.

* not a high-protein breakfast but rich in agrarian foods with high nutrient density

Be sure to enjoy your food. Again, eat slowly. Focus all your attention on the natural pleasure of eating food that delivers high-intensity well-being. Collect some Joy Points as you eat. Connect with yourself and eat slowly, savoring every bite:

- Notice the mouth-feel, taste, and pleasure in chewing and swallowing.
- Feel gratitude for your health to be able to eat.
- Be aware of your sensory pleasure in eating.
- Appreciate the joy of eating only when you are hungry.
- Feel grateful for your abundance, that you have access to food.
- Think about the people who contributed to your nourishment.

Appreciate yourself for taking a few moments to eat food that sustains your positive mood, high energy, and personal vibrancy throughout the morning and beyond.

Take Sanctuary Time for 10 Minutes
The tools of EBT can be used solo or with other people, however, most people find that they like taking 10 minutes per day to be alone and use the tools to clear away the day's stress. Find a quiet place and enjoy closing your eyes and relaxing as you use the tools.

Establishing that pattern of taking 10 minutes daily, much like you would with a meditation practice, can have a grounding impact on your day. By setting limits and taking this time, there are many benefits to you and those around you.

Sanctuary Time
- A safe time to cycle through daily emotions
- A way to honor the deeper work you are doing
- Training the brain that emotional connection matters

My children are used to having constant access to me when I am home, and by telling them that they could not interrupt me for 10 minutes because I was having solo time, they perked up. Their mother has limits and cares about her inner life!

I schedule my Sanctuary Time when I come home from work. My habit had been to discuss the day with my partner, but most of my stories were complaints about people or projects. By taking those 10 minutes, I get myself to Brain State 1 or 2 and our entire conversation goes better. I like myself better when I'm at Brain State 1 or 2, rather than at Brain State 3 or 4.

The EBT Food List
Joy Foods

Hunter-Gatherer Foods

These foods are rich in nutrient density (nutrition per calorie) and can decrease hunger, boost energy, and promote vibrancy.

1. The Fiber Group

Vegetables
- ☐ Acorn squash
- ☐ Artichokes
- ☐ Arugula
- ☐ Asparagus
- ☐ Bamboo shoots
- ☐ Banana squash
- ☐ Bean sprouts
- ☐ Beets
- ☐ Bok choy
- ☐ Broccoli
- ☐ Brussels sprouts
- ☐ Butternut squash
- ☐ Cabbage
- ☐ Carrots
- ☐ Cauliflower
- ☐ Celery
- ☐ Chard
- ☐ Chayote

- ☐ Corn
- ☐ Cucumbers
- ☐ Eggplant
- ☐ Endive
- ☐ Fennel
- ☐ Green onions/scallions
- ☐ Green peas
- ☐ Hubbard squash
- ☐ Jicama
- ☐ Kale
- ☐ Leeks
- ☐ Mushrooms
- ☐ Mustard greens
- ☐ Okra
- ☐ Onions
- ☐ Parsnips
- ☐ Pea pods
- ☐ Peppers
- ☐ Potatoes

- ☐ Pumpkin
- ☐ Radishes
- ☐ Romaine
- ☐ Scallions
- ☐ Shallots
- ☐ Snap peas
- ☐ Snow peas
- ☐ Spaghetti squash
- ☐ Spinach
- ☐ Sprouts
- ☐ Summer squash
- ☐ Sweet potato
- ☐ Swiss chard
- ☐ Tomatoes
- ☐ Water chestnuts
- ☐ Yams
- ☐ Yellow summer squash
- ☐ Zucchini

Fruits
- ☐ Apples
- ☐ Apricots
- ☐ Bananas
- ☐ Blackberries
- ☐ Blueberries
- ☐ Cantaloupe
- ☐ Cranberries
- ☐ Cherries
- ☐ Grapefruit
- ☐ Grapes
- ☐ Guavas
- ☐ Figs
- ☐ Honeydew melon
- ☐ Kiwis
- ☐ Lemons
- ☐ Limes
- ☐ Mangoes

- ☐ Melons
- ☐ Nectarines
- ☐ Oranges
- ☐ Papayas
- ☐ Peaches
- ☐ Pears
- ☐ Persimmons
- ☐ Pineapples
- ☐ Pomegranates
- ☐ Plums
- ☐ Prunes
- ☐ Raisins
- ☐ Raspberries
- ☐ Strawberries
- ☐ Tangelos
- ☐ Tangerines
- ☐ Watermelon

2. Healthy Fats

- ☐ Avocados
- ☐ Olives
- ☐ Omega 3 eggs
- ☐ Salmon
- ☐ Sardines

Nuts
- ☐ Almonds
- ☐ Hazelnuts
- ☐ Macadamias
- ☐ Peanuts
- ☐ Pecans
- ☐ Pistachios
- ☐ Walnuts
- ☐ Butters from the above

Seeds
- ☐ Flaxseeds
- ☐ Pumpkin seeds
- ☐ Sesame seeds
- ☐ Butters from the above

Oil
- ☐ Almond
- ☐ Avocado
- ☐ Canola
- ☐ Flaxseed*
- ☐ Hazelnut
- ☐ Macadamia

- ☐ Olive, extra virgin*
- ☐ Peanut
- ☐ Pecan
- ☐ Walnut

Salad Dressings
- ☐ Dressings made with vinegar or lemon and healthy oils

3. The Protein Group

Fish & Shellfish
- ☐ Barramundi
- ☐ Calamari
- ☐ Clams
- ☐ Cod
- ☐ Crab
- ☐ Halibut
- ☐ Haddock
- ☐ Herring, Atlantic
- ☐ Mackerel, Atlantic
- ☐ Mahi-mahi
- ☐ Mussels
- ☐ Ono

- ☐ Oysters, farmed
- ☐ Prawns
- ☐ Red snapper
- ☐ Salmon, Alaskan, wild
- ☐ Sardines
- ☐ Scallops, farmed
- ☐ Shrimp
- ☐ Sole
- ☐ Squid
- ☐ Tilapia
- ☐ Trout
- ☐ Tuna, albacore
- ☐ Tuna, yellowfin

Poultry & Meat
- ☐ Beef round steak
- ☐ Beef round, ground
- ☐ Beef flank steak
- ☐ Beef sirloin tip roast
- ☐ Buffalo
- ☐ Canadian bacon
- ☐ Chicken, ground
- ☐ Chicken breast
- ☐ Chicken drumsticks, skinless
- ☐ Chicken thighs, skinless
- ☐ Goat meat
- ☐ Ham, all fat removed

- ☐ Lamb steaks
- ☐ Pork chops, lean
- ☐ Pork tenderloin
- ☐ Sausage links, low-fat
- ☐ Sheep meat
- ☐ Turkey, ground
- ☐ Turkey breast
- ☐ Veal lean
- ☐ Venison

More
- ☐ Eggs
- ☐ Egg substitute
- ☐ Egg whites
- ☐ Protein powder

Agrarian Foods

These food are whole foods that provide important nutrients. For some people, these foods increase stress, hunger, and inflammation.

Grains
- ☐ 100% whole grain bread
- ☐ 100% whole grain cereals
- ☐ 100% whole grains cooked

Beans
- ☐ Legumes
- ☐ Beans

Milk Products
- ☐ Milk
- ☐ Yogurt
- ☐ Cheese

Stress Foods

Post Industrial Revolution Foods

The post-industrial revolution foods cause even more stress, hunger, and inflammation in humans.

Everything else!

Questions? Speak with a registered dietitian, physician, or nurse practitioner about the amounts of agrarian and industrial foods that are appropriate for you given your health status and risk factors for obesity, diabetes, heart disease, cancer, depression, anxiety, addiction, and other conditions.

In the Fiber Group, choose vegetables and fruits that are organic and farmed locally when possible. Rather than consuming juices, eat whole fruits and vegetables. In the Healthy Fats group, (*) these oils have exceptionally good healthy fat contents. In the Protein Group, emphasize consumption of fish and choose red meat in moderation, choosing natural, grass-fed meats cooked without frying or grilling when possible.

Success Check Day 13

- **Daily Success**

☐ I continued my Power of One Practice with 10 Check Ins and 10 Joy Points.

☐ I reset my lifestyle in these four ways: Exercise, Play, Joy Breakfast, and Sanctuary Time.

☐ I made one or more community connections for support with my lifestyle reset.

- **Did I pass the Success Check?   YES   NO**

If you did not, stay with this activity for one more day, then move on.

- **My Amazing Learning:**

_____

- **My Biggest Accomplishment:**

_____

- **My Biggest Challenge:**

_____

Congratulations!

You have completed Day 13 of The Power of One Challenge.
Your next step is Day 14. Discover Your Love Circuit.

Day 14. Discover Your Love Circuit

Today, we begin focusing on the Love Circuit. When we shift that circuit, a small but important flash of loving feelings and sensations appears. Even passing waves of these feelings override stress and light up our lives.

In the next three days, we'll discover the Stress Circuits of merging and distancing that block us from feeling love. We'll develop a Power Grind In for Love so that when in stressful situations we'll be able to short-circuit merging and distancing drives and feel a burst of love.

The Love Circuit

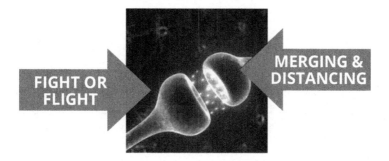

Why

Love is an emotion we experience when we are at One. We can't get to One when these Stress Circuits block us.

These wires are encoded early in life – or sometimes later during periods of stress overload. If we have some of these wires, try as we might, our brain will not allow us to give and receive love. We're intimate when stress is low, but when stress ramps up, the reptilian brain activates merging or distancing – or seesaws back and forth between the two.

The Brain and Love Circuits
MERGING The prefrontal cortex attunes excessively to the emotional brain of the other person. We abandon ourselves.
DISTANCING The prefrontal cortex attunes excessively to our own emotional brain. We abandon others.

The Stress Circuits come in two forms: merging with another or distancing from them. The goal of these three days is for you to find the merging or distancing wire that blocks you from giving and receiving love. Then you will develop a Power Grind In that provides immediate deactivation of the drive to merge or distance. With repeated use over time, the same Power Grind In transforms the Love Circuit. The new circuit stops merging and distancing and activates a drive to be intimate, staying close but retaining our own essential boundary.

Love Circuits	Examples
Merging	rescuing, people pleasing, seeking validation, indulging others, denying my own needs, being the victim, relentlessly seeking others, being overly available, being needy, making everyone else happy
Distancing	hiding, judging, persecuting, criticizing, neglecting others, abusing others, putting up walls, manipulating, objectifying, ignoring their needs, taking too much, rejecting others, being sought by others, disappearing

What does merging look like?

How do you know if you have a Merge Circuit? You won't be able to tell when stress is low. When we're running wires that are activated by the neocortex, we can easily connect with others. We get our survival needs – our safety, protection, power, nurturing, and existence – from the emotional connection between our thinking and feeling brains.

However, in stress, one fundamental brain function changes. Our prefrontal cortex stops attuning to our emotional brain and instead excessively focuses on the emotional brain of another. If we could just get something from them, we would be fine. We forget about our fundamental aloneness, that we are responsible for taking care of our own basic needs. We look for them to do it for us. We borrow their functioning.

If two people with Merge Circuits are in a committed relationship, and are chronically merged, the implicit agreement is that each will take care of the other. That way neither person will evolve beyond the circuits they downloaded from their parents. Neither one must grow.

My husband and I love each other very much. We feel love for each other, but we are excessively close. I don't set limits with him and he doesn't set limits with me. After dinner, he disappears into the kitchen and I can hear him grazing in the fridge. I shop on the internet, drink too much wine, and go to sleep early.

Even one person with a Merge Circuit in a relationship or family can block the system's emotional evolution. The purpose of relationships is to support each other's development, giving warm nurturing, emotional honesty, and effective limits. Sometimes friends won't do that for us; only those who really love us will! The Merge Circuit makes us so reactive to another person that we cannot tolerate allowing them to experience the pain that they need in order to grow.

I cannot stand it when my daughter is upset. I get an instant stomach ache and feel like I am going to die. I coddle her and obsess about how to prevent her from having pain. She is now 28 years old and is so adversity deficient that she has the maturity of a 12-year-old.

Merge Circuit Examples

- I get my safety from you.
- I get my security from rescuing you.
- I get my power from pleasing you.
- I get my safety from your approval.
- I get my power from not upsetting you.

What about distancing?

How do you know if you have a Distancing Circuit? In stress, your prefrontal cortex stops attuning to the emotional brain of others. It's not that you do not care or are insensitive, but the brain shuts down awareness of others as if our life depended on it. We forget about our fundamental need to emotionally connect with others. We have no idea how they feel or what they need. In fact, without emotional connection, all we care about is getting what we want when we want it, without regard to the needs of others or our own need for connection in the longer term.

If two people with Distancing Circuits are in a committed relationship, and chronically disengaged, the implicit agreement is that each will take care of themselves. That way neither person will evolve beyond their comfort zone from childhood.

My partner and I are very busy people and we care about each other, but we live our own lives, perhaps to a fault. I am not a nurturing person so it doesn't bother me, and he has never been emotional. We are both addicted to our work and our relationship is functional. Yet our lack of closeness shows up in our sex life and in a sense that something is missing.

Like merging, even one person in a relationship or family with a Distancing Circuit can change the growth trajectory of the individuals involved. The Distancing Circuit makes us so unresponsive to another person's feelings and needs that we do not disrupt their circuits because we are not that impacted by them. We can either avoid conflict for decades or use high drama and conflict as a smokescreen that keeps real change from happening.

My husband and I are happily coupled, but he ran up more than $100K of debt by investing in a start-up business with a partner who activated his Merge Circuit. It frustrated me that he is so irresponsible with money. I don't bring it up because I start judging him, and we have big blow-ups, then I go back to overspending and overeating.

Distancing Circuit Examples

- I get my security from putting up walls.
- I get my safety from hiding.
- I get my power from neglecting you.
- I get my protection from persecuting you.
- I get my existence from ignoring your needs.

The Seesaw – Merging AND Distancing

Most of us have both types of circuits. Some people find that they activate vastly different circuits with different people. They switch circuits or seesaw between them to both merge and distance.

My unconscious mind activates merging with my younger daughter. I want to rescue her from all pain. My son, who is 10 and a carbon copy of my husband's dad, brings out my Distancing Circuit.

The Love Circuit Seesaw

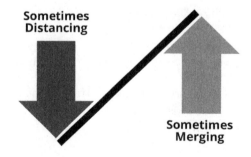

Sometimes
Distancing

Sometimes
Merging

Many people are raised with one type of Love Circuit, and when they tire of the stress and loneliness it causes, they switch to the other.

My mother was a merger and so was every woman in my family. I'm not sure of my dad's circuits, but I stopped merging after I married a distancer who was depressed and drained my resources.

Rewiring Love Circuits – the new frontier of neuroplasticity

Until 10 years ago, the Stress Circuits that control emotional connection were thought to be hardwired. Now we know that they are plastic and open to change.

The idea that you can take this course and attack an unwanted Merge or Distancing Circuit is nothing less than revolutionary. There is mounting evidence which suggests that we have the power to change our attachment styles. The most important research is that of Joseph LeDoux and Elizabeth Phelps, who demonstrated our power to change our emotional circuitry. Also, the research of attachment scientist Phillip Shaver, from University of California, Davis, demonstrates that emotional connection is learned. In fact, 70 percent of our emotional connection style in stress can be predicted by our mother's attachment style. That connection appears to be environmental, not genetic.

Studies by Michael Meaney, from Montreal's McGill University, overturned the concept that genetics determine attachment style. He demonstrated in an elegant series of studies on rats (which are remarkably similar to humans) that even among offspring that had been birthed to stressed-out mothers (and so shared their genetics and in-utero experience of stress) if put in a nurturing environment, the rats evidenced signs of a secure connection.

Getting into the 5th Drawer

How do we rewire the way we connect? The traditional way is to seek psychotherapy. A supportive relationship can be helpful. Another way is to find love. Loving relationships heal. However, we tend to find partners who are at our set point, so if our set point is in stress, our partner will have either Merge or Distancing Circuits or both.

The EBT solution is to keep our sense of humor and appreciate that if we've had stress, we have a few of these circuits of disconnection. Let's go after those circuits, begin to raise our set point, and bring upgraded wires to our relationships. In the best of all worlds, we target and change a wire that is in the 5th Drawer. It's the most disruptive. Just bring to mind the relationship that bothers you the most and use the Zap a Glitch Cycle to discover it. Always start by complaining, and make sure to use A+ Anger to unlock that circuit.

The Travel Back Experience

Sometimes the brain activates an old memory so that you can change it by using your imagination. Every time a circuit is activated, the hippocampus reconsolidates it, shifting it to long-term memory with alterations based on that experience. We are always updating our wiring.

The Travel Back Experience

- Do a Cycle about any deep hurt and be sure to use A+ Anger.
- Hope for an "unlocking moment" to discover circuits in the 5th Drawer.
- After finding the unreasonable expectation, focus on the place in your body that you experience the most stress.
- Relax and say, "I have felt that before." Allow your mind to travel back.
- Notice images that appear and settle on one of them. See yourself in that image, and feel love for yourself.
- If you like, imagine yourself as you are now, stepping into that image and giving your past self whatever you needed at that time to feel safe.
- Feel the glow in your body. You are wiring into your brain a secure connection to yourself.

When you do a deep Cycle – using A+ Anger and getting well into the 5th Drawer – right as you are discovering the circuit ("Of course I would do that, because my unreasonable expectation is . . . ") an image from the time the circuit was encoded might appear. If it does, you can "travel back" to that time and re-experience it.

You can imagine how you might have responded differently in that situation or reach a depth of understanding of yourself that can be profound. This can change the circuit and can provide a "reattachment" experience, which is among the deepest work you will do in EBT.

The nature of circuits – we can change our reality
Why does the Travel Back work? It's the nature of neural circuits. We think we are experiencing reality, but our reality is the experience that the activation of circuits delivers to us. As we change our circuits, we change our reality.

How do we travel back? We complain about a situation in our lives, such as a relationship. Those thoughts activate legions of wires stored in our unconscious mind. We notice activations of sensations and emotions in our body triggered by those wires. By turning our attention to our body, we block the prefrontal cortex from the overthinking that curtails the force of our imaginal mind. We focus on our body sensations of stress, further targeting the most egregious circuit, the memory of an experience that encoded the strongest Stress Circuit. We allow our mind to travel back via the images formed by the memories and one memory triggers another and another.

For example, the wire of an alarming scene of feeling invisible can trigger another wire that elicits feelings of being invisible, even though the people and situations were vastly different. Traveling back gives us a pathway to changing the root memory, as our mind seeks to find the deepest hurt.

By discovering it we more fully activate the memory, and that activation gives us the power, using our consciousness, to choose to intervene by imagining, and to update that wire.

We change the wire by choosing to see our present selves enter into the image and say or do whatever our younger selves needed to avoid or minimize harm. The actual circuit, now updated, is reconsolidated by the hippocampus so that our reality changes.

I was using the Cycle Tool to find my Love Circuit and complaining about my boyfriend who is volatile. I arrived at the unreasonable expectation which is I get my safety from distancing from and judging him. Suddenly, I had this pit in my stomach. I realized that I was in the 5th Drawer and had unlocked a strong fear memory. It was a doozy of a Stress Circuit. I focused on my stomach and that stress, locked my mind into those sensations and said to myself: I've felt this way before. I allowed my mind to travel back and bring up images, each one leading to another that happened still earlier in my life. In about 30 seconds an image appeared that must have been from when it was encoded. I could see myself in the living room of our apartment and my dad booming his rant. I was so scared and distancing from him and judging him. It was how I emotionally survived that incident. I could see myself and I felt love for myself. The oddest part was that I chose to imagine me, the adult I am now, taking charge and entering the image to comfort her. I told her that she didn't have to judge him or distance emotionally. She could scream at him to stop or leave the room or get help from another adult. She could use her power without needing to judge or distance. The experience was a turning point for me in raising my set point. It was a reset.

How
To discover your Love Circuit, bring to mind the relationship that causes you the most stress. Use the Zap a Glitch Cycle one or more times until you discover the unreasonable expectation that would make it perfectly reasonable for you to merge or distance.

Discover Your Love Circuit
I get my _____(need)_____ from _____(merging or distancing)_____ .

Discover the hidden message of your Love Circuit
Settle on a Love Circuit that you have a strong drive to rewire! Follow the lead-ins for Zap a Glitch and the Rewiring Checklist later in this chapter to guide your way.

Experiment until the words ring true
The words of the unreasonable expectation for Love Circuits follow the formula "I get my (need) from (merging or distancing)." They are a false association made by the brain between a basic need and whatever relationship pattern we used to try to meet it. They are crossed wires. By "uncrossing" this wire, fantastic things happen! We stop doing something that harms us, and open our mind to meeting our true need.

The *"I get my . . ."* checklist in the left column includes the five basic needs that the brain seeks: safety, love, comfort, pleasure, and purpose. Additional words that may more accurately convey safety needs are: survival, existence, protection, security, power, and nurturing. A checkbox for "other" has been provided for you to pinpoint your specific need if you don't see it on the list.

The set of two checkbox columns on the right offer common approaches to relationships that do not bring us love. Beneath the *". . . from"* heading are columns of phrases for merging and distancing.

Enjoy discovering the hidden message in your second circuit.

The Rewiring Checklist
Day 1. Discover Your Love Circuit

Say What Is Bothering You

- The situation is . . . (Complain about a relationship.)
- What I'm most stressed about is . . . (Say what bothers you the most about this relationship.)

Unlock the Circuit

- I feel angry that . . .
- I can't stand it that . . .
- I hate it that . . .

Discover the Hidden Message

- I feel sad that . . .
- I feel afraid that . . .
- I feel guilty that . . .
- OF COURSE I would do that, because my unreasonable expectation is . . .

I get my:	from:	
	MERGING	**DISTANCING**
☐ Safety		
☐ Love	☐ Others, not from myself	☐ Hiding
☐ Comfort	☐ Rescuing others	☐ Judging others
☐ Pleasure	☐ People pleasing	☐ Persecuting
☐ Purpose	☐ Seeking you	☐ Neglecting others
☐ Survival	☐ Others validating me	☐ Abusing others
☐ Existence	☐ Indulging others	☐ Shaming others
☐ Protection	☐ Denying my own needs	☐ Being sought by you
☐ Security	☐ Being the victim	☐ Putting up walls
☐ Power	☐ Making you happy	☐ Taking too much
☐ Nurturing	☐ Never making you angry	☐ Disappearing
☐ Other _____	☐ Other _____	☐ Other _____

Success Check Day 14

- **Daily Success**

☐ I continued my Joy Practice with 10 Check Ins and 10 Joy Points.

☐ I discovered my Love Circuit.

☐ I made one or more community connections for support with discovering my circuit.

- **Did I pass the Success Check?   YES   NO**

If you did not, stay with this activity for one more day, then move on.

- **My Amazing Learning:**

_____

- **My Biggest Accomplishment:**

_____

- **My Biggest Challenge:**

_____

Congratulations!

**You have completed Day 14 of The Power of One Challenge.
Your next step is Day 15. Negate Your Love Circuit.**

Day 15. Negate Your Love Circuit

Today, we'll negate that message that tells us to merge or distance. Negating a circuit is the easiest of the three stages of rewiring. You're telling your brain that losing yourself in another person is not the "genuine article" of love. Distancing isn't either.

The odd part about distancing and merging is that even though our original intent in being in a relationship was to give and receive love, once a Love Circuit has been encoded, that changes. Inadvertently, we use the relationship to fulfill another need, such as safety or comfort. Our need for love goes unmet, which increases our stress!

Why

We rewire this circuit because we need love. Pseudo love simply does not impress the emotional brain. It needs us to find love inside, lock in that secure connection to ourselves, then to give and receive love. We cannot do that easily as long as a circuit triggers us to merge or distance.

What's more, rewiring our Love Circuit is a practical strategy for improving the quality of our lives. We need to clear our Work Circuit and Habit Circuit. They are so much easier to clear when our set point is higher. We have more emotional bandwidth to roust out those wires and do them in. Soon we'll have not one but two Power Grind Ins to use in daily life: Mood and Love. Our set point will be higher so that our Work and Habit Circuits will begin to weaken quite naturally.

Merging does not give me the safety that I need.

Once I had created Power Grind Ins for both Mood and Love, my stress level plummeted. I was functioning better at work and feeling more compassion for myself in general. I had put off dealing with my various excesses, but at that point, I was motivated to reconsolidate them. It was pretty straightforward. Much easier.

Distancing does not give me the safety that I need.

How

Use the same negation process you used with your Mood Circuit. For the expectation, **"I get safety from making everybody happy all the time,"** say **"I can NOT get safety from making everybody happy all the time."** Again, state it very slowly at first, then ramp it up and ridicule the circuit. If you like, sing or dance or stomp when you are negating it. Making community connections helps tremendously. The more emotionally-charged the experience, the better the rewiring results.

Example (All Grind In Clusters count as 10 Grind Ins)

SLOW

- I . . . can . . . NOT . . . get . . . SAFETY . . . from . . . YOU . . . (pause)
- I . . . can . . . NOT . . . get . . . SAFETY . . . from . . . YOU . . . (pause)
- I . . . can . . . NOT . . . get . . . SAFETY . . . from . . . YOU . . . (pause)
- I . . . can . . . NOT . . . get . . . SAFETY . . . from . . . YOU . . . (pause)
- I . . . can . . . NOT . . . get . . . SAFETY . . . from . . . YOU . . . (pause)

RAMP UP

- That's ridiculous! I can NOT get safety from YOU!
- Plugging into you does NOT make me safe.
- Obsessing about YOU does NOT give me the safety that I need.
- That's ridiculous! I can NOT get my core safety from YOU!
- Totally ridiculous! I can NOT get my core safety from YOU!
- I CANNOT GET MY SAFETY from YOU or from ANYONE ELSE!!!

2 Stages of Negating a Love Circuit		
SLOW	I . . . can . . . NOT . . . get . . . my . . . protection . . . from judging you. I . . . can . . . NOT . . . get . . . my . . . protection . . . from judging you. I . . . can . . . NOT . . . get . . . my . . . protection . . . from judging you.	
RAMP UP	That's ridiculous! I can NOT get my protection from judging you! Judging you can NOT protect me. That's ridiculous! Even if I judged you all the time, that would NOT protect me.	

Grieving is normal – Do 5 Cycles

Our relationship circuits are strong because they are encoded early in life. Updating any strong circuit will cause grieving. Even if that circuit harmed us a great deal, it's familiar to the reptilian brain. Changing it is a loss. Be very careful to do as much grieving as you need to do before negating this circuit. Use any and all of the Cycles. Clear away that emotional clutter so that you feel charged up and ready to negate this wire!

The situation is . . . my Love Circuit is merging. I people please. I have been trying to please my father since I was six. My mind is traveling back as I say that, and I can see my father. I had to please him, or I would be a goner. I would lose his approval. What I'm most stressed about is . . . My father didn't give me love. He made me disconnect from myself and do whatever I thought he wanted me to do so that I could please him and feel safe. I feel angry that . . . he put that circuit in me. I can't stand it that . . . I am a big people pleaser. I hate it that . . . he did that to me. I HATE THAT!!! . . . I feel sad that . . . I have merged . . . I feel afraid that . . . I will always disconnect from myself, feel intense anxiety, and people please. I feel guilty that . . . I didn't scream at him to stop making me into someone I wasn't and to just love me!!! OF COURSE I would not scream at him, because my unreasonable expectation is . . . I have no power. That rings true. I'm going to change that expectation! I do have power. I DO have power . . . That's ridiculous. OF COURSE I have power. I DO HAVE POWER. Yes I do. I have POWER and I'm going to use it . . . to bust this Love Circuit.

I think I merged early in my life, but at some time in high school, I encoded a distancing circuit. I drank and partied. I did not care about anyone but myself. People liked me, but I didn't like myself, which made me distance more. I didn't want anyone to see me – really know me – because they might reject me. The situation is . . . I have been distancing for decades and what I'm most stressed about is . . . how much opportunity for happiness I lost. What I'm most stressed about is . . . how unhappy I have been because I have not built a family life. I am successful in my work but in love, I have not invested in satisfying relationships. What I'm most stressed about is . . . I do not have love in my life. I feel ANGRY that . . . I do not have love in my life. I can't STAND IT that . . . I am so lonely. I HATE it that . . . actually, I'm sad. I feel sad that . . . I have no friends . . . I feel afraid that . . . I'll continue to put up walls. I feel guilty that . . . I put up walls. OF COURSE I put up walls, because my unreasonable expectation is . . . I get my safety from people not rejecting me. OH MY GOSH. Under my Distancing Circuit is a Merge Circuit!

Let's add some Power Boosters

Continue to use the Power Boosters you have learned so far but add to them ways to share your Grind Ins with others. The brain experiences the Grind Ins differently when we are being seen, heard, and felt by another.

Power Boosters for your Love Circuit
• Grind it in whenever you sense you are distancing or merging.
• Say it to a Connection Buddy.
• Ask a family member or friend to listen to you grind it in.
• Post your Grind In on the EBT Community Forum Boards.
• Record yourself saying it, then listen to your recording.

Keep having fun with these circuits. Be sure to crush this circuit with passion and zeal. It's an old rusty wire that is blocking your Power of One. Let's fry this wire!

The Rewiring Checklist
Day 2. Negate Your Love Circuit

I negated my Love Circuit:

- **SLOW**

  I can NOT get my _____ from _____.

- **RAMP UP**

  That's ridiculous! I can NOT get my _____ from _____.

  I did it: 50   75   100   125   150   200 _____ times.

I boosted the power of my Grind In (one or more ways):

- ☐ Grinding it in whenever I sense I'm distancing or merging
- ☐ Saying it to a Connection Buddy
- ☐ Asking a family member or friend to listen to me grind it in
- ☐ Posting my Grind In on the EBT Community Forum Boards
- ☐ Recording myself saying it, then listening to my recording

Success Check Day 15

- **Daily Success**

☐ I continued my Joy Practice with 10 Check Ins and 10 Joy Points.

☐ I negated my Love Circuit.

☐ I made one or more community connections for support with negating my circuit.

- **Did I pass the Success Check?   YES   NO**

If you did not, stay with this activity for one more day, and then move on.

- **My Amazing Learning:**

_____

- **My Biggest Accomplishment:**

_____

- **My Biggest Challenge:**

_____

Great Work!

**You have completed Day 15 of The Power of One Challenge.
Your next step is Day 16. Transform Your Love Circuit.**

Day 16. Transform Your Love Circuit

Today you will create a Power Grind In for your Love Circuit. Once you have created it, then you can use it to zap a drive to merge or distance and rewire your experience of love in daily life.

Why

Transforming this circuit brings us so much happiness. Our work can bring us a sense of purpose, but our loving relationships are the basis for our happiness. We have a natural capacity to target and rewire the very circuits that block our happiness. It makes perfect sense to rewire them! In the short term, you can put your Power Grind In for Love to immediate use. For instance, whenever you sense the reptile might launch a merging or distancing drive, use your Power Grind In. Zap that wire to activate the drive to give and receive love!

My mom called last night. I knew she was going to give me advice and tell me how to run my life. Instantly, I reached for my Power Grind In and zapped my Distancing Circuit. I was so proud of myself because I tenderly told her that I loved her, but I was not up to hearing advice at that moment. She heard the kindness in my voice. She sensed that I loved her but was setting some reasonable limits. I was being emotionally honest with her. I felt close to my mom and spiraled up to One.

You can use your Power Grind In when you sense that you may be repeating old patterns. The reptile does a great job of convincing us that we are smart to replay an old pattern, even if it harms us. By using our Power Grind In, we can speak back to the reptile. It stops controlling us!

**Freedom from that wire
would change my life!**

163

Right after my divorce, I started dating Ken, whom I merged with immediately. My friends told me I was making a horrible mistake, that the relationship was a replay of my dysfunctional marriage. The Power Grind In saved me. I must have repeated it 50 times, which deactivated my unreasonable merging drive to get my safety from fixing emotionally unavailable men. I stopped merging with Ken and ended the relationship. I used the stress of the breakup with Ken to make my new circuit solid. I have not been in a merged relationship since and am dating a man now who is emotionally available.

How

There are three parts to your new instruction to your brain about how to approach experiencing more loving connection in your life.

Connect: Tell yourself to connect with the deepest part of yourself. That connection – strong, loving, and wise – is the foundation of your ability to give and receive love.

Approach: State your approach to love. Try out different words until you find some that short-circuit merging and distancing and activate a healthy drive to give and receive love. Below are four approaches to this statement plus some examples and a visualization activity. Use them to construct your approach statement.

Reward: The reward is not always Intimacy! It can be any of the seven rewards, whichever is your motivating force. Some people stop merging for the reward of Integrity. Others want to stop distancing to intensify their Vibrancy. Some want to deepen their Spirituality. Still others want more love in their lives because they sense that without Intimacy they will not let go of using common excesses. Their reward is Freedom.

Where is your circuit stored?

Consider where your Love Circuit is stored. For example, **if your Love Circuit is activated gradually and moderately then it's probably in the 3rd Drawer**. A gentle reminder to give love, while stopping short of abuse or neglect, might be enough to help you not merge or distance. **If it is stronger or activates more rapidly, it's probably in the 4th Drawer.** Be more directive and quite specific. **If it activates an overwhelming drive to distance or merge, then it is in the 5th Drawer**. Don't hold back with the message of your Power Grind In. All 5 Circuits are survival circuits, the most extreme drives we have. Be commanding, as the reptile doesn't listen if we are not committed to having our way and expressing that forcefully!

My history has been merging with someone, and then when I couldn't stand the loss of control anymore, leaving them. The drives were really strong. I think my Merge Circuit was in the 4th Drawer and my Distancing Circuit in the 5th Drawer. I will go after my Distancing Circuit because it is in the 5th Drawer. Perhaps crushing that wire will weaken or clear my merge wire.

My main love affairs are computers and alcohol, and I'm a sucker for potato chips, too. My Distancing Circuit is in the 5th Drawer and I am reluctant to open that drawer. I negated it for three days and need to do another five Cycles before I transform it. This wire is going to require me to stop trying to control it. The rewiring has to be in small steps.

What is your new approach to relationships?

The reptilian brain needs directions, particularly when it comes to love. Choose an approach that helps you move toward intimacy as a personal skill, something you know how to do, a competency!

The Bolster Boundaries Approach

This approach works well if you are a merger, particularly someone whose urge to merge wire is stored in the 5th Drawer of the brain. This approach is so rewarding because by setting limits, not only does merging fade, but the associated anxiety can fade, too.

When my wife starts becoming anxious and needy, I cannot stop myself from giving her advice and trying to fix her. I have to stop this Merge Circuit from controlling my responses to her before our intimacy will pick up again. This is hard for me!

Bolster Boundaries Approach Examples
• Do not rescue people.
• Stop seeking validation from others.
• Do not accept neglect or abuse.
• Speak up about how I feel and what I need.
• NO MERGING!

The Unconditional Love Approach

If you have a Distancing Circuit, this approach can be highly effective as it not only can short-circuit distancing but often improves the most common Mood Circuit associated with distancing: depression.

How do you use it? Just tell your reptilian brain that you are going to love, not judge. Be matter of fact! It's a policy switch! What if you do not have love to give? Use the tools. Spiral up to One and you'll have so much love to give that it will shock you. That's right! Abundant love. Then give some away. The giving of love manufactures even more love.

Unconditional Love Approach Examples
• Do my best to give love.
• Feel compassion for others.
• NO DISTANCING!
• Ask how they feel and what they need.
• It's a policy. I love rather than judge.

I am in abject terror at the thought of getting close to anyone. My Mood Circuit is to go numb and this wire is to judge, hide, or overwork. I can direct myself to love more. Something has to change. At this point, I do not like EBT. That must be my lizard brain revolting. EBT has me cornered and that's probably what it's going to take to get me to change.

The Finding the Sweet Spot Approach

If your Love Circuit is in a higher drawer in the brain, your prefrontal cortex can direct the emotional circuits in elegant ways. It can attune to your emotional brain and check how you feel and what you need, then attune to the emotional brain of another person and check how they feel and what they need. This "reading" by the brain enables us to shift our boundary rapidly. One moment we can have a tissue-paper-thin boundary when love is safe, and the next, a vault-thick boundary when there is danger. This keeps relationships vibrant, emotionally honest, and growing.

How do you find the sweet spot?

The sweet spot of love starts with feeling grounded in our own unconditional love for ourselves. At that point, we have enough love to give without triggering a 5 State. We stay connected to ourselves and enjoy giving love. However, we are always aware of our inner state. The moment giving that love is more than we can do without merging with the other person or triggering a strong desire to distance, we pull back somewhat. This is the dance of healthy intimacy. It is hard work, requires being present, and is the greatest joy of all.

The fact that I have to find love inside me as a first step in intimacy is news to me. I thought I depended upon outside relationships for love. The fact that it starts with the love I have for myself changes a lot of things for me. I need to think about that.

Finding the Sweet Spot Approach Examples
• Give and receive love.
• Stay separate but close.
• Be emotionally honest.
• Get to One before speaking up.
• Give love but set limits.

This approach is right for me. I can love people and I can set limits with them. Recently, I moved to Chicago to be with my boyfriend and went back to school, so stress is high. I need to up my skills so I can find that sweet spot even when I am highly stressed.

The Meet My Need Approach

The last approach is to identify why the brain encoded your Love Circuit and be sure to meet that original need. It's a simple solution and can be quite effective.

My unmet need that caused my brain to encode a Merge Circuit was safety. I grew up in a family that was very chaotic. I didn't feel safe and didn't know what to do about it. I committed early to a friendship with David and eventually married him. That leftover unmet need of not knowing how to make myself safe remains. If I deal with my safety issues, my relationship might improve.

The unmet need that led my reptilian brain to encode distancing was comfort. I felt safe growing up and I had my mother's love, but never learned how to ground my life in basic comforts. The reason I don't date is that I wouldn't want to bring someone into my apartment. It is full of clutter. I want to learn how to develop a lifestyle that comforts me.

Meet My Need Approach Examples

- Meet my true need, rather than distancing or merging.
- Get my core safety from inside me, not from others.
- Get my basic love from myself, rather than from others.
- Learn how to comfort myself, then learn how to comfort others.
- Choose healthy pleasures, rather than unhealthy relationships.
- Bring my purpose to mind when I am with others.

The Love Circuit Imagine

Develop your transformation statement by using the brain's ability to activate circuits based on an Imagine. Use this visualization to generate, verify, or fine-tune the instructions your brain needs to transform your Love Circuit.

Relax: Create a situation in which you have privacy and will not be interrupted. Find a comfortable location for yourself and begin to relax. Focus your attention on your body and your breathing. Breathe in through your nose, out through your mouth, or in any way that is comfortable and comforting to you. When you are ready, begin to imagine.

Imagine: See yourself walking through your day, moving through the whole range of brain states and doing what you need to do. Notice your boundary changing, sometimes very thick for protection and sometimes quite thin – allowing for the giving and receiving of love. Be aware that you have emotional range and your boundary varies to some degree.

Now see yourself about to encounter someone who is important to you and with whom you know for sure that your Merge or Distancing Circuit could be activated. Take a deep breath and continue to see yourself move through your day. See that wire about to fire. Take a few moments and be aware of where you are . . . who is around you . . . how your body feels . . . and the thoughts that appear in your mind. Notice what you do . . .

Last, imagine yourself taking out your Power Grind In and saying words to yourself . . . words that give you a clear instruction to connect with yourself. Then imagine words appearing in your mind to express the approach statement you need to hear. Take a few deep breaths . . . Notice that if you stay focused on your body, imagining that scene, the words will bubble up into your mind. Finally, which reward would motivate you to connect with yourself and use that approach? Would it be Sanctuary, Authenticity, Vibrancy, Integrity, Intimacy, Spirituality, or Freedom?

Use the upcoming checklist to record the transformation statement that feels right to you.

When you're alone, you're in good company
As you rewire your Love Circuit, be sure to honor your need to strengthen your relationship with yourself. The first four Advanced EBT courses focus on building a secure base within. The rewards of Sanctuary, Authenticity, Vibrancy, and Integrity are fundamental to a secure attachment to self. With that base, we can nurture others more deeply and set limits with them, too. Also, we can heal from the past.

We need to be securely connected to ourself in order to be intimate with others. If we are not, we will return to merging and distancing, which is not only harmful to us, but to them. It is normal

The Power Grind In for Love: Merging Example

Stage	Statements
1 SLOW	I can NOT get my safety from pleasing everyone.
2 RAMP UP	That's ridiculous! I can NOT get safety from pleasing everyone. That's ridiculous. I can NOT get safety from pleasing everyone!
3 JOY	I get my safety from connecting to myself and being emotionally honest with people. Reward: Authenticity. I get my safety from connecting to MYSELF and being emotionally honest with people. Reward: It's Authenticity. Yes I do! I GET my safety from connecting to myself and being emotionally honest. Reward: AUTHENTICITY!

for relationships to activate old hurts, hurts that stay dormant if we are alone. That's the job of relationships, to activate those hurts, so that we can heal them. By being intimate with others, we find our intimacy with ourself deepening, too.

The Power Grind In for Love: Distancing Example

Stage	Statements
1 SLOW	I can NOT get my safety from hiding.
2 RAMP UP	That's ridiculous! I can NOT get safety from hiding. That's ridiculous. I can NOT get safety from hiding.
3 JOY	I get my safety from connecting to the love inside me and showing up in people's lives. Reward: Integrity. I get my SAFETY from connecting to the love inside me and showing up in people's lives. Reward: Integrity. I get my safety from connecting to the love inside me and showing up in people's lives. Reward: Integrity!

Nothing can hurt us the way people can and nothing can make our spirits soar the way relationships can. Now that we have the Cycle Tool we can clear away past hurts, and find more safety and fulfillment in our relationships. Each Cycle we do has two benefits. One is opening us to love and the other is replacing an unreasonable expectation with a reasonable one, providing a nugget of wisdom. As we heal, we love more deeply, and become far wiser.

My Distancing Circuit triggered me to cheat on my partner, and then blocked me from really understanding how much hurt I had caused. For 11 years after that horrible time, I was numb and self-loathing. A year ago, I started using EBT and cycling through that experience. I went through every recollection, and circuit by circuit, I came to peace with what I did. I became far more empathetic and loving, and the sting of that hurt is gone.

Create your Power Grind In for Love

Create your Power Grind In that will guide your way in rewiring your Love Circuit. Grind it in 50 to 200 times today, so that you begin to transform that circuit. Use the checklist that follows. Once you've developed your Power Grind In, use it in daily encounters. Appreciate that you will break and transform that circuit during the Second 30 Days. However, right now, use your Grind In as often as possible, at least four times per day. Celebrate creating your second Power Grind In and prepare to move forward for a lifestyle reset and onward to your Work Circuit!

The Rewiring Checklist
Day 3. Transform Your Love Circuit

I transformed my Love Circuit:

- **SLOW**

    I can NOT get my _____ from _____.

- **RAMP UP**

    That's ridiculous! I can NOT get my _____ from _____.

- **JOY**

I get my _____ **from:**

CONNECT	APPROACH	REWARD
☐ Connecting with myself	☐ Being emotionally honest	☐ Sanctuary
☐ Checking in	☐ Living for a higher purpose	☐ Authenticity
☐ Taking a deep breath	☐ Feasting on natural pleasure	☐ Vibrancy
☐ Being aware of myself	☐ Choosing healthy comforts	☐ Integrity
☐ Staying connected	☐ Giving and receiving love	☐ Intimacy
☐ Honoring my feelings	☐ Creating safety from within	☐ Spirituality
☐ Connecting inside	☐ Staying separate but close	☐ Freedom
☐ Listening to my body	☐ Giving love but setting effective limits	
☐ Knowing my number	☐ Loving people, but not rescuing them	
☐ The deepest part of me	☐ Saying how I feel and what I need	
☐ Feeling my feelings	☐ Giving love stopping short of self-neglect	
☐ Other _____	☐ Other _____	

I did it: 50   75   100   125   150   200 _____ times.

Success Check Day 16

- **Daily Success**

☐ I continued my Power of One Practice with 10 Check Ins and 10 Joy Points.

☐ I transformed my Love Circuit and created my Power Grind In.

☐ I made one or more community connections for support with transforming my circuit.

- **Did I pass the Success Check?   YES   NO**

If you did not, stay with this activity for one more day, then move on.

- **My Amazing Learning:**

_____

- **My Biggest Accomplishment:**

_____

- **My Biggest Challenge:**

_____

Great Work!

You have completed Day 16 of The Power of One Challenge.
Your next step is Day 17. Lifestyle Reset #4
Joy Lunch and Balancing Sleep.

Day 17. Lifestyle Reset #4
Joy Lunch and Balancing Sleep

Our fourth lifestyle reset is a huge step forward in training the brain to appreciate the natural pleasures of life. It includes a Joy Lunch and eight hours of Balancing Sleep. Also, you'll track changes in the Power of One Inventory, your progress in reaping the richest rewards of life.

Why

We have been using the Spiral Up Tools and rewiring Stress Circuits to control which gear we're using. These gears command changes in the chemicals and electricity in every cell of our bodies. In first gear (Brain State 1) everything is in balance, in harmony, and performing optimally and in fifth gear (Brain State 5) is quite the opposite.

However, from this point forward in EBT, you'll be adding more lifestyle control options to change your brain state (and ultimately, your set point). In the past, you may not have taken your lifestyle seriously. Without the EBT Tools, most of us reside in stress, which makes lifestyle changes difficult. You are not in that situation anymore, so you can make lifestyle changes quite easily and have the joy of manipulating your brain state not by chance but by choice!

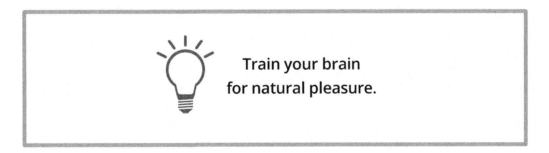

Train your brain
for natural pleasure.

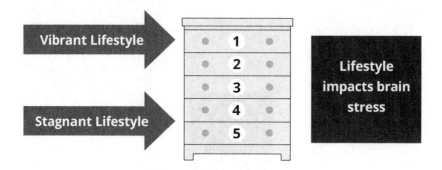

A Joy Lunch sustains our productivity

Our hunter-gatherer ancestors had their largest meal at midday. This is why you've probably noticed that there are a lot of growling stomachs around that time.

The goal is to eat a substantial lunch, consisting mainly of Joy Foods, particularly fiber foods, healthy fats, and lean protein. If you like, have agrarian foods, as they are whole foods and many people do well on them. Check how your lunch impacts your mood and performance in the afternoon. Food is a way we self-medicate. It's a substance, having a direct chemical impact on our physiology. Overeating Stress Foods can cause high insulin levels which can increase anxiety. We are controlling our chemicals with the EBT tools and also through lifestyle.

Your mind stays clearer, your relationships stay more connected, and your energy stays strong all afternoon. By evening you have enough stamina and energy to create a pleasurable evening, an Evening at One.

> ### Why insulin matters!
> Eating Joy Foods can tame the blood sugar
> highs and lows that cause
> anxiety, irritability, and cravings.
>
> **"I eat Joy Foods to balance my moods."**

Sleep is like food for the brain

If you do not sleep well or long enough, the work you do during the day to check in and rewire circuits is largely flushed away at night. Sleep is when the brain consolidates the learning we have done during the day and locks it into long-term memory. For example, today I did a cluster of Cycles about my mother, grieving what she went through in the last days of her life. It was "heavy" emotional lifting, and I was proud of doing them, so I am planning to get plenty of sleep tonight, to be sure that the changes stick.

The better your sleep habits, the lower your levels of the stress hormone cortisol, so you are less apt to trigger brain glitches. By developing the habit of sleeping long and well, you can alter two important hormones: ghrelin and leptin. As these hormones change, they stop causing food cravings and constant hunger, which can be a relief for the 70 percent of us in the U.S. who have food cravings or weight issues.

Changing sleep patterns is not easy, but sleep is so important to brain stress, that finding a way to get enough sleep is worth it. Do Cycles, get coaching, talk to your doctor, do whatever you need to find a healthy sleep pattern that works for you!

 **Track your Progress.
Be at ONE!**

How

First, plan your Joy Lunch and Balancing Sleep. Check off ideas below. Then make it easy by using the tools so that you naturally spiral up.

Then take the Power of One Inventory, total your scores, and compare them to your baseline scores. Reflect on the changes, then move on. Next up: taking charge of short-circuiting work stress.

Joy Lunch Ideas

- ☐ Emphasize lean protein, healthy fats, and fiber to boost productivity.
- ☐ If you need Stress Foods, have them without guilt.
- ☐ If you cannot control the type of food you eat, choose half portions.
- ☐ In restaurants, order by ingredients – "I want greens with chicken on top."
- ☐ Eat only when you are hungry.
- ☐ Choose salads topped by a protein source, drizzled with olive oil.
- ☐ Eat half a deli sandwich and bring the other half home for dinner.
- ☐ Drink four glasses of water or more during the workday.
- ☐ Keep healthy snacks on hand: nuts, fruit, a piece of chicken, olives . . .
- ☐ Bring a sack lunch to eat when you are hungry.
- ☐ If you overeat at lunch, check in three times in the early afternoon.
- ☐ Reward yourself with "dessert" after lunch – go outside and move!

Balancing Sleep Ideas

- ☐ Consider your relationship with sleep as important.
- ☐ Learn to calm and quiet yourself – it is a developmental task.
- ☐ Get enough exercise during the day so your body is tired.
- ☐ Do not eat or exercise for two hours before sleep.
- ☐ Stop use of all technology an hour before sleep.
- ☐ Overcome problems: snoring, uncomfortable bed, body pain . . .
- ☐ Make your bedroom dark and cool.
- ☐ Use natural sleep triggers, such as reading, a bath, or lovemaking.
- ☐ Check in and spiral up before going to sleep.
- ☐ Conclude your day with three Joy Points.
- ☐ If you awaken in the night, consider it a Moment of Opportunity.
- ☐ Do Power Grind Ins or use the tools until you to drift off to sleep.

The Power of One Inventory

Needs

In the last week, how often did you meet each of your basic needs?

Purpose
    1 = Rarely   2 = Sometimes   3 = Often   4 = Very Often

Pleasure
    1 = Rarely   2 = Sometimes   3 = Often   4 = Very Often

Comfort
    1 = Rarely   2 = Sometimes   3 = Often   4 = Very Often

Love
    1 = Rarely   2 = Sometimes   3 = Often   4 = Very Often

Safety
    1 = Rarely   2 = Sometimes   3 = Often   4 = Very Often

Total Needs Score _____

Rewards

In the last week, how often did you experience these rewards?

Sanctuary: Peace and power from within
    1 = Rarely   2 = Sometimes   3 = Often   4 = Very Often

Authenticity: Feeling whole and being genuine
    1 = Rarely   2 = Sometimes   3 = Often   4 = Very Often

Vibrancy: Healthy with a zest for life
    1 = Rarely   2 = Sometimes   3 = Often   4 = Very Often

Integrity: Doing the right thing
    1 = Rarely   2 = Sometimes   3 = Often   4 = Very Often

Intimacy: Giving and receiving love
    1 = Rarely   2 = Sometimes   3 = Often   4 = Very Often

Spirituality: Aware of the grace, beauty, and mystery of life
    1 = Rarely   2 = Sometimes   3 = Often   4 = Very Often

Freedom: Common excesses fade
    1 = Rarely   2 = Sometimes   3 = Often   4 = Very Often

Total Rewards Score _____

Connection

In the last week, how often did you connect in this way?

Being aware that I can create joy in my life
    1 = Rarely   2 = Sometimes   3 = Often   4 = Very Often

Choosing to create a moment at One
    1 = Rarely   2 = Sometimes   3 = Often   4 = Very Often

Spiraling up from stress to One
    1 = Rarely   2 = Sometimes   3 = Often   4 = Very Often

Enjoying sensory pleasures
    1 = Rarely   2 = Sometimes   3 = Often   4 = Very Often

Eating healthy food
    1 = Rarely   2 = Sometimes   3 = Often   4 = Very Often

Exercising in ways that are fun
    1 = Rarely   2 = Sometimes   3 = Often   4 = Very Often

Feeling love for myself
    1 = Rarely   2 = Sometimes   3 = Often   4 = Very Often

Feeling love for others
    1 = Rarely   2 = Sometimes   3 = Often   4 = Very Often

Feeling love for all living beings
    1 = Rarely   2 = Sometimes   3 = Often   4 = Very Often

Total Connection Score _____

The Power of One Inventory Summary

Category	Baseline Score	Current Score	Progress	Power of One Range
Needs	_____	_____	_____	15 to 20
Rewards	_____	_____	_____	21 to 28
Connection	_____	_____	_____	27 to 36
Power of One Total	_____	_____	_____	63 to 84

What is your amazing learning about your needs?

_____

What is your amazing learning about your rewards?

_____

What is your amazing learning about your connection?

_____

Success Check Day 17

- **Daily Success**

☐ I continued my Power of One Practice with 10 Check Ins and 10 Joy Points.

☐ I reset my lifestyle in these six ways: Exercise, Play, Joy Breakfast, Sanctuary Time, Joy Lunch, and Balancing Sleep.

☐ I tracked my progress in creating the Power of One.

☐ I made one or more community connections for support with my lifestyle reset.

- **Did I pass the Success Check?   YES   NO**

If you did not, stay with this activity for one more day, then move on.

- **My Amazing Learning:**

_____

- **My Biggest Accomplishment:**

_____

- **My Biggest Challenge:**

_____

Congratulations!

**You have completed Day 17 of Power of One Challenge.
Your next step is Day 18. Discover Your Work Circuit.**

Take Charge

Day 18. Discover Your Work Circuit

After rewiring your Love Circuit, what comes next? Productivity is essential to life, so it makes sense that work would be a magnet for stress wires. Today you will discover your Work Circuit.

I have a procrastination wire that I need to clear. That would change my productivity and probably, my income.

I acquired my dad's wire to be perfect at work. I don't want anyone criticizing me, but that perfectionism keeps me from closing on projects. I am never perfect enough!

The wires that block the joy of productivity are brain glitches. We have an illusion that work is work and personal life is personal life. However, emotional circuits don't know when you are at work and when you are at home. Work can activate wires that trigger replays of childhood coping strategies and latent drives to go to excess. Perfect! Raise your set point and become more productive at work, too.

I had no idea why I didn't like my boss. Then I did a Cycle and realized that she activated my stepfather wires. He was a critical man who was 6'4" and weighed 250 pounds. My boss is a 5'4" skinny woman. However, both activate the same wire!

What's a Work Circuit?
A wire that blocks
the joy of productivity.

Two types of Work Circuits

Two types of stress-activated circuits can readily block the joy of productivity. One is our work style, for example, being late. The other is work roles, like adopting the role of being the good employee or the failure. Both block our productivity and each one is a sign that we have an unmet need. By discovering that circuit, and unlocking its synaptic connections, not only can we stop the Work Circuit from blocking our Power of One at work, but we can meet the original unmet need that caused it to be encoded.

The Work Circuit

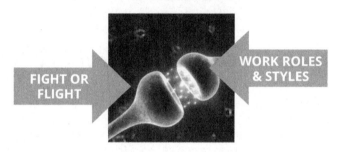

The Roles We Play Circuits

The most common blockers to success at work are the replays of roles we established in childhood. Roles are false selves we develop because we did not get the recognition and love we needed. Basically, the reptile concocted a role we played to gain love, then locked it into our 4th or 5th Drawer. Work stress activates these roles and we find ourselves playing them out!

I was the oldest child and it was my job to be The Best. I put down my sister and easily outshined my brother. At work, I have a fight-or-flight drive to outdo the others, which works well up to a point. But it puts me under horrendous stress and I irritate some of my co-workers.

My role in our family was to be The Invisible One. This role is impacting my income because I am the highest producer in our division but my boss pays me less and gets away with it. They do not see me because . . . I am The Invisible One!

The Work Styles Circuits

If we do not get our needs for emotional connection and loving limits met early in life, we develop drives and habits that interfere with work joy and success. This can take many forms! The most common Work Circuit is working too much.

"I get my love from overworking."

We're stressed because we do not get the love, recognition, or validation we need, and the fight-or-flight response latches onto overworking as a solution. Like all glitches, overworking makes sense up to a point. Overworking is not the problem. Overworking so much that it blocks our power is the problem. It's that last five percent of the excess that is the work of the reptile.

We are on a dopamine high all day at work, not because of the work, but because we are in joyful anticipation of finally getting the love we need! Then our dopamine high crashes in the evening, and we have no energy to find love. So we settle for drinking, overeating, internet excesses, and anything that helps us not face the fact that our need for love has yet again gone unmet.

I work 14-hour days and weekends. I take Saturdays off every few weeks and sleep all day. I have no idea how to comfort myself. My condominium is a trash heap and I do no maintenance on my life. I haven't had a vacation for five years and I'm not sure I want one. I comfort myself by overworking, even though it does not make me feel comforted!

"I get my safety from underworking."

Sometimes the Work Circuit triggers underworking. People around us can't figure out why we don't get busy and take on a new job. It's simple. It's a circuit that keeps us in a dopamine low and sporting a strong drive to underachieve. It's our safety, because if we ever tried to do the best we could do, chances are we would fail. Where would that leave us? The underworking circuit, like all circuits, covers up an unmet need.

I took an early retirement and have been somewhat lost since then. I stay busy with my computer and small tasks, but I am definitely underutilized. My circuit is: I get my comfort from wandering around and doing nothing, from underworking.

"I get my comfort from repeating old patterns."

Work Circuits can also be various other patterns that block our productivity. These seemingly simple quirks about us are nearly impossible to change because they are fueled by a glitch. Common patterns are procrastinating, perfectionism, lateness, and quitting. These wires trigger small differences that interfere with our productivity and work relationships.

My review came up last week and my supervisor rated my work high but said that I would not be promoted. Her complaint was that I was often late for meetings. I went to Brain State 5 and used my Damage Control PLUS Tool. After my review, I cycled until I found my Work Circuit. It was: I get my pleasure from being late. How ridiculous! Then I did a Travel Back and saw this image of myself as a kid, wanting to have things other kids who weren't poor and in foster care had. I always showed up late as an attention grabber. No wonder I kept doing it. I got my pleasure from being late.

Why

We need to work. Our hunter-gatherer brain needs us to work hard, stopping short of abusing or neglecting ourselves, and to feel rewarded for our work. But Work Circuits get in our way.

They are particularly important to rewire because Work Circuits travel with us everywhere. We can change our boss, profession, or organization, but about six months to a year into the new situation, the circuits start firing again!

We rewire them because Work Circuits are so sticky! We would be tempted to consider them as just skill deficiencies or bad habits. However, they are emotional wires. They are exceedingly persistent.

What's more, our emotional wires reach into the emotional brains of others. They create toxic work relationships and organizational dynamics even when there is no logical reason for them to exist!

My old boss could never keep employees more than six months because she was a tyrant. I took the role of The Victim, but finally left. I made a point of taking a new job being the direct report to a really nice boss. I had not bothered to clear my victim circuit, and before long, she became The Tyrant and I became The Victim again! What I didn't rewire came back to haunt me.

Discover Your Work Circuit

I get my _____(need)_____ from _____(work style or role)_____.

How

Discover this circuit by complaining about work, then following the natural flow of your feelings until you uncover the unconscious expectation that is driving you to respond in that way. Most of us have several Work Circuits. As always, complaining about what bothers you the most gives the brain the stimulus to find circuits in the 5th Drawer.

Which Work Circuit
blocks my power to be at One?

The situation is . . . I am nice to everyone and work harder than my co-worker who is also an escrow specialist. I close more deals and she is paid more. What I'm most stressed about is . . . I am nice but I'm not getting ahead. I feel ANGRY that . . . they don't see me. I can't stand it that . . . I work hard and get no credit for it. I hate it that . . . I think my A+ Anger skill could use some improvement. I'll go to sadness. I feel sad that . . . nobody gives me credit. I feel afraid that . . . I will never get a raise. I feel guilty that . . . I don't speak up and ask for a raise. OF COURSE I don't ask for a raise, because I get my safety from . . . being the nice passive girl who is unseen by other people. I get my safety from . . . being a nice person. I HATE THAT! I HATE IT THAT I AM ALWAYS NICE and get shortchanged by everyone I work with! I HATE THAT. Great work. That was my best Cycle ever.

Examples of Work Role Circuits

- I get my safety from being The Perfect One.
- I get my comfort from being The Invisible One.
- I get my security from being The Failure.

The situation is . . . I have high standards and people like working for me because our team achieves a lot and I have the Power of One a lot. But then something switches and I go to Brain State 5. Instead of having high standards, there is this stress rush, and I am outright demanding. I call this my Obnoxious Tyrant Circuit. What I'm most stressed about is . . . I am obnoxious! I feel angry that . . . I am so stupid. I can't stand it that . . . I don't even know I am doing it. I hate it that . . . I have been so obnoxious that I'm sure people judge me . . . I feel sad they judge me . . . I feel afraid I can't stop doing it . . . and I feel guilty that . . . I can be so stupid. OF COURSE, I can be that stupid, because I get my safety from being an Obnoxious, Demanding Tyrant. Now I'm at Brain State 1. It's a wire. I'm going to rewire that one!

Examples of Work Style Circuits

- I get my love from complaining about work.
- I get my comfort from procrastinating.
- I get my protection from overworking.

The situation is . . . I work seven days a week and stay late most evenings. My wife is lonely and I hardly see my 4-year-old daughter. What I'm most stressed about is . . . I work too much. I HATE it that . . . I can't stop working. I feel FURIOUS that . . . all I think about is work. I AM ANGRY . . . actually I'm sad. I feel sad that . . . I don't do something about it. I feel afraid that . . . I am so removed from my family. I feel guilty that . . . I don't care. It really doesn't bother me that much. OF COURSE it doesn't bother me that I work so much, because my unreasonable expectation is . . . that I get my LOVE from work. That is really sick. I can't GET LOVE from work. Wait a minute. My mother got love from work. I have her wire!

What are common work roles and styles?

• The Overachiever	• Overworking
• The Rescuer	• Underworking
• The Authority	• Procrastinating
• The Victim	• Doing everything perfectly
• The Failure	• Complaining about work
• The Clown	• Regularly being late
• The Nice One	• Taking on too much
• The Troublemaker	• Rebelling against rules
• The Invisible One	• Not checking my work
• The Tyrant	• Making snap decisions
• The Perfect One	• Judging my co-workers

Feel your feelings, then continue processing your discovery

As always, after discovering your Work Circuit, be aware of your emotions for as long as possible. This emotional awareness (up to six hours after unlocking the wire) helps dismantle the circuit, preparing it to be transformed. Then analyze the wire, considering when it might have been encoded (often we never know) and whether or not it is an intergenerational circuit, acquired from someone close to you.

Last, be sure that you have grieved the losses of having encoded and lived with that wire, or even mourning the loss of it. Even procrastination brings with it the joy of familiarity. We can "count on" procrastinating! Perhaps do five Cycles, and if the circuit was deep, considering doing a Travel Back. An important note about grieving losses: NEVER grieve having to "give up" the excess. In EBT, we rewire the drive so that change becomes easy and natural.

Enjoy discovering your Work Circuit. Then, when you are ready, move on to the next day's activities and begin dismantling that wire.

The Rewiring Checklist
Day 1. Discover Your Work Circuit

Say What Is Bothering You

- The situation is . . . (Complain about work.)
- What I'm most stressed about is . . . (Say what bothers you the most about work.)

Unlock the Circuit

- I feel angry that . . .
- I can't stand it that . . .
- I hate it that . . .

Discover the Hidden Message

- I feel sad that . . .
- I feel afraid that . . .
- I feel guilty that . . .
- OF COURSE I would do that, because my unreasonable expectation is . . .

I get my:	**from being:**	**or from:**
☐ Safety	☐ The Overachiever	☐ Overworking
☐ Love	☐ The Rescuer	☐ Underworking
☐ Comfort	☐ The Authority	☐ Procrastinating
☐ Pleasure	☐ The Victim	☐ Doing everything perfectly
☐ Purpose	☐ The Failure	☐ Complaining about work
☐ Survival	☐ The Clown	☐ Failing at work
☐ Existence	☐ The Nice One	☐ Taking on too much
☐ Protection	☐ The Troublemaker	☐ Rebelling against rules
☐ Security	☐ The Invisible One	☐ Not checking my work
☐ Power	☐ The Tyrant	☐ Making snap decisions
☐ Nurturing	☐ The Perfect One	☐ Judging my co-workers
☐ Other _____	☐ Lost	☐ Other _____

Success Check Day 18

- **Daily Success**

☐ I continued my Power of One Practice with 10 Check Ins and 10 Joy Points.

☐ I discovered my Work Circuit.

☐ I made one or more community connections for support with discovering my circuit.

- **Did I pass the Success Check?   YES   NO**

If you did not, stay with this activity for one more day, then move on.

- **My Amazing Learning:**

_____

- **My Biggest Accomplishment:**

_____

- **My Biggest Challenge:**

_____

Congratulations!

**You have completed Day 18 of The Power of One Challenge.
Your next step is Day 19. Negate Your Work Circuit.**

Day 19. Negate Your Work Circuit

Let's weaken your Work Circuit today. This prepares you to transform an aspect of your life that blocks the joy of productivity.

Our hunter-gatherer genes prepare us to go into battle, to right wrongs, fix issues, and contribute to the greater good. We need to be industrious, challenged, and rewarded by doing hard things in order to be happy.

By weakening and transforming the Work Circuit, we can honor our fundamental drives to get things done and experience more success and fulfillment in doing so.

That way of working will not give me the love that I need.

Why
The circuits that crop up at work are of immediate consequence in disparate areas of our lives. You'd think that we would have dealt with them long ago. If they were simple wires, we would have. They are not simple wires, but constellations of neural connections stored in the elusive emotional brain.

My father was an accountant and partner at his firm and didn't spend much time with me. I had so many wires of resenting him for being absent that I encoded a failure circuit: I get my safety from failing at work. I revised that expectation to: I get my existence from being fired from every job my father's connections ever got for me. This unconscious circuit was my way of expressing my abandonment rage at my father.

We rewire these circuits because, without the precise and repeated use of the emotional processing tools, these patterns can easily stay with us for the rest of our lives. Coming to terms with the fact that these patterns have emotional roots is a breakthrough of its own.

I do outside sales for technology companies and as I get older, it's harder to find work. Prospective employers see that I last one or two years at a firm. My supervisors always complain that I do not follow through with clients. I have used calendar reminders and sales apps to improve. Nothing ever worked. Now, I have a second wife and we have four teenagers between us. I need to make a good income. So, I'm frying this wire. It's already started changing me. Today I followed through with a client and it wasn't hard. I even got a dopamine zing when I did it!

These patterns that impact productivity are even more challenging to change because our own circuits are part of a larger pattern of circuits of those we work with and those we love. Wires are not just a personal concern but a systems issue.

Denny and I have two children ages six and nine and my marriage is going downhill due to Work Circuits. We have matching circuits. Both of us get our love from overachieving. Either we work through the weekend or we are so distraught about work problems that we can't relax. Our younger daughter is self-medicating with sugar and our older daughter has started biting her nails and pulling out her hair. Our family is under more stress than I realized. Fortunately, I'm already teaching my children the tools and Denny and I have committed to using EBT together.

As you negate your Work Circuit, avoid trying to change your work behavior. Forcing behavior change is accomplished by the prefrontal cortex, whereas the root cause of the problem is a wire that is stored in the emotional brain. Instead, use your prefrontal cortex to crush, destroy, and transform the faulty circuit!

Tips on Negating Your Work Circuit

- Do not change your work habits.
- Instead, change the circuit.
- Weaken that wire.
- Changes in work will naturally follow.

Grieve before you negate

Work Circuits can be rooted deep in the brain and be entangled with other wires. We don't want to disturb these wires because we sense that it is complicated. But complicated is good in EBT. It means that we can gently trigger, then clear, suppressed emotions that could otherwise rumble around inside and cause one problem after another in our lives. Instead of experiencing a narrow healing, while changing the Work Circuit we can clear related wires. This helps us move up our set point more rapidly.

The situation is . . . when I start something I don't finish it. I procrastinate and then activate my Ridiculous Anxiety Circuit, which drains my creativity. Then my Sappy Merge Circuit starts ramping up and I think nobody will be pleased with what I do. They never are! Then I'm at a stuck Brain State 5. What I'm most stressed about is . . . how unproductive I have been. I have talent but I don't use it. Okay, keep to ONE topic here. What I'm most stressed about is . . . I have not achieved my potential. I feel angry that . . . I have slacked off. I can't stand it that . . . I have so much talent and I'm not using it. I HATE it that . . . the time has gone by and I've made so many mistakes . . . I feel sad that . . . I have not been more successful . . . I feel afraid that . . . I will keep underachieving . . . I feel guilty that . . . I don't do anything about it . . . OF COURSE I don't do anything about it, because my unreasonable expectation is . . . I am doomed to fail. What a horrible wire. I know just where I got that wire, from my mother . . . I am NOT doomed to fail . . . I AM NOT doomed to fail. I AM REALLY NOT DOOMED to fail. That's ridiculous. I have POWER. I am NOT doomed in any way. THAT IS RIDICULOUS! I do have power. I'm going to use it. I am getting out of my own way and using my POWER!

How

Use the same negation process you used with your Mood and Love Circuits. For the expectation, **"I get safety from being The Perfect One,"** say **"I can NOT get safety from being The Perfect One."** Again, state it very slowly at first, then ramp it up and ridicule the circuit. If you like, sing, dance, or stomp when you are negating it. Making community connections helps tremendously. The more emotionally-charged the experience, the better the rewiring results.

Next, ramp up your energy. Make fun of the circuit. Say something like: "That's completely ridiculous! That makes no sense! How can I get my safety from being The Perfect One?" Keep expressing your disbelief that you could ever think it could give you safety. Have some fun at the circuit's expense! Make these mocking statements until a surge of feel-good dopamine locks in your new learning. Pause, and enjoy the glow!

2 Stages of Negating a Work Circuit	
SLOW	I . . . can . . . NOT . . . get . . . my . . . comfort . . . from underworking. I . . . can . . . NOT . . . get . . . my . . . comfort . . . from underworking. I . . . can . . . NOT . . . get . . . my . . . comfort . . . from underworking.
RAMP UP	That's ridiculous! I can NOT get comfort from slacking off. Slacking off does NOT give me comfort. It just makes me feel bad. That's completely ridiculous! Goofing off is NOT COMFORTING!

Example (All Grind In Clusters count as 10 Grind Ins)

SLOW

- I . . . can . . . NOT . . . get . . . LOVE . . . from . . . procrastinating . . . (pause)
- I . . . can . . . NOT . . . get . . . LOVE . . . from . . . procrastinating . . . (pause)
- I . . . can . . . NOT . . . get . . . LOVE . . . from . . . procrastinating . . . (pause)
- I . . . can . . . NOT . . . get . . . LOVE . . . from . . . procrastinating . . . (pause)
- I . . . can . . . NOT . . . get . . . LOVE . . . from . . . procrastinating . . . (pause)

RAMP UP

- That's ridiculous! I can NOT get love from procrastinating.
- Putting things off does NOT give me love.
- I could procrastinate for weeks and it would NOT bring me love.
- That's ridiculous! I can NOT get love from procrastinating!
- No matter how long I put things off, it will NOT give me LOVE!
- HOW UTTERLY RIDICULOUS!!!

The Ladder Tool

**Start with the 5 Tool and then go up the "ladder,"
using each tool in order and getting to One.**

The Ladder Tool . . . a fresh new way to spiral up!

Use this tool when you are in the 5th Drawer of the brain for a highly productive rewiring experience. You will clear away some neuronal clutter in each of the five drawers.

It's really easy and there is no guesswork involved. All you do is use the lead-ins for each tool. If you are using the app or mobile check in on your member home page, then it will move you through the lead-ins with ease. Start using the tools. First, use the 5 Tool, then the 4 Tool, then the 3 Tool, then the 2 Tool, and finally, the 1 Tool!

My Mood Circuit is depression and my Love Circuit is distancing. My outward personality gives people the impression that everything is fine when it's not, so I have been successful at work. When I realized that work was my addiction of choice, it hit me hard. Without being perfect at work, who would I be? I wouldn't exist! I went right to Brain State 5. I went to bed but awoke in the middle of the night in stark terror. I didn't know what to do, so I tried the Ladder Tool. About 10 minutes later, I must have fallen back to sleep. When I awoke the next morning, I was at Brain State 2, or perhaps even Brain State 1. I love this tool!

The Ladder Tool

- Use the 5 tool – Ease your stress.
- Use the 4 tool – Feel more connected.
- Use the 3 tool – Enjoy positive emotions.
- Use the 2 tool – Be present and aware.
- Use the 1 tool – Celebrate the Power of One!

Let's add some Power Boosters

Continue to use the Power Boosters you have already learned, but try a few more that pertain directly to work. When you are ready, tear into that circuit. Have at this wire. It was encoded by some random life event through no fault of your own. It resides in your emotional brain and only you can take charge and clear it. Let's clear that wire!

Power Boosters for Your Work Circuit

- Grind it in when you arrive at work.
- Take a lunch break and use your Grind In.
- Grind it in at night when work is on your mind.
- Feel like complaining about work? Do your Grind In instead.
- Do your Grind In on the commute to and from work.

The Rewiring Checklist
Day 2. Negate Your Work Circuit

I negated my Work Circuit:

- **SLOW**

    I can NOT get my _____ from _____.

- **RAMP UP**

    That's ridiculous! I can NOT get my _____ from _____.

    I did it: 50   75   100   125   150   200 _____ times.

I boosted the power of my Grind In (one or more ways):

☐   Grinding it in when I arrive at work

☐   Taking a lunch break and using my Grind In

☐   When work is on my mind, using my Grind In

☐   When I feel like complaining about work, doing a Grind In instead

☐   Doing my Grind In on the commute to and from work

Success Check Day 19

- **Daily Success**

☐ I continued my Power of One Practice with 10 Check Ins and 10 Joy Points.

☐ I negated my Work Circuit and tried out the Ladder Tool.

☐ I made one or more community connections for support with negating my circuit.

- **Did I pass the Success Check?   YES   NO**

If you did not, stay with this activity for one more day, then move on.

- **My Amazing Learning:**

_____

- **My Biggest Accomplishment:**

_____

- **My Biggest Challenge:**

_____

Congratulations!

**You have completed Day 19 of The Power of One Challenge.
Your next step is Day 20. Transform Your Work Circuit.**

Day 20. Transform Your Work Circuit

Today you will create a personalized Power Grind In to short-circuit that Work Circuit. That Power Grind In will not only give you the security of knowing that you have the capacity to deactivate that wire on the spot, but your new message will spiral you up to Brain State 1.

My Work Circuit is being The Authority. I was so charged up yesterday when my co-worker took issue with my part of the project that I was about to say things I would regret. Instead I repeated my Power Grind In to myself. I calmed down. A few moments later, I was at One.

Why

Transforming this circuit is really important because work takes up an average of 8.8 hours per day, so if a brain glitch is triggered and stays stuck on, that's a lot of cortisol cascading all day! Day by day, in small but important ways, our set point moves up or down. How we respond to work stress is a major contributor for most people.

Whether your work is caretaking, teaching, running a start-up, raising children, or whatever it takes to cover expenses, you can express your talents and feel rewarded. Work is challenging! If that old circuit remains, it can be triggered in a nanosecond, and work stress can be bad for us. It activates our 5 Circuits (Survival Circuits) and they become stuck on, activating common excesses. Our set point goes down.

On the other hand, if we have our Power Grind Ins handy, we know that our synaptic connections have become fluid. Our most powerful survival circuits, the 5 Circuits, become unhinged. If we connect with our body, and use our Power Grind Ins with passion, we turn work demands into productive stress. Not only will that stress weaken our Work Circuit, but it will yield a strong and powerful Brain State 1. We become exceptionally productive.

A bonus of being at One involves emotional contagion. When we are at One, the 4 Circuits and 5 Circuits in others go on holiday! We bring out the best in others.

Work Stress Can be Bad for Us

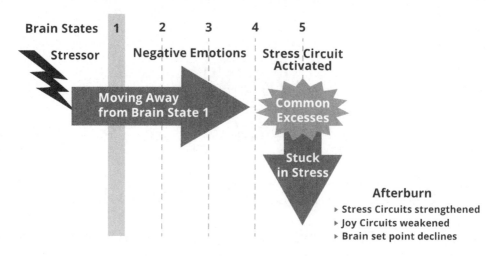

I was considering leaving my job but decided to stick it out for a while because it is stressful! I can use this dysfunctional work situation to raise my set point. In my next position, I will have transformed my Work Circuit and will be able to automatically access the Power of One.

Most of our customers are reasonable and as a customer service employee, I enjoy them. About five percent of our customers are aggressive. My reptile activates my Work Circuit and I tense up. Now my defense is to state my Power Grind In for Work and zap that wire.

Work Stress Can be Good for Us

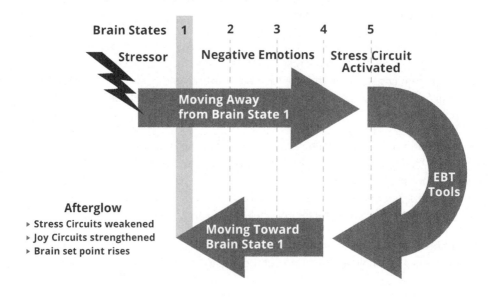

As your set point rises, your work will change. You are experiencing a different reality because you are activating different circuits. Worries about work fade and actions that previously seemed impossible happen with remarkable ease.

I am an ER nurse and I love my job. I have seen others who have endured stress for far too long and I don't want to be like that. Nor do I want to be relying on pills all the time. My choice is to raise my set point, to be wired at One, and stay in this job.

The stress of not working enough is making me slide back to using excesses. I can see that my life is not about recovering from addiction to painkillers or alcohol, but to my old set point. I need to be wired at One, and breaking my Work Circuit will help.

How

We are going to construct a Power Grind In for Work. Use the three-pronged approach to reconsolidate that wire!

Connect: Use your favorite connect statement so that you can lock into your inherent strength, goodness, and wisdom. Switch from checking out to checking in!

Approach: State your new approach to work. Whether it's to work more or less, to use a different style, or to revamp a role, make sure the approach is so responsive to your needs that you relax when you hear yourself say it.

Reward: Your reward is any of the seven higher-order rewards, whichever one soothes you and energizes you to move forward with making that change. It may be Sanctuary, Authenticity, Vibrancy, Integrity, Intimacy, Spirituality, or Freedom?

Where is your circuit stored?

Your Work Circuit may be a minor habit, a wire stored in your **2nd or 3rd Drawer**. A gentle instruction might be enough to change it. As work is survival-based, check to be sure it is not stronger, a wire stored in the **4th or 5th Drawer** that will require a much stronger new instruction. If circuits in the higher drawers speak softly to the reptile yet make their mark, the wires in the lower drawers require that we come out fighting and, in essence, punch the reptile in the nose.

What is your new approach to work?

What would be a fresh approach to work that would change your day or perhaps your career, your finances, and your productivity? Encode that message in your brain, the one that will change your work life in ways that matter to you.

The Freedom from Roles Approach

The roles we play are part of normal family dynamics, harkening back to such realities as sibling rivalry and reflecting imperfect fits between the personalities of parents and children. When we do not feel seen and validated, we become someone else!

Sometimes they are subtle, or variable, only arising in certain situations. Other times, they are so survival-driven that it feels nearly impossible to step out of that role. If we could not play that role, what role would we play? This is a particularly fun circuit to rewire. Don't hold back, warmly tease yourself about your role!

I call my Work Circuit my "drive to be so perfect that nobody could hate me, not even my mom" wire. My desire to over-please at work is the boy who wanted mom to love him the most. My resultant "Perfect Employee" wire is a 5 Circuit. My transformation statement is "I get my survival from connecting to myself and breaking free of my Perfect Employee Wire. Reward: Authenticity."

I get a rush when there is a problem at work. My "The Fixer" role circuits start jangling, and I overcommit, then come up short on follow-through. It's deflating to me that I can NOT get my love from being The Fixer. I get my love at home and I get my paycheck at work. If I overcommit less, my job performance will improve.

Freedom From Roles Approach Examples

- Be genuine, rather than playing a role.
- Stop striving to be The Authority.
- Be real, not The Perfect One!
- Let go of The Tyrant role.
- Stop repeating my childhood.

The Getting Unstuck Approach

When the problem is a bad habit, like procrastinating, or being late for meetings, start with five robust Cycles. Then do five more. These stuck habits are often products of emotional hurts. The habit wire itself is not that strong. These habits are driven by strong yearnings to be seen, heard, and felt, in combination with an upbringing in which effective work habits were not always modeled and taught. This getting unstuck approach is especially effective when the circuit is in the top three drawers of the brain.

I enjoy being late for meetings. I have a rebellious streak and I feel important when I make people wait for me. I did five Cycles on this and started laughing myself silly. Of course I would do that! I get my safety from being naughty. I cannot get safety from being naughty and offending my co-workers. I get my safety from showing up and being a team player.

I think my Work Circuit co-activates with my Mood Circuit, which is powerlessness. To get unstuck, I'm going to use the approach statement: NOT ACTIVATING MY POWERLESS CIRCUIT, and charging forward! Just saying that gives me a dopamine surge! No wonder I've been stuck. I've been activating two obnoxious circuits and the cortisol cascade has been killing my motivation. No wonder my back hurts and I have trouble sleeping. The stress chemicals have been putting me on edge, as if I am always looking around for someone who is about to attack me. That sounds like a wire from childhood.

- Arrive five minutes early for the fun of it.
- Instead of procrastinating, work on it for five minutes.
- Quitting is not an option. Make it work!
- Choose to do things I don't want to do.
- Put my heart into it!

The Meet My Needs Approach

The tendencies to overwork and underwork can be based upon survival drives. When stress is high, and the reptile is aggravated, there is no way to find work-life balance. In fact, the idea of it is ludicrous. Work is so central to survival, that when the brain is stressed, we resort to overwork or underwork. Until we meet our basic need, the imbalance will not let up!

My Work Circuit is that I get my comfort from overworking. I work at home and never have to leave. I work all day every day and it's so comfortable. If I got comfort in healthy ways, maybe I'd be able to break that wire. I can get comfort from connecting with myself and heaping on the natural pleasures and comforts of life OTHER THAN WORKING. That's frightening. The idea that I would meet my actual need is revolutionary. I will try that.

I have a good time. The day goes by and I have empty food wrappers strewn around. I watch the news on TV. For 20 years, I worked in a very stressful, unhappy, dog-eat-dog environment. Then I was laid off. My Work Circuit is that I get my pleasure from doing nothing. I'm going to break that circuit. I can NOT get pleasure from doing nothing. Sure, I can, but it's not that pleasurable. I get my pleasure from natural, healthy pleasures. A lot of them. If I encode that, then the drive to underwork may fade.

Meet My Need Approach Examples

- Meet my true needs, rather than overworking.
- Get my safety from inside, not from work.
- Get love from people, not from overworking.
- Comfort myself in healthy ways.
- Enjoy natural pleasures.
- Bring to mind my reward for working harder.

The Work Circuit Imagine

Enjoy this Imagine as a way to generate, verify, or fine-tune the instructions your brain needs to transform your Work Circuit.

Relax: Create privacy for yourself and find a comfortable location to relax. Focus your attention on your body and your breathing. Breathe in through your nose, out through your mouth, or in any way that is comfortable and comforting to you. When you are ready, begin to imagine.

Imagine: See yourself awakening in the morning and saying to yourself, "I am creating joy in my life." Notice that you are aware that it will be a great day and you have a zest for life. You are ready to be happy, healthy, and productive.

See yourself moving along through the day including being at work, no matter what you do that involves effortful control. This involves a certain amount of stress and a need to produce, to be productive. Now, see yourself in a work situation, aware that you are vulnerable. Your Work Circuit may be activated and just that "thing" you do not want to do – you find yourself about to do "it"!

See yourself in slow motion, just about to do precisely what you do not want to do. Respond in just the way you have done so many times before, the response orchestrated by the reptilian brain. But this time, you pull out your Power Grind In and you say to yourself . . . words that give you a clear instruction to connect with yourself . . . Then state your new approach to this situation . . . and last, state your reward, whether it is Sanctuary, Authenticity, Vibrancy, Integrity, Intimacy, Spirituality, or Freedom.

Please take all the time you need and then, use the upcoming checklist to record the transformation statement that feels right to you.

Circuits co-activate – it's a party!
The Work Circuit is so diverse that is it helpful to read the cycles of others as you prepare to transform this important wire. Typically, more than one wire is involved, which is why during the Second 30 Days, we'll break all four wires we identify in this challenge.

The situation is . . . I am the assistant manager of a family-owned restaurant chain. I work long, late hours and there is a lot of stress. These days it is harder to find good employees and the margins are smaller, so one slow day and we are in the red again. The owner blames me and so does his 24-year-old son, who enjoys bossing me around. What I'm most stressed about is . . . I am in the middle. I feel angry that . . . I am in the middle. I can't stand it that . . . it is always my fault. I HATE it that . . . I am the punching bag. I HATE it that . . . I take being the punching bag. I AM FURIOUS they dump on me . . . (unlocking moment) . . . I could feel that one! . . . (Deep breaths) . . . I feel sad that . . . I'm in a bad job. I feel afraid that . . . the son is going to squeeze me out. I feel guilty that . . . I take their blame. OF COURSE I take their blame, because I have an unreasonable expectation that . . . I get my survival from IGNORING PROBLEMS. That's right. I avoid conflict at home and at work, just the way I did as a child. I get my survival from activating my Mood Circuit, which is a false high and my Work Circuit which is ignoring problems. Now it all makes sense. The problem is two wires. My transformation statement for my Power Grind In is . . . I get my survival from connecting solidly to myself and bringing up my concerns. Reward: Integrity. I think I nailed that one!

The Power Grind In for Work: Role Example

Stage	Statements
1 SLOW	I can NOT get my comfort from being The Perfect One.
2 RAMP UP	That's ridiculous! I can NOT get my comfort from being perfect. That's ridiculous. I can NOT get my comfort from being PERFECT!
3 JOY	I get comfort from connecting inside and BEING REAL. Reward: Authenticity. I get comfort from connecting inside and BEING REAL. Reward: Authenticity. I get comfort from connecting inside and BEING REAL. Reward: AUTHENTICITY!

The situation is . . . I attract the most abusive bosses. If there are five supervisors in a division, I am always assigned to the one who is going to hide key information from me, favor other workers, and evaluate me unfairly. What I'm most stressed about is . . . there must be a wire in me that is contributing to this. What I'm most stressed about is . . . all my bosses have been bullies. I feel ANGRY that . . . all my bosses have been bullies. I can't stand it that . . . I have the worst luck in bosses. I HATE IT that I have bad bosses. (That is B minus anger.) I FEEL $@&% that I have such $@&% bosses. I HATE it that they treat me like $@&%. I HATE IT! I HATE IT! I HATE IT!!!! . . . . (Ahhh! The unlocking moment!) . . . I feel sad that . . . I am picked on . . . I feel afraid that . . . I deserve it . . . I feel guilty that . . . I cower when the boss is around. OF COURSE I cower when the boss is around, because I have an unreasonable expectation that. . . I get my . . . love from . . . being The Victim. I HATE THAT!!! How could I get love from being a victim? Maybe there's another circuit there . . . OF COURSE, I get love from being a victim, because the wire under that is that . . . I get my . . . survival from merging with other people, just like I did with my mother. Maybe it's a pile-up of circuits. What's the Mood Circuit that is co-activated by this wire? Well, it would have to be . . . ANXIETY. That's it. Three circuits co-activated and there I am, a willing victim of bosses, bringing out the worst circuits in them. I HATE that . . . but I understand it now. I have compassion for myself. Already I have Power Grind Ins for Mood and Love. My transformation statement for my Work Circuit is . . . I get my love from checking in, getting to One, and never cowering again! Reward: Freedom!

The Power Grind In for Work: Style Example

Stage	Statements
1 SLOW	I can NOT get my love from overworking.
2 RAMP UP	That's ridiculous! I can NOT get my love from overworking. *That's ridiculous.* Work will never give me the love I need.
3 JOY	I get love from staying checked in, getting LOVE from people, not from overworking. Reward: Vibrancy. I get love from staying checked in, getting LOVE from PEOPLE, not from overworking. Reward: Vibrancy. I get love from staying checked in, getting LOVE from PEOPLE, not from overworking. Reward: Vibrancy!

Create your Power Grind In for Work

Create the words of your Power Grind In for Work and grind it in 50 to 200 times today. If you find many Work Circuits and notice that other circuits are co-activated with them, do not worry. That is normal, which is why we are going to smash four circuits that are very low in the brain during the Second 30 Days. We are now preparing for those 30 days by fine-tuning four Power Grind Ins. Focus on creating the Power Grind In for Work that will enhance your joy of productivity the most.

Celebrate creating your third Power Grind In. After the lifestyle reset tomorrow, we will move forward to rewiring your Habit Circuit.

The Rewiring Checklist
Day 3. Transform Your Work Circuit

I transformed my Work Circuit:

- **SLOW**

    I can NOT get my _____ from_____.

- **RAMP UP**

    That's ridiculous. I can NOT get my _____ from _____.

- **JOY**

I get my _____ from:

CONNECT	APPROACH	REWARD
☐ Connecting with myself	☐ Stop overworking!	☐ Sanctuary
☐ Checking in	☐ Feasting on natural pleasure	☐ Authenticity
☐ Knowing my number	☐ Accepting my limitations	☐ Vibrancy
☐ Honoring my feelings	☐ Showing up on time	☐ Integrity
☐ Loving myself	☐ Not playing roles	☐ Intimacy
☐ The compassion within	☐ Doing hard things	☐ Spirituality
☐ Honoring my strengths	☐ Sticking with it	☐ Freedom
☐ Believing in myself	☐ Not complaining	
☐ Trusting myself	☐ Doing the right thing	
☐ Listening to my body	☐ No more procrastinating	
☐ Being present now	☐ Not having to be the best	
☐ Other _____	☐ Other _____	

I did it: 50   75   100   125   150   200   _____   times.

Success Check Day 20

- **Daily Success**

  ☐ I continued my Power of One Practice with 10 Check Ins and 10 Joy Points.

  ☐ I transformed my Work Circuit and created my Power Grind In.

  ☐ I made one or more community connections for support with transforming my circuit.

- **Did I pass the Success Check?   YES   NO**

  If you did not, stay with this activity for one more day, and then move on.

- **My Amazing Learning:**

  _____

- **My Biggest Accomplishment:**

  _____

- **My Biggest Challenge:**

  _____

Beautiful Work!

**You have completed Day 20 of The Power of One Challenge.
Your next step is Day 21. Lifestyle Reset #5 Evenings at One.**

Day 21. Lifestyle Reset #5
Evenings at One

Let's take back the night! Today you will plan and experience an Evening at One. You will meet your most important needs and experience an abundance of the natural pleasures of life.

Why

It's time to integrate your inner life, your rising set point, and your increasingly secure connection within, with your lifestyle.

We have worked on resetting lifestyle before, but this fifth lifestyle reset is unlike any other. Anyone can meet their needs in the morning after a good night's sleep. But what happens between 4 p.m. and midnight is the true story of our skill in meeting our needs and soaking in life's richest rewards. What's more, it's those evening hours that largely determine our health and happiness.

Why is that? If we stay emotionally checked in, connected, processing our emotions effectively, and spiraling up to the Power of One during the day, we are running Joy Circuits in the evening. The neocortex is in charge and happy. We are running homeostatic circuits.

Take Back the Night
- Identify your deepest needs.
- Determine your reward.
- Experience an Evening at One.

If we check out, lose sight of the Power of One during the day, we are running Stress Circuits in the evenings, and these allostatic circuits are in control. The reptile is happy. Extremes take over and block our capacity to have Sanctuary, Authenticity, Vibrancy, Integrity, Intimacy, Spirituality, and Freedom. Today, we will change that!

How

What I love about EBT is that it is so basic. Our brains are vastly different from one another when it comes to thoughts, but remarkably the same in terms of what rewards and satisfies us. We all have basic needs and when we meet them, we run Joy Circuits in the evenings.

Step 1. Identify your deepest needs

Stand back from the evening and identify your most fundamental needs. By the time the evening arrives, which needs will you have met and which ones will you want to start meeting in the evening?

Take Back the Night
Step 1. Identify Your Deepest Needs

Check off the unmet needs you will meet this evening:

☐ Safety ☐ Love ☐ Comfort ☐ Pleasure ☐ Purpose

Step 2. Determine your reward

To marshal the drive to effectively meet those needs, the brain's reward center must light up from feel-good chemicals. These chemicals come from tapping into the deeper rewards of life. Check in more deeply with yourself to determine which reward will take you up and over to meeting those needs.

Take Back the Night
Step 2. Determine Your Reward

Which reward will motivate you to meet these needs?

☐ Sanctuary ☐ Authenticity ☐ Vibrancy ☐ Integrity

☐ Intimacy ☐ Spirituality ☐ Freedom

Step 3. Make your plan to take back the night

Pull out all the stops. Make this ONE evening meet your needs. A cornerstone of an Evening at One is a natural pleasures binge. See ideas that bring sensory pleasures and any other natural joys that our hunter-gatherer ancestors used. No technology. Nothing that uses substances, artificial pleasures, or addictive devices. Be a hunter-gatherer for one night and experience long-overlooked joys and an easy way to be at One. Be sure to plan for support. If you have a circle of connection buddies, plan connections with each of them. A one- to five-minute call boosts oxytocin, which quiets appetite and makes natural pleasures more satisfying. Also, invite family members and friends to share your "Take Back the Night" or "Evening at One." Spend the evening together or connect by telephone so the richness of one another's voices activates your reward center. You can't have too much support with EBT! The emotional brain loves connection even more than artificial rewards!

Take Back the Night
Step 3. Experience an Evening at One
Check off what you plan to do:

ESSENTIAL

☐ A Natural Pleasure Binge
☐ A Joy Dinner
☐ Freedom from Artificial Pleasures

OPTIONAL

☐ Move in Joy
☐ Play
☐ Sanctuary Time
☐ Community Connections
☐ Sleep
☐ Emotional Connection
☐ Sensual Pleasure
☐ Sexual Pleasure
☐ Loving Companionship
☐ Spiritual Practices
☐ Social Activities
☐ Home/Life Upkeep
☐ Reading
☐ Caring for Others

*What I need is **Safety**. I'm so tired when I get home that I know my blood pressure is up and I'm on the edge of quarreling with my wife or drinking too much. To encode wires that bring me safety I need to take 30 minutes of time alone in the garage. What reward would motivate me to do that? **Intimacy**. I want a loving evening, not one that goes south. I am on board for a Joy Dinner: steak, salad, and fruit, will skip drinking scotch, but will have one glass of wine (that's natural right?). I will go on a bike ride for my pleasure and see if my wife will play strip poker with me, like she did before we were married. That is my Evening at One.*

*My need is for **Love**. I have a good paying job, but the office is very cold and my day is lonely. I am going to start taking five-minute breaks to make community connections, a couple in the morning and a couple in the afternoon, so I am not completely 5ish and feeling love-deprived by the time I come home. In the evening, I like having time alone (even though love is what I need). I live alone, have a cat, and am not ready to date. I have a neighbor friend I like and my strategy is to go out one night per week to a community event. My reward? It's Integrity. It's the right thing to stop being so cut off. My pleasure binge is going to be an evening basketball game with my neighbor, soaking in my hot tub, and eating fish with veggies, and strawberries. Technology is out. I'm going to have a ball.*

Natural Pleasure Binge rules

The rules for your natural pleasure binge are simple: Do not do anything that our hunter-gatherer ancestors did not do. Our brain is set up for these natural pleasures so their potential to become Stress Circuits is low, and they do not bring artificial happiness, but a deep, natural joy! When doing them, you are MORE connected to yourself, not less! What a great way to live!

What about having a Joy Dinner?

That's easy. Be sure to have some lean protein, healthy fat, and plenty of fiber foods that are veggies or fruit. Eat agrarian foods if you like but skip the post-industrial-revolution foods ("Stress Foods"). Eat early enough in the evening that you can take a food rest for 12 hours minimum to clear excess glucose and glycogen from your system and perhaps burn up some triglycerides (fat). Your dessert – as many natural pleasures as you like!

Freedom from Artificial Pleasures

This means no technology, texting, computers, tablets, except to use the phone to call a person. No devices or equipment that our hunter-gatherer ancestors did not have. No gambling, video games, or anything else that has high addiction potential. If you choose, avoid all alcohol. (If you prefer, some wine in cooking or not more than four ounces with the meal is permissible.) Take all regular medications and do not abstain from drugs you currently use if doing so would cause withdrawal or negative consequences.

Ideas for Your Natural Pleasure Binge

☐ Taking a long, hot shower

☐ Enjoying the sensory pleasure of sight – looking at the stars

☐ Playing with my dog or cuddling with my cat

☐ Enjoying the sensory pleasure of sound

☐ Drawing, painting, sculpting, or playing with clay

☐ Singing, dancing, or playing an instrument

☐ Discovering adult coloring books

☐ Enjoying the sensory pleasure of smell – a plant or flower

☐ Lighting candles all over, then sitting in the semi-darkness

☐ Having a spa night at home – bathing and grooming

☐ Savoring the sensory pleasure of taste – eating food slowly

☐ Curling up in a ball and listening to my favorite music

☐ Going for a swim or playing an evening sport

☐ Celebrating the sensory pleasure of touch – enjoying my skin

☐ Asking neighbors to come over and visit

☐ Learning something or taking up a new hobby

☐ Calling an old friend and catching up

☐ Writing three pages of Cycles by hand

☐ Playing classic games like checkers, cards, dominoes

☐ Making a community connection by telephone

☐ Making love or giving backrubs

☐ Sharing my hopes and dreams

☐ Reading to myself or aloud to my partner or child

Joy Dinner Ideas

☐ **Chicken and Veggie Salad**

A plate of fresh greens, topped with 6 oz. sliced chicken breast and 2 c. veggies, dressed with olive oil and balsamic vinegar.

☐ **Avocado and Shrimp Salad**

A plate of fresh greens, topped with one sliced avocado, ½ sliced cucumber, and 6 oz. cocktail shrimp, dressed with olive oil and sherry vinegar.

☐ **Turkey Breast, Artichoke, Greens, and Cherry Tomatoes**

Coat a turkey breast with olive oil and seasonings, bake, and slice. Meanwhile, cook an artichoke. Toss greens and cherry tomatoes in olive oil and vinegar. Arrange a plate of turkey, artichoke, and salad.

☐ **Teriyaki Chicken and Strawberry Pecan Salad**

Grill chicken breasts marinated in teriyaki sauce. Serve with salad greens topped with sliced strawberries and pecans, dressed with olive oil and balsamic vinegar.

☐ **Sautéed Snapper, Sliced Oranges, and Asparagus**

Sauté snapper or other fish in healthy oil, and top with sliced almonds, capers, and lemon juice. Serve with sliced oranges and steamed crisp asparagus.

☐ **Joe's Special Scramble**

Sauté ½ diced onion and ½ lb. ground round or ground turkey until the meat has browned and the onions are golden. Add 2 eggs, 2 c. leaf spinach, garlic, salt, and pepper to taste. Continue cooking until the eggs are firm and the spinach is wilted.

☐ **Freedom Salad**

Bed of greens of your choice, topped with 5 oz. of grilled wild-caught salmon, chicken breast, or flank steak, and your favorite veggies, dressed with olive oil, balsamic vinegar, and seasonings.

☐ **Nutty Chicken Salad**

Top a plate of fresh greens with a warm sliced chicken breast, and top with dried cranberries, sliced green onions, and walnut pieces. Drizzle with olive oil and vinegar.

☐ Turkey and Peppers

Shape ground turkey into ¼ lb. patties and season. Grill, then serve with sautéed red, green, and yellow peppers, and sliced tomatoes topped with olive oil.

☐ Pork Tenderloin, Avocado Salad, and Watermelon Wedges

Marinate pork tenderloin in hot mustard, vinaigrette, and peppers, then grill. Serve with sliced avocados and wedges of watermelon.

☐ London Broil Smothered in Mushrooms and Caesar Salad

Marinate meat in vinaigrette plus garlic and sweet hot mustard to taste. Sauté mushrooms in olive oil, broil steak, and serve with romaine, tomatoes, and cucumbers tossed with Caesar dressing.

☐ Quick Dinner Bowl

Sauté 2 c. of broccoli florets in extra virgin olive oil. Add leftover chicken, fish, or meat, and sauté until brown. Toast ½ c. nuts in frying pan on low heat until brown and fragrant. Season with favorite herbs, salt, and pepper. Combine ingredients and serve.

☐ Quick Vegan Bean Salad*^

Place dark greens (e.g., baby spinach and kale) on a plate. Heat up ¾ c. cooked beans of your choice in the microwave while slicing toppings of ½ avocado, ½ tomato, and ¼ chopped cucumber. Slide the beans onto the greens and add toppings. Drizzle with olive oil and vinegar. Add seasonings to taste.

☐ Fruit and Cottage Cheese Plate*

Slice up fruits that you love – cantaloupe, watermelon, peaches, bananas, kiwis, apples, oranges. Place a bed of lettuce on a plate and cover with 1 c. cottage cheese. Top with fruit and sprinkle with toasted wheat germ and sliced almonds.

☐ All Veggies and Nuts*^

Use a frying pan over medium to high heat and pour in 2 to 4 T. olive oil. Slice up onions, mushrooms, garlic, peppers, and other vegetables (e.g., cubed squash, yams, fennel, turnips, or carrots) and sauté each one separately, then combine them in the frying pan. Toast ¼ cup nuts in the frying pan until golden and add them with seasonings (e.g., salt, pepper, thyme, basil) and a splash of wine or broth and simmer for 5 minutes.

*contains agrarian foods
^not a high-protein meal

Success Check Day 21

- **Daily Success**

☐ I continued my Power of One Practice with 10 Check Ins and 10 Joy Points.

☐ I reset my lifestyle in these eight ways: Exercise, Play, Joy Breakfast, Sanctuary Time, Joy Lunch, Balancing Sleep, Natural Pleasure Binge, and Joy Dinner.

☐ I made one or more community connections for support with my lifestyle reset.

- **Did I pass the Success Check?   YES   NO**

If you did not, stay with this activity for one more day, then move on.

- **My Amazing Learning:**

_____

- **My Biggest Accomplishment:**

_____

- **My Biggest Challenge:**

_____

Beautiful Work!

**You have completed Day 21 of The Power of One Challenge.
Your next step is Day 22. Discover Your Habit Circuit.**

Day 22. Discover Your Habit Circuit

We've plumbed our depths! Emotions, relationships, work, and now, what about our habits? A Habit Circuit is an observable behavior that is triggered by a fight-or-flight drive, causing us to repeat the response. Then we say, "Why do I keep doing that? I tell myself I won't do it again, but then I do. What's wrong with me?"

There is nothing wrong with us. Let's get back to basics. We all have a Stress Triangle, in which the amygdala, the reward center, and the hypothalamus all collude to activate and strengthen our Love Circuit – causing the stress of merging and distancing, our Mood Circuit – with false highs, unnecessary lows, or numbness, and our Work Circuit – causing problems with our survival-based need to be productive.

Stress not only takes the prefrontal cortex offline, so our executive functioning and impulse control are on the fritz, but it drives the release of dopamine. Too much dopamine and we burn out our dopamine receptors, further increasing our need to feel better by getting a rush of endorphins as a reward. Although there are other genetic, epigenetic, and environmental factors at play, this can lead to dopamine lows and lethargy so that we have no energy to access natural rewards, and it's so easy to rely on and become addicted to artificial ones.

What's a Habit Circuit?
A wire that triggers
unwanted behaviors

The Habit Circuit

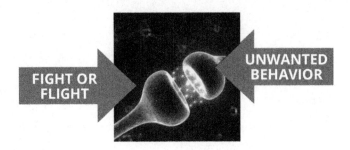

Stress drives dopamine release and unhealthy lifestyles (sleep, technology, diet . . . all the things we've been addressing) and drains our "feel comforted" chemical serotonin. The combination of low serotonin, dopamine extremes, and stress causes depression. (See Robert Lustig's *The Hacking of the American Mind* for a discussion of this.) How do we cope? We encode or strengthen our Habit Circuit, increasing our stress and furthering our set point decline, effectively causing the stress buzzer to get stuck on and strengthening these unwanted circuits day by day, year by year!

Why serotonin matters!

Serotonin is the happiness hormone.
Exercise, eating Joy Foods, and being
at One boost serotonin levels.

"Life at One is my serotonin solution."

What's the solution? It's taking really good care of our Stress Triangle, targeting and clearing unwanted circuits, and then raising our set point. Changing that Habit Circuit begins by not judging our behavior, and instead remembering that all behaviors are just circuits. It's being logical about our wires and pushing up our sleeves and beginning to rewire them. When it comes to the Habit Circuit, the first step is to identify our type of circuit. There are three of them.

Dabbler Habit Circuits

We categorize Habit Circuits based on the three most common ways we use them. The most common for those with high set points is the "Dabbler." Attachment to any specific behavior is not strong, and you do not see yourself as addicted to any of them. However, you may stay disconnected from yourself much of the day because of these seemingly inconsequential wires.

I use a steady stream of excesses. I hand off one excess for another, starting with heavy-duty coffee in the morning, then texting, social media, checking stocks and news, overworking, and so on. Until EBT, I never was conscious of plugging into myself. I didn't know how to connect with myself emotionally.

Habit Circuit Types

Type	Examples
Dabbler Circuits	Several behaviors during the same period Stored as: 2 Circuits or 3 Circuits
Serial Circuits	One behavior at a time, transferring one habit for another Stored as: 4 Circuits or 5 Circuits
One Circuit	One behavior and stick with it over time Stored as: 4 Circuit or 5 Circuit

Serial Habit Circuits

The Serial Circuit type is unmistakable because we do identify a "problem" behavior, and when we fix it or abstain from it, all seems well. But because the root problem is the brain set point in stress, we spend a lot of time in chronic stress. For example, if our set point is in the 4th Drawer, every moment we're at Brain State 4, we are strengthening 4 Circuits. Imagine how many unbalanced emotions, behaviors, and thoughts are becoming stronger and more easily activated due to our chronic stress.

Habit Circuit Types: Where are they stored?

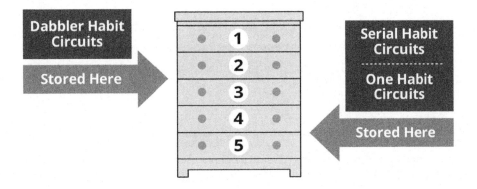

*I was drinking heavily by age 11, sneaking vodka and rum, and got busted by my parents, who scared the *&$% out of me. I never drank again. Instead, I started using marijuana and vaping. After a while, I found I didn't like either of them and took up sexual experimenting. My last shift was to food, and I gained about 50 pounds.*

Habit circuits are particularly interesting because they can include both emotional and chemical drives. If the Habit Circuit is watching television, then it's only emotional, and although you may want to rewire it, until you have raised your set point, either the wire is likely to return or a substitute will emerge ("addiction transfer"). If the habit involves ingesting, injecting, or inhaling a chemical, then rewire that circuit. Gaining freedom from that wire will improve your vibrancy, and help you raise your set point faster.

One Habit Circuits

Sometimes a circuit seems so perfect for us, as if we were meant to be connected to that excess for the rest of our lives. Sometimes it's because it was encoded with a mammoth fight-or-flight drive so the wire itself is ironclad. Some of us have brains that light up to one excess more than another. Since these wires are often in the 5th Drawer, there is a singular drive for an excess, but, in truth, a whole bevy of 5 Circuits are driving it.

You could give me any type of alcohol, even one taste, and my mind would shut off. I'd drink the entire bottle until I was sick. I am the One Habit Circuit type.

Programming. The first time I tried programming was in college, and I did not eat, drink, or sleep for 18 hours. I do hackathons on weekends, will program anything at any time, as I am in a zone that makes me not eat (I lost 20 pounds of extra weight). It's definitely an addiction for me.

I have an addiction I don't talk about because it is an issue with my wife. She does not like me watching porn. I am so controlled that this is my one way to act out. It's a 4 Circuit, but that doesn't change the fact that my type is a One Habit Circuit.

The Special Joy of Rewiring Habit Circuits

- **The habit changes – we have evidence of success**
- **For chemical excesses – we radically reduce stress**
- **Other lifestyle changes follow – we have a more vibrant life**

Why

The Habit Circuit appears last of the four circuits we rewire in this challenge – our four pillars of well-being – because after weakening the other three, our set point is on the rise. It becomes easier to target and crush the Habit Circuit. Also, the Habit Circuit can be the most rewarding circuit of all to rewire for three reasons:

Think of habit change as a rewiring game

First, once we've made the paradigm shift to appreciate that the problem is our wiring, then as in any game, we want to know that we have won. Behavior is observable and measurable. When we rewire enough to stop the excess because we don't need it anymore, there is a lot to cheer about.

My spending circuit is the one I targeted, and once I broke the connection between rampant careless spending and love, I checked my bank account every day. My goal is to get out of debt, and my husband and I made a game out of it. We started liking to eat at home and it became fun to pinch pennies. Success is intoxicating!

Double the benefit: Clear both psychological and chemical stress

Second, imagine that alcohol, sugar, processed foods, or drugs are battery acid. Pouring it into our digestive system, shooting it into our veins, or inhaling it into our lungs can add to our stress. This has a direct chemical impact on our brain and body that sabotages our brain state and resets our body chemistry and organ functioning. Changing that can help.

My wife and I drink at night. We don't drive when we drink and we both enjoy it, but then she was diagnosed with breast cancer. Alcohol is a risk factor for breast cancer and in solidarity with her decision to stop drinking, I stopped, too. I had a lot more time in the evenings, because I wasn't sleepy after dinner, and between our discussions about our mortality and how busy we were dealing with her treatment, we grew closer. Clearing my body and brain of alcohol made my recovery from my other circuits (distancing, depression, overworking, overspending) easier. I was no longer chemically impacted by booze.

Third, whatever your set point or stress habit, any change engenders hope, and that hope opens up the prefrontal cortex. The broaden and build theory of development proposes that opening ourselves to positive emotions – like the ones we feel when we are successful in some way – inspires our conscious mind to make even more profound changes. We inspire ourselves.

Type	Examples
Dabbling	a little shopping, a bit of wine, and some clutter, biting my nails, overusing meds at times, video binges, excessive texting, comfort eating, pulling out hair
Serial Circuits	compulsive spending followed by compulsive saving, ending overeating only to begin overdrinking, excessive technology dependency turns to over-exercise
One Circuit	problem drinking, drinking binges, alcohol addiction, overeating, binge eating, purging, sugar addiction, excessive shopping, extreme hoarding, binge spending

I didn't think I would ever exercise again, with my back pain and getting older. I broke my "I like to sit" circuit, joined a gym, and had a great time. I started drinking less in the evenings. I surprised myself by how great I started feeling.

I dabble all day, so I have no idea how to find my wire or what to complain about. The situation is . . . I am disconnected continuously. I have to be with people and connect with them, obsess about my diet or my weight, or drink water, coffee, or wine. I am very oral. I have to be doing something or consuming something to be happy. What I am most stressed about is . . . I am addicted to consuming. I feel ANGRY that . . . I CONSUME. I can't stand it that . . . I have to be putting something in my mouth all the time . . . I HATE IT that . . . I do that. Truthfully, I rather like it. Okay, I hate it that I like it so much. I HATE THAT!!!! . . . I feel sad that . . . I'm so dependent . . . I feel afraid that . . . I'm a big baby, and I will never stop having to have something in my mouth . . . I feel guilty that . . . I consume. OF COURSE I consume, because my unreasonable expectation is . . . I get my comfort from . . . putting things in my mouth. Eeeek, that's so true. Great, I nailed my circuit. That's the one.

My current habit of choice is consuming too much wine, to the point that I wake up in the middle of the night and can't sleep. It's getting out of hand. The situation is . . . I drink more than I should. My sleep is disturbed, my energy level is low. I don't feel healthy. What I'm most stressed about is . . . I drink too much. I feel ANGRY that . . . I can't drink as much as I want to. I can't stand it that . . . I have to deal with this. I HATE it that . . . I can't do whatever I want when I want to . . . I HATE THAT . . . I really $&%&ing HATE that I can't DO WHATEVER I WANT WHEN I WANT TO!!! I HAAAATTTEE THAT!!!! . . . My mind just turned off. Great. The unlocking moment . . . a few deep breaths. I feel sad that . . . I can't drink as much as I want to drink . . . I feel afraid that . . . I'll feel unhealthy for the rest of my life . . . I feel guilty that . . . I don't want to give up alcohol. OF COURSE I don't want to give up alcohol, because my unreasonable expectation is . . . that I get my love from drinking . . . I get my . . . nurturing . . . from drinking . . . I get my comfort . . . from drinking. But I do get comfort from drinking. Okay. I can ONLY comfort myself in one way: alcohol. I'll make it briefer. I get my comfort ONLY from alcohol. That's true. I believe that. Now I'm laughing. Okay, that's my circuit!

Which Habit Circuit Matters Most to Me?
I get my _____(need)_____ from ____(habit)____ .

How

Once you have identified a habit that matters to you, then use the same technique you used on your three other circuits. Complain, activate effective A+ Anger to unlock the circuit, then feel your feelings until you discover the circuit.

Feel your feelings, travel back, and grieve, too – Do whatever you need to do to sit with your feelings after your Cycle. Travel back if you like, and finally, six hours or more afterward, track when that circuit could have been encoded and whether or not it is intergenerational.

I did a Travel Back on my drinking circuit, and my mind went right back to the time of my parent's divorce when I was taking care of them, rather than them taking care of me. My best friend became a bottle of vodka. I brought up the image of me being in the other room while my parents were arguing

224

and me slipping into the kitchen to find the bottle. I stepped into the image as the adult and talked to myself as an 11-year-old boy, and told him that his feelings mattered, that drinking would not help him heal, and said to him that it was not his job to make his parents happy. It was his job to speak up for himself and get support from others, even if his parents weren't doing their job of giving him support. I felt the Power of One and a great deal of healing from that Travel Back.

Outsmart the Reptile – Use Humor!

Be Creative and Playful – Have Fun	
Dabbler Circuits	I have three loves: eating, drinking, and spending! There isn't an artificial reward that I can't like!
Serial Circuits	My weight goes down, my spending goes up! I flip flop: marathon runner, then couch potato.
One Circuit	I am merged at the hip with alcohol. I bite my nails. I don't have to clip them!

When you are ready, please do a Cycle and begin to discover your circuit, so that you can create a Power Grind in for Habit. After the next two days, we'll move into jumpstarting the Second 30 Days, and raising your set point so that the Power of One is your brain's natural habit.

The Rewiring Checklist
Day 1. Discover Your Habit Circuit

Say What is Bothering You:

- The situation is . . . (Complain about a habit that matters to you.)
- What I'm most stressed about is . . . (Say what bothers you the most that habit.)

Unlock the Circuit

- I feel angry that . . .
- I can't stand it that . . .
- I hate it that . . .

Discover the Hidden Message

- I feel sad that . . .
- I feel afraid that . . .
- I feel guilty that . . .
- OF COURSE I would do that, because my unreasonable expectation is . . .

I get my:	**from:**	
☐ Safety	☐ Clutter	☐ Drugs
☐ Love	☐ Hoarding	☐ Misusing medications
☐ Comfort	☐ Over-exercising	☐ Smoking or vaping
☐ Pleasure	☐ Inactivity	☐ Partying
☐ Purpose	☐ Television	☐ Marijuana
☐ Survival	☐ Technology	☐ Overspending
☐ Existence	☐ Texting	☐ Underspending
☐ Protection	☐ Sleeping too much	☐ Drinking too much
☐ Security	☐ Food	☐ Binge drinking
☐ Power	☐ Pornography	☐ Gambling
☐ Nurturing	☐ Video games	☐ Sexual excesses
☐ Other _____	☐ Nail biting	☐ Other _____

Success Check Day 22

- **Daily Success**

☐ I continued my Power of One Practice with 10 Check Ins and 10 Joy Points.

☐ I discovered my Habit Circuit.

☐ I made one or more community connections for support with discovering my circuit.

- **Did I pass the Success Check?   YES   NO**

If you did not, stay with this activity for one more day, then move on.

- **My Amazing Learning:**

_____

- **My Biggest Accomplishment:**

_____

- **My Biggest Challenge:**

_____

Congratulations!

**You have completed Day 22 of The Power of One Challenge.
Your next step is Day 23. Negate Your Habit Circuit.**

Day 23. Negate Your Habit Circuit

You may have more fun today than any other day in this challenge. You are in a great position to zap that Habit Circuit with gusto.

You are not just changing a habit, but going to its root cause. In fact, unless that circuit is tremendously deleterious to your health and happiness, you don't even think about changing that habit. If you change it without rewiring the drive within that circuit, the habit will return. Instead, you stay the course and address the root cause!

I can't stand that I overspend. I was tempted to call a budget coach and cut up my credit cards. Instead, I used my A+ Anger skill and did a "last ditch effort" Cycle and found a huge wire that told me that I get my safety from abusing myself. It was completely illogical, but rang true. I am frying that wire and have stopped overspending. I needed that 5 State to find the real wire that caused my spending issue.

The wire's ridiculous message is so convincing!
One of the truths about the emotional brain is that when the reptile is activated, the ridiculous messages it sends are completely convincing. If that were not the case, humans would be extinct. If the fight-or-flight message didn't stop rational thought, we would never follow our survival drives. One of my biggest awakenings in developing EBT was that my survival brain made me completely irrational at times, and convinced me that I was being rational!

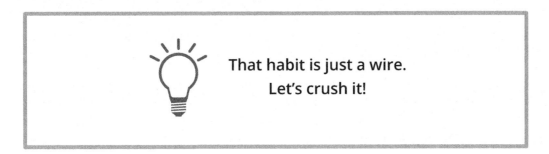

That habit is just a wire.
Let's crush it!

I never thought about the idea that the Stress Circuit is a survival drive, like gulping down water when we're thirsty or finding shelter in a storm.

Whenever a Stress Circuit is the product of the collision of a survival drive and any artificial reward that does not implicitly meet our basic needs, the response activates stress overload in the brain. The circuit that triggers us to binge on junk food, work, anxiety, exercise, or drugs is fueled with fight-or-flight chemical surges.

That's the nature of stress wires. Based on evolutionary biology, the job of the wires is to convince us that following the instructions of the Habit Circuit is our only possible reality. There is no other world beyond using this habit, and nothing else on earth could possibly make us feel this safe, loved, comforted, or pleasured.

The great news is that when we break this circuit, it's a whole new world! When we break that wire and those that co-activate with it, it is a new universe! We have an expansive freedom that we have not known before. What we felt would be impossible to do before is now not just possible, but easy, spontaneous, and sometimes even fun.

My habit was drinking a couple of glasses of wine at night. On my way home from work I would see myself going to the refrigerator, and reaching for the wine bottle, and that activated my circuit. When I got home, it was a mad dash from the front door to the fridge. Then I broke my alcohol wire! Now, I look at people drinking, and it doesn't interest me. Alcohol does not do it for me anymore. My brain changed.

I was consumed by my exercise addiction. It was ruining my relationship with my kids because I was either at work or at the gym. If something prevented me from exercising, I was snarly and irritable. Breaking the wire saved my marriage and my relationship with my kids. Once I broke that connection, it wasn't hard. Now I laugh with my kids, and my wife is happier.

Focus on one circuit at a time
The challenge of EBT is to do the work. Think of it as a personal project of raising your set point. It takes rewiring circuits, one by one, all the while devoted to having the precious opportunity to really know yourself, one circuit at a time.

You are getting to know your Habit Circuit now. Think of the rewiring process as the prefrontal cortex's love affair with one wire, knowing it well then carefully transforming it. One day I was on my way to work, driving across the Golden Gate bridge and doing a Cycle and not expecting any rapturous moment to arrive. I was in stress and wanted relief. However, I activated a love-seeking wire and when the words bubbled up into my conscious mind, I felt love for myself, awe that I could have this "big reveal" and love for the circuit.

This one transformed on the spot. Sometimes they do that! The rewiring results are related to where it is stored and its strength, however, it is most related to the intensity of the emotional experience. This is why it's important to focus on one circuit, one love affair at a time, so all your passion goes into that circuit. Sometimes multiple circuits will be activated when you do a Cycle, but be sure to focus on one wire at a time. You might have several habits you want to clear, all

Transform one wire at a time

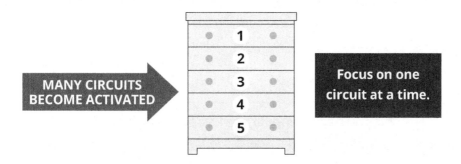

stored in the same drawer of the brain, however, select only one. You can rewire the others as you move up your set point in time.

However, right now, focus on zapping one wire only. This is the art and science of emotional plasticity. It's a skill and you are learning it!

Why

You are changing this habit because it bothers you, because it blocks you from raising your set point and experiencing an abundance of the rewards of purpose. If this habit does not bother you, take an extra day to circle around and find something that bothers you enough to attack it with 100 to 200 negations, to really tear apart that wire.

I had planned to rewire my Clutter Circuit because my house is such a mess. There is clutter everywhere. However, what really bothers me is the money I spend on all the things that clutter up my house. I did more discovery work and came up with a wire that I can get behind rewiring: I get my comfort from buying things. Saying that makes me shiver. That must be the right circuit for me. That's the one.

I have the right circuit: I get my power from partying. It's not alcohol only or socializing only or escaping into pleasure only. It's all three. I get my power from partying. I'm going to do five Cycles to grieve the losses of how much my partying has cost me, then maybe another five Cycles, and when I feel charged up to zap it, I'm going to zap it with gusto!

How

Use the same negation process you used with your other circuits. For the expectation, **"I get my existence from spending money I do not have,"** say **"I can NOT get my existence from spending money I do not have."** Again, state it very slowly at first, then ramp it up and ridicule the circuit. If you like, sing, dance, or stomp when you are negating it. Making community connections helps tremendously. The more emotionally charged the experience, the better your rewiring results!

2 Stages of Negating a Habit Circuit	
SLOW	I . . . can . . . NOT . . . get . . . my . . . love . . . from . . . watching videos. I . . . can . . . NOT . . . get . . . my . . . love . . . from . . . watching videos. I . . . can . . . NOT . . . get . . . my . . . love . . . from . . . watching videos. I . . . can . . . NOT . . . get . . . my . . . love . . . from . . . watching videos.
RAMP UP	That's ridiculous! Bingeing on videos every night is NOT love. I need love. Watching videos is NOT meeting my need for love. How ridiculous! Videos do NOT give me the LOVE I need!

Example (All Grind In Clusters count as 10 Grind Ins)

SLOW

- I . . . can . . . NOT . . . get . . . safety . . . from . . . drinking wine . . . (pause)
- I . . . can . . . NOT . . . get . . . safety . . . from . . . drinking wine . . . (pause)
- I . . . can . . . NOT . . . get . . . safety . . . from . . . drinking wine . . . (pause)
- I . . . can . . . NOT . . . get . . . safety . . . from . . . drinking wine . . . (pause)
- I . . . can . . . NOT . . . get . . . safety . . . from . . . drinking wine . . . (pause)

RAMP UP

- That's ridiculous! I can NOT get safety from drinking wine.
- I could drink wine all night and I would NOT get safety.
- That's ridiculous! I can NOT get safety from wine!
- No matter how hard I try to rely on drinking, it will NOT give me safety!
- Numbness is NOT my safety blanket. No Way!
- HOW RIDICULOUS!!!

Only negate when you can do it with fervor

Pause before negating the circuit and do Cycles about how the circuit was encoded or how it impacted you. Each Cycle clears away internal stress and relieves the constant burden of pushing down our emotions. Each Cycle lightens the emotional load so that we are naturally calmer and more securely connected to the deepest part of ourselves.

The situation is . . . when I was in my late 20s I had a stress eating problem and was tired of feeling fat, and tired of controlling my food. One night I had a second glass of wine and noticed that I stopped wanting the food. I thought I was out-smarting the system, but my drinking triggered my temper, which led to the loss of my marriage, financial chaos, and raising two children largely on my own – and in near-poverty. My chest aches when I talk about it. What I'm most stressed about is . . . I really &$%#&ed up my life. I feel ANGRY that . . . I was so &$%$&&@ stupid. I can't stand it that . . . I tried to game the system. I HATE IT THAT . . . drinking made it worse . . . I need more anger . . . I AM &%$#@ FURIOUS that I did that to myself. WHAT IS MY PROBLEM???!!! . . . Oh, that did it, now I'm laughing. I feel sad that . . . I did that. I feel afraid that . . . I have poor judgment at times. I feel guilty that . . . I wasn't smart enough to stop overeating AND not take up drinking. OF COURSE I feel guilty about that, because my unreasonable expectation is that . . . I get my safety from . . . being perfect. How ridiculous! I can NOT get safety from . . . being perfect. I can NOT . . . get safety from being perfect . . . I can NOT get safety from . . . being perfect! I DO NOT HAVE TO BE PERFECT!!!!

No need to do profound Cycles. Just let it rip!

When you have cleared away the grieving emotions and feel charged up and ready to negate, then go for it! State your negation very slowly at first, then ramp it up and ridicule the circuit. Be sure to do it with fervor, so you activate a spurt of dopamine to lock in the circuit. Definitely sing it, dance it, share it!

I can NOT . . . get . . . the . . . safety . . . I . . . need . . . from . . . sitting on the couch. I can . . . NOT . . . get the . . . safety . . . I . . . need . . . from sitting on the couch . . . I can NOT . . . get the safety . . . I . . . need . . . from . . . sitting on the couch . . . even though . . . it seems . . . like . . . I can . . . I can . . . NOT get . . . the safety . . . that I need from . . . the STUPID COUCH. THE COUCH IS NOT MY SAFETY. I can NOT get safety from SITTING there, even though I want to sit there. THAT'S RIDICULOUS. This couch WILL NOT give me the SAFETY that I NEED!!!! Wha-hoo!

Let's tromp that circuit with Power Boosters

This circuit only departs if we give it no other option. We are going to mince it up and cast it out! Use your fury. Repeat the negation 50, 100, 150, even 200 times. Get rid of that rusty old wire. Throw it out!

Make this your best day in the challenge yet! Bust that circuit!!!

Power Boosters for your Habit Circuit

- Sing your Grind In to your dog or cat.
- Jump up and down while you say it.
- Listen to music and dance as you say it.
- Lie on the floor and scream it out.
- Say it while playing a musical instrument.

The Rewiring Checklist
Day 2. Negate Your Habit Circuit

I negated my Habit Circuit:

- **SLOW**

  I can NOT get my _____ from _____.

- **RAMP UP**

  That's ridiculous! I can NOT get my _____ from _____.

  I did it: 50 75 100 125 150 200 _____ times.

I boosted the power of my Grind In (one or more ways):

- ☐ Singing my Grind In to my dog or cat
- ☐ Jumping up and down while saying it
- ☐ Listening to music and dancing as I say it
- ☐ Lying on the floor and screaming it out
- ☐ Saying it while playing a musical instrument

Success Check Day 23

- **Daily Success**

☐ I continued my Power of One Practice with 10 Check Ins and 10 Joy Points.

☐ I negated my Habit Circuit.

☐ I made one or more community connections for support with negating my circuit.

- **Did I pass the Success Check?   YES   NO**

If you did not, stay with this activity for one more day, then move on.

- **My Amazing Learning:**

_____

- **My Biggest Accomplishment:**

_____

- **My Biggest Challenge:**

_____

Great Work!

You have completed Day 23 of The Power of One Challenge.
Your next step is Day 24. Transform Your Habit Circuit.

Day 24. Transform Your Habit Circuit

Today you transform your Habit Circuit! This is the day when you develop a Power Grind In that short-circuits the desire for this behavior. When the drive quiets down, habit change naturally follows.

**Your Power Grind In makes
it so easy to change!**

Why

You change this wire because you made a personal decision to change this habit. What bothers one person doesn't bother another. You made a decision to change the habit, so let's change it!

How

You are going to construct a Power Grind In for your Habit Circuit. Again, confront the reptile. Use the 3-pronged approach.

Connect: For your connect statement, use words that have a strong emotional impact. All 4 and 5 Circuits block the brain's capacity to connect with ourselves and others. Our connect statement must penetrate the stress overload barrier! Consider such options as: connect to the profound love inside, check in with my amazing inner strength, or access my spiritual connection. Don't hold back!

Approach: State your new approach to habit change with particular sensitivity to the power of the specific habit you are rewiring. If your habit triggers extreme highs and lows, then use an approach statement that is very strong. Fight fire with fire! If your Habit Circuit is stored in the 4th or 5th Drawers it carries a chemical wallop. So consider blunt statements, such as No Alcohol. None! No Gambling. Ever! or Stop Overspending! Speak to your reptile as if you were talking to a headstrong toddler who was about to walk out into the street in front of a car. Don't mince words. What if the circuit is higher in the brain? Overwhelm it with kindness; say words that gently guide you to use a new and effective approach.

Reward: Choose your reward carefully. Saying that reward must be so emotionally impactful that you are profoundly moved when you say it. It may be Sanctuary, Authenticity, Vibrancy, Integrity, Intimacy, Spirituality, or Freedom.

Why set point and circuit storage matter

Take these two factors – set point and storage of circuits – into account when you develop your approach to rewiring your circuit. Stress causes the Stress Triangle to start spinning and makes it harder to change behavior easily for lasting results. Dopamine and serotonin are neurotransmitters (chemical messengers) in our brain which control countless functions and processes in our body. Stress causes changes in the levels of both dopamine and serotonin. The lower in the brain our circuit is stored, the more it triggers chronic cortisol secretion, dopamine extremes, and serotonin lows. The lower your set point, the more your stress buzzer will be stuck on. What's the solution? Zapping these wires and raising your set point. If your set point is in the low 4 to 5 range, be sure to access external support. When allostatic circuits are firing, the help of one-on-one support or a small group can help connect the brain so that the tools can activate and change deeper, more powerful wires. Also, err on the side of accessing more medical support as needed. You'll see better results faster!

Where is your circuit stored?

The effectiveness of your Power Grind In for the Habit is even more impacted by where it is stored than for other circuits. Again, the fact that the response may have its own addictive impact, beyond the fight-or-flight drives, means you need to carefully modulate your statement based on storage location. Again, with a **weaker habit, a wire stored in the 2nd or 3rd Drawer,** be even more loving and gentle than with other Grind Ins. Your power is in kindness. With a **stronger habit, a wire stored in the 4th or 5th Drawer,** the reptile is in charge, and a loving but strong and clear statement that sets limits may serve you better. Use the Imagine below to help you fine-tune and verify the most effective transformation statement for you.

What is your "new approach" to habits?

Consider whether your Habit Circuit is a dabbler circuit, serial circuit, or one circuit, and where it is stored in the brain. If the habit delivers both an emotional charge that activates the stress chemical cascade AND a direct chemical impact, such as alcohol, drugs, medications, or processed foods, be sure to speak with your physicians about the potential need for a detoxification schedule or other support.

The Dabbler Approach

If you are a dabbler, the problem is not the individual behaviors. Talk straight to your reptile. Give a clear message that you are short-circuiting the whole range of wires.

I am as much of an addict as anyone because I cannot stop disconnecting. I go from one excess to the next all day long. Early in the day I'm on overdrive, and late in the day I completely poop out. My circuit is: I get my comfort from disconnecting from myself and connecting to whatever works for me in the moment. That gives me a nauseous feeling, so it must be right! My transformation statement is: I get my comfort from finding that secure, loving place in my body, and not needing to disconnect from myself. My reward? Freedom.

Dabbler Approach Examples

- STOP escaping into substances.
- Use internal solutions, not external solutions.
- Be present rather than escaping.
- STOP disconnecting from myself.
- Steer clear of addictive substances.

The Serial Circuit Approach

When you observe that one Habit Circuit turns into another, there are two divergent pathways to go down in formulating your approach statement.

One option is to call the reptile on the pattern and say, "cut it out." The approach is to rewire this Habit Circuit at such a depth that quitting it does not result in sprouting a substitute. This "clear the decks" approach is best when the circuit is in the 4th Drawer.

The other option is to focus on rewiring one circuit well. Go as deep as the brain will allow you to go at the time. Then, when another Habit Circuit crops up, clear that circuit and as much of its emotional roots as the brain will allow you at that time. With each rewiring, you'll raise your set point. This "one circuit at a time" approach is often best for wires that are in the 5th Drawer.

My painkiller addiction is in the 5th Drawer, and I want to short-circuit that wire first. I don't know how deep the rewiring will go, as I have never been emotional. No one in our family is emotional. I have never seen my wife cry, and she has never seen me cry. I'll take the gradual approach, rewire that painkiller addiction, and no doubt after that, there will be other circuits. I am devoted to my faith, so that has to be part of my transformation statement. It is: I get my existence from connecting to the God within and asking for help. My reward? Spirituality. The asking for help part, asking to receive guidance from the spiritual, seems to make all the difference for me. I will take it slowly, and see how it goes, step by step.

Serial Circuit Approach Examples
Clear the Decks Option
• Stop drinking and all of its substitutes.   • Quit smoking and all artificial rewards.
One Circuit at a Time Option
• Stop hoarding, then rewire the next one.   • Fry this habit, then zap the next one.

I want freedom from thinking about my spending habit and the ones that I have gone to historically when I stopped overspending: food, alcohol, and (not a Habit Circuit but a Love Circuit) rescuing people. I merge with all these things. I have to address my Merge Circuit, or I know I cannot clear this Habit Circuit, or the alcohol, or food. They are all 4 Circuits, and the transformation statement I came up with is: I get my love from inside me, not from merging with anything, not possessions, food, or alcohol. None of them. My reward? Intimacy . . . That reward surprised me, but it's true. I want intimacy with people, not with my habits.

The One Circuit Approach

If your pattern is one circuit, the approach is usually simple: break the wire that is causing it.

When we set breaking the circuit as our goal, we are not in complete control of the outcome. Sometimes the wire is cleared and other times traces of that memory remain. Some people prefer an abstinence approach to lessen the chances of reinstating an old wire. Others use a harm reduction approach, minimizing the behavior.

My set point is in the 3 range and my Habit Circuit is gambling. I don't have any other habits that are questionable. When it comes to gambling, I know I can stop, but it's comforting to me. I only gamble now and then. I want to tone down the gambling. My transformation statement is . . . I get my comfort from checking in and comforting myself in healthy ways, not by gambling. My reward? Integrity.

One Circuit Approach Examples
• Cut back on alcohol, but still drink.   • QUIT TEXTING SO MUCH!   • No More Overspending. CUT IT OUT!   • Clear away the hurts, and rewire the drive.   • Whether I want to or not, STOP DOING THIS!

My set point is in the 4 to 4.5 range. Nobody knows me very well, as I am a consummate distancer and live alone. But if they did, they would tell me that I'm at set point 5 and should detox from the anti-anxiety pills I take and the bottle of wine I drink each night. I have always used this mix of alcohol and meds and to me, the combination is my lifeline. I get my life from drugging myself. My transformation statement is . . . I get my life from loving myself and getting my lifeline from natural pleasures, not from chemicals. My rewards? Sanctuary and Vibrancy. I need medical support and have already made an appointment.

The Meet My Needs Approach

Identify the unmet need that triggers you to activate your Habit Circuit. If the encoding of that wire occurred early in life, or later during a traumatic episode, it is probably a 5 Circuit, a survival circuit. If your Habit Circuit has a chemical component to it, it is probably a 5 Circuit, too. Be sure to break the old connection before trying to meet your need. The priority is break first, meet the need second.

Meet My Needs Approach Examples

- Meet my true needs, rather than overspending.
- Get my safety from inside me, NOT from DRUGS.
- Get my love from people, not from MONEY.
- Find comfort in the simple joys of life.
- Access pleasure from natural sources
- Bring to mind my reward for being healthy.

My Habit Circuit is binge drinking and it's a 5 Circuit. My mind shuts off and I'm going to drink to excess no matter what. My approach is this: I get my safety from NOT DRINKING! My mind hears: Stop drinking, you idiot! You are ruining your life. Get serious about your life and just STOP IT! I need that strong limit or I will take the first drink and after that, there is no stopping me!

If that wire is not as deep in the brain or as strong, and there is no added wallop of a chemical excess, it is probably not a 5 Circuit. In that case, focusing on the need can be more helpful. Essentially, the stronger the drive to engage in that behavior, the more your transformation statement must tell you to NOT do it! This is the art of developing a transformation statement.

My Habit Circuit is pornography. It's a 4 circuit. My approach is this: I get my love from connecting with myself and my husband, not from porn. It's a clear statement but not overly harsh. It tells me to stop the porn habit, but makes that easier because it is telling me to meet my real need. That feels right to me!

The Habit Circuit Imagine

Use this Imagine to fine-tune your transformation statement for your Habit Circuit.

Relax: Create privacy for yourself and find a comfortable location to relax. Focus your attention on your body and your breathing. Breathe in through your nose, out through your mouth, or in any way that is comfortable and comforting to you. When you are ready, begin to imagine.

Imagine: See yourself awakening in the morning and being aware that you are creating a simple statement that will be so rewarding that it will short-circuit your drive for a particular habit.

See yourself going through your day not engaging in that habit, but be aware that every single temptation that could occur, instantly occurs. Imagine yourself surrounded by temptations that would make it seem absolutely impossible for you not to trigger your Habit Circuit.

See yourself in slow motion, saying the words you most need to hear in that moment. You have pulled out your Power Grind In, words that give you a clear instruction to connect with yourself – words that are so powerful and nurturing that they shake you to your core. You feel that loved. Then state your new approach to this situation. Use words that are so emotionally honest and authentic that you can feel an awakening in your body and a sense of urgency to follow through. Last, consider which reward would be so meaningful to you that every last temptation could not phase you: Sanctuary, Authenticity, Vibrancy, Integrity, Intimacy, Spirituality, or Freedom.

Use the upcoming checklist to record the transformation statement that feels right to you.

Watch for reptilian brain sabotage

As you transition from establishing your four Power Grind Ins, the reptile could be very snappish. Keep your sense of humor, and when your success in raising your set point is significant enough to cause a Brain State 5, use the tools and appreciate your progress.

Reptilian Brain Shenanigans

Count on the reptile to appear at least once a week. Keep your sense of humor when you:

- "Forget" your Power Grind In
- Start analyzing your childhood, instead of rewiring circuits
- Decide that your set point is fine, thank you
- See dozens more circuits, rather than rewiring The Big Four
- Figure that EBT will work for everyone, but not for you
- Skip using the tools and sign up for a marathon instead
- Feel so much better that you are "done"
- Fall in love – the relationship will solve everything

Stage	Statements
1 SLOW	I can NOT get my existence from drinking too much.
2 RAMP UP	*That's ridiculous!* I can NOT get my existence from drinking. That's not possible. *In fact, that's ridiculous!* My existence does NOT come from alcohol. That's absurd.
3 JOY	I get my existence from inside me, from knowing and loving myself, NOT from drinking too much. My reward: Sanctuary. I get my existence from inside me, from knowing and loving myself, NOT from drinking too much. My reward: Sanctuary. I GET my existence from inside me, from *knowing and really loving myself*, NOT from drinking. My reward: SANCTUARY!

Create your Power Grind In for Habit

Develop your Power Grind In for Habit. Find the words that ring true for you, making your circuit an offer it cannot refuse. Do not ask more of yourself than is right for you. The problem is not the behavior, but the faulty message your brain has been trained to send. We are retraining our brain with messages that take us up and over to our joy.

Celebrate creating your fourth Power Grind In, settling on the new message and grinding it in. Then you will have a secure base with each of your four Power Grind Ins and be ready to turn to a welcome respite from rewiring by focusing on body pride and sensual pleasure!

The Rewiring Checklist
Day 3. Transform Your Habit Circuit

I transformed my Habit Circuit:

- **SLOW**

    I can NOT get my _____ from_____.

- **RAMP UP**

    That's ridiculous. I can NOT get my _____ from _____.

- **JOY**

I get my _____ **from:**

CONNECT	APPROACH	REWARD
☐ Connecting with myself	☐ STOP escaping into substances	☐ Sanctuary
☐ Checking in	☐ Avoiding external solutions	☐ Authenticity
☐ Knowing my number	☐ Quitting addictions one at a time	☐ Vibrancy
☐ Honoring my feelings	☐ Zapping one wire at a time	☐ Integrity
☐ Loving myself	☐ Cutting back on drinking	☐ Intimacy
☐ The compassion within	☐ Meeting my true needs	☐ Spirituality
☐ Honoring my strengths	☐ Getting my love from myself	☐ Freedom
☐ Believing in myself	☐ Comforting myself in healthy ways	
☐ Trusting myself	☐ Accessing pleasure from natural sources	
☐ Listening to my body	☐ Knowing my reason for being healthy	
☐ Being present now	☐ Being present rather than escaping	
☐ Other _____	☐ Other _____	

I did it: 50 75 100 125 150 200 _____ times.

Success Check Day 24

- **Daily Success**

☐ I continued my Power of One Practice with 10 Check Ins and 10 Joy Points.

☐ I transformed my Habit Circuit and created my Power Grind In.

☐ I made one or more community connections for support with transforming my circuit.

- **Did I pass the Success Check?   YES   NO**

If you did not, stay with this activity for one more day, then move on.

- **My Amazing Learning:**

_____

- **My Biggest Accomplishment:**

_____

- **My Biggest Challenge:**

_____

Beautiful Work!

You have completed Day 24 of The Power of One Challenge.
Your next step is Day 25. Lifestyle Reset #6
Body Pride and Sensual Pleasure.

Day 25. Lifestyle Reset #6
Body Pride and Sensual Pleasure

You've changed so much on the inside, it's time to reset your relationship with your body and the Power of One in two areas. One is body pride, enjoying your body, and the other is sensual pleasure, amplifying the sensory rewards you experience at Brain State 1.

Why

As your set point rises, you will continue to experience your body in a new way. Stress causes us to disconnect from our bodies and treat them like objects. We become self-critical, judgmental, dismissive, or detached, and stop short of enjoying the sensory pleasure inherent to our physical nature. That state of connection becomes more apparent as you spend more moments of the day at One.

I was dressing for work this morning and these words bubbled up to my consciousness, "You look good, Sweetie." I was shocked. When have I ever spoken to myself with such kindness – and been so accepting of my body? Never!

Lately, I have been enjoying using my senses to make me happy. I was driving my six-year-old to school and I told him to look out the window and name three colors he saw in the clouds. I never would have done that a month ago!

- **Reset your connection with your body.**
- **Enjoy a new level of body pride.**
- **Celebrate your sensual nature.**

> **Body Pride**
> Knowing, honoring, and celebrating your appearance
>
> **Sensual Pleasure**
> Enjoying your body's senses, appetites, and passions

All bodies are perfect bodies

As our set point continues to rise, the hypercritical reptile voice about our bodies seems so frighteningly immature. In its place comes not only a desire to take really good care of our bodies, adorn them, and celebrate them, but a great deal of respect and appreciation for our physical presence on the planet.

After I found out about my husband's affair, my set point went to 4.5. I did not have the emotional skills to process the betrayal. I did exactly what I needed to do at the time: eat and drink my way through the pain. I hated how I looked: puffy and big. I did a deep Cycle and realized that my body was perfect in its own way. My body showed what I had been through. Accepting that this happened and that my body showed the hurt, energized me to get healthy, take care of my body, and begin again.

I was in the store looking for tops with long sleeves and couldn't find many. I complained to the salesperson. I said, "The skin on my arms is starting to sag. I need to cover them up." She looked back at me and said, "Well, at least you have arms. Perhaps you should celebrate that!" I bought a sleeveless dress. Away went body shame and I switched over to body pride. All bodies are good bodies, including mine.

Enjoying sensual pleasure

Stress not only causes the disconnect between the neocortex and the emotional brain that shuts down sensory awareness, but it also distorts the sensual nature of life. The four most common sexual issues in men and women are caused by stress. If we are stressed, the first thing to go is sex drive (arousal and desire).

The basis for deepening love and emotional connection shuts down while the deprivation of sensual pleasures activates our Stress Circuits. The emotional brain is the #1 sex organ, so as our set point rises, often we renew our awareness first of our senses, then of the sensual pleasures of life.

I am enjoying all my senses more, particularly touch. When I can't sleep at night, I run my hands over my skin and notice how it feels. I have bumps on my skin and I feel them. I run my fingertips down my arm. It sounds like an inconsequential thing, but I didn't do that in the past. Now I enjoy my senses.

After we had children, my wife and I distanced from each other. Our son has developmental delays and our daughter has a heart defect so our stress levels are in the 4 to 5 range. My wife has low desire and I am the opposite. After dinner, she goes into the kitchen to eat and I go to my computer to work and fume. Last night we made love. EBT is starting to work!

Celebrate your body!

Your task today is to celebrate your amazing body. Give your body the unconditional love and appreciation that is precisely the way it needs to be to reflect your personal history and life journey. On that sturdy foundation of loving, honoring, and celebrating your body, have fun!

How

See how many of the strategies listed on the following two pages you will try out to give yourself moments of Body Pride and Sensual Pleasure. Check off each one.

Enjoy the natural pleasures of life. You have created four Power Grind Ins and have trained your brain to honor, celebrate, and enjoy your body and yourself.

Body Pride Moments

☐ **Celebrate your Hair:** Style it, cut it, change it!

☐ **Honor your Eyebrows:** Brush them, move them, admire them.

☐ **Check out your Face:** Pull your ears, wiggle your nose, smile wide.

☐ **Ah, that Neck. Oh, those Shoulders:** Strong, gorgeous, sexy!

☐ **Perfect arms. Just right for you:** Perfect for giving hugs.

☐ **Super sturdy Pecs:** Strong and lean, soft and welcoming.

☐ **Good Hands:** Great fingers, nice knuckles, capable in every way.

☐ **Nice Torso there:** Nicely rounded, like a washboard, gorgeous!

☐ **Flex your Biceps:** Strut your stuff, show it off, be strong.

☐ **A great Behind:** Round and wonderful, jiggling and exciting!

☐ **Oh, those Thighs:** Soft to the touch, alluring, muscles galore!

☐ **Good looking Knees:** Square, rounded, fleshy, fantastic!

☐ **Fond of your Feet:** Toes that wiggle, new shoes, nice ankles.

☐ **Decorate Yourself:** Try out new looks, update your style.

☐ **Stand with Body Pride:** Shoulders back, stand tall, feel pride!

☐ **The whole package:** Look in a mirror. You are a great specimen!

☐ **Feel gratitude:** Feel grateful for your body.

☐ **Curl up to sleep:** Feel pride in your body and yourself.

Sensual Pleasure Moments

☐ **Awaken to Sensual Pleasure:** how does your skin feel on the sheets? Stroke your body with love.

☐ **Morning Stretch:** notice how great you feel when you stretch your arms and legs.

☐ **Enjoy your food:** the smell and taste of it, and how it feels to swallow it.

☐ **Water Play:** Be aware of the shower or bath water on your skin. What pleasure!

☐ **Dress with body pride:** Choose clothes that bring you joy and have fun with your appearance.

☐ **Sensual dressing:** As you clothe yourself, be aware of your sensory pleasure.

☐ **Walk intentionally:** Move your body with pride, enjoying each step.

☐ **Use your fingertips wisely:** Pass your fingertips over your hand, thigh, calf, cheek. Wonderful!

☐ **Massage your neck:** Place your hand on the back of your neck (think oxytocin release!) and rub!

☐ **Be aware of your genitals:** We are sexual beings and that awareness is pleasurable.

☐ **Sit with body pride:** Sit up tall in your chair and enjoy being present.

☐ **Get to One:** Take a sensuality break, a minute to appreciate your body.

☐ **Move with joy:** Be grateful for your arms, legs, belly, hips – all of you!

☐ **Find one muscle on your body:** Even a finger. Delight in your strength!

☐ **Put your hands over your eyes and smile:** It feels GOOD!

Success Check Day 25

- **Daily Success**

☐ I continued my Power of One Practice with 10 Check Ins and 10 Joy Points.

☐ I reset my lifestyle in these ten ways: Exercise, Play, Joy Breakfast, Sanctuary Time, Joy Lunch, Balancing Sleep, Natural Pleasure Binge, Joy Dinner, Body Pride, and Sensual Pleasure.

☐ I made one or more community connections for support with my lifestyle reset.

- **Did I pass the Success Check?   YES   NO**

If you did not, stay with this activity for one more day, then move on.

- **My Amazing Learning:**

_____

- **My Biggest Accomplishment:**

_____

- **My Biggest Challenge:**

_____

Congratulations!

**You have completed Day 25 of The Power of One Challenge.
Your next step is Day 26. Strengthen Your Core.**

Celebrate
The Power of One

Day 26. Strengthen Your Core

Today we will launch the completion of our Power of One Challenge, transitioning from solving problems to accessing purpose.

We will strengthen our core in three steps. We'll update how we view Brain State 5, add a meditation to our EBT Practice that encodes the core circuits of emotional evolution, and turn our attention to becoming wired at One.

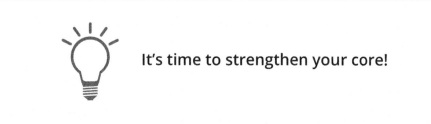

I have already changed more than I had imagined but want more. I want to raise my set point. I want the seven rewards!

Why

We are going to create a secure base inside and raise our set point. Our innate biology instills in us a hunger to be at One, and to use our energies to make the world a better place.

The joy of the human condition is that we have a brain that enables us to think magnificent thoughts – to do things for the right reasons. By doing that we self-administer a surge of neurotransmitters and discover that we have a great deal of courage. Learning how to train our brain to accomplish that is not only essential to the survival of the species, but it brings us profound pleasure, the elevated emotions of love, compassion, gratitude, hope, forgiveness, awe, and joy.

In his book, *Spiritual Evolution*, George Vaillant, a Harvard professor, research psychiatrist, and pioneer in human development, describes a special area in the emotional brain: the septal area. It is famous for giving us the ability to have an endless and even addictive drive to please ourselves. However, this area is also activated to bring pleasure from a thought of higher purpose. Our brain gives us the power to activate surges of neurochemicals that reward us in ways that artificial pleasures never could. We can have paradise inside by using our brain well.

My set point is already moving up. My brain randomly triggers a Brain State 5 and I shrug it off. I see a glimmer of joy, then I feel awash in joy. That is not the person I was 30 days ago. I want to keep going.

I can feel my neocortex taking charge. It is highly effective at checking out the wires that are triggered, liking them, and either using them or switching them off. It likes the tools and being aware of my purpose right in the moment – even right now. What's my purpose in saying this? Authenticity.

How

Take three steps to strengthen your core and move from focusing on problems to focusing on higher-order purpose. These are specific actions that help the circuitry in our brain change, so this natural transition becomes smoother and faster.

Step 1. Update the 5 Tool

In the past, when we would go to Brain State 5, our residue from random moments of stress (brain glitches), would take control. We'd activate a Mood Circuit, trigger a Habit or Work Circuit, or distance or merge in relationships.

Now we have four Power Grind Ins so these circuits are largely under our control. However, the 5 State remains our pathway to ongoing improvement of our set point. We must reset our relationship with Brain State 5 in order to evolve.

After Brain State 5, we often have a clearing. We are at a strong Brain State 1, on a natural high, making us wonder: could Brain State 5 be good for us? Yes, if we use our tools with precision and grace. The brain is wide open to change then, so if we stay emotionally connected in those moments, we can wire in that state of connection. However, when we are in the 5th Drawer of the

Update your approach to Brain State 5
• This is a productive 5 State!
• Brain State 5 is part of the process.
• If I can love myself at 5, I can do anything!
• Brain State 5 is a Moment of Opportunity.
• At 5, I connect with the spiritual.
• Before Brain State 1 comes a moment at 5.

brain we are apt to activate a real garage band of circuits, not a symphony. So, we must take charge and tell the lizard brain that we are not going to be a willing victim of its stress hormone cascade.

We are going to avoid secondary stress, the stress buzzer getting stuck on. It's not the initial strike of a circuit that is most treacherous, but the chronic stress or prolonged stress reactivity that follows. Secondary stress can easily become our new addiction, a way of life focusing on problems and seeing glitches everywhere. The reptile would love that!

So, we must update our 5 Tool. We must say a few words that clearly announce that this state is good for us! Experiment with different phrases until one feels good to you. Then slip in your personal phrase prior to using the 5 Tool. If you bring up a strong nurturing voice and connect with yourself in those moments, Brain State 5 is productive. It will deepen your self-compassion. Oxytocin is higher in that state, perhaps a sign of grace, making it easier to connect with ourselves and the spiritual in challenging moments.

As the brain is highly plastic then, even a tiny bit of self-compassion is strongly remembered. That experience helps us move up our set point. In a way, stress is the new joy!

Step 2. Use the Core Grind In

The Core Grind In is a fundamental practice of EBT. You take about five minutes and read through the seven circuits of emotional evolution. Included are the most fundamental expectations of life, the essential pain we must face to live an exceptional life, and the rewards we receive in abundance from doing so. This practice strengthens our circuits that anticipate, experience, and value the seven rewards.

The Core Grind In
7 Circuits to Strengthen Your Core

Reasonable Expectation	Essential Pain	Earned Reward
I do exist.	I am alone.	Sanctuary
I am not bad.	I am not perfect.	Authenticity
I do have power.	I am not in complete control.	Vibrancy
I can do good.	It takes work.	Integrity
I can love.	Some people may reject me.	Intimacy
I am worthy.	I must receive.	Spirituality
I can have joy.	I must give.	Freedom

This Core Grind In has some meanings that differ from other uses of the words, so at first you may read this and wonder at some of them. Learn more about them below, and also, let your mind take time to adjust to these ideas. Often, they will begin to ring true for you over time. If you need to personalize them, then by all means do so. Make it your own. Here is a starting place, the meanings of each of the seven circuits of emotional evolution:

Sanctuary – Peace and Power from Within

I do exist asserts that we are alive. If we recognize that we are alive, we must face our separateness. No matter how much we love others and how much they love us, **we are alone**. We alone are responsible for how we use our gift of life. By facing our aloneness, we are motivated to cultivate a rich inner life, a **Sanctuary**, so we have peace and power from within.

Authenticity – Feeling Whole and Being Genuine

I am not bad means that we have overcome the drive for stress to "split" us and make us think that we are either all good or all bad. When we face the essential pain that **we are not perfect**, we relax, access humility, and feel whole. We can be genuine and experience **Authenticity** in our daily life.

Vibrancy – Healthy with a Zest for Life

I do have power means that we are neither powerless nor all-powerful, either of which leads to suffering and health problems. We face the essential pain that **we are not in complete control** and access far more energy to be healthy with a zest for life, that is, **Vibrancy**.

Integrity – Doing the Right Thing

I can do good means that we are industrious and can take purposeful initiative. When we face the essential pain that **it takes work**, we stop blaming ourselves for the many "failures" and the inevitable pain involved in growth. We stop blaming others too, for life takes work for all of us. No one gets a free ride. The reward is **Integrity**, that gut feeling that we are doing the right thing.

The first four circuits of emotional evolution form the basis for intimacy with self and a secure connection within. Only with that security within can we safely and effectively expand and connect in more profound ways through Intimacy, Spirituality, and Freedom.

Intimacy – Giving and Receiving Love

I can love means that we have accepted that our nature is to love, and we have enough to give to others. The essential pain as we give love is that **some people may reject us**. Although that may hurt, we can take the risk of loving others because we have a secure base within (the first four circuits). Our reward is **Intimacy** in the form that it takes at the time.

Spirituality – Aware of the Grace, Beauty, and Mystery of Life

I am worthy means that we are functional enough to give back to the world. We have evolved enough to give back for the greater good and face the essential pain that **we must receive**. Asking for support from the spiritual as we define it or the greater good stops the overcontrol of outcome that blocks joy. That essential step of humility opens us to experience more of the grace, beauty, and mystery of life, that is, **Spirituality**.

Freedom – Common Excesses Fade and We Move Forward in Life

I can have joy means that instead of despairing, we are in hopeful anticipation of the next amazing thing that will happen in our lives. We open ourselves to using our talents in just the way that completes our lives. That takes facing the essential pain that **we must give** at a deeper level. Only then will the whole range of common excesses fade and bring to us the reward of **Freedom**.

Please experiment with this Core Grind In at least once each day. Whether it becomes part of your daily practice or you use it as a "run through" now and then on your way home in the evening, it can be connecting and grounding. What's more, it primes the brain for Advanced EBT and raising your emotional set point.

Share the Core Grind In during connections

I have a weekly connection on Fridays at 8 a.m., and one of us reads the Core Grind In to the other. We have it memorized now. I feel closer to my buddy because we do this.

Use the Core Grind In when you are at Brain State 5

My Mood Circuit is numbing. Sometimes I don't want to deal with my feelings. This Grind In helps a lot. I say it to myself, and it has a stabilizing effect. It helps me put whatever I was worrying about in perspective.

Use it in meditation, prayer, or Sanctuary Time

My morning routine is to check in with myself. Usually, I say a prayer, feel my feelings, and commit to creating joy in my life that day. I use the Core Grind In as a way of focusing on what matters to me: these seven rewards.

Create your own ways to use it, such as a Family Grind In

I sing this Grind In to my three children when we are driving, and they are arguing. They always calm down. Now my 10-year-old is telling me that he is kind to his friends out of integrity. We keep it light and fun, and it is working.

Step 3. Reset your focus: Raising your set point

The most powerful thing anyone can do is raise their set point. Whatever situations arise in your day, consider them opportunities to raise your set point. Think in terms of your Check Ins, Spiral Ups, Power Grind Ins, and Joy Points. Be aware of the earned reward upon which you base each of your actions throughout the day.

I am interested in the reward of Sanctuary right now. My mind is turning to peace and power from within. I want to grab hold of my Power Grind Ins and use them for freedom from worrying all the time. I want all seven rewards, so I have an ever-deepening experience of life. I want to be wired at One, and then after that, deepen my One.

By taking these three steps – updating your 5 Tool, using the Core Grind In, and resetting your focus to raising your set point, you are tapping into the perfection of your emotional brain. What could be more powerful than that?

Success Check Day 26

- **Daily Success**

☐ I continued my Joy Practice with 10 Check Ins and 10 Joy Points.

☐ I updated my 5 Tool, used the Core Grind In, and reset my focus to raising my set point.

☐ I made one or more community connections for support with these activities.

- **Did I pass the Success Check?   YES   NO**

If you did not, stay with this activity for one more day, then move on.

- **My Amazing Learning:**

_____

- **My Biggest Accomplishment:**

_____

- **My Biggest Challenge:**

_____

Wonderful Work!

**You have completed Day 26 of The Power of One Challenge.
Your next step is Day 27. The Vibrancy Plan Day 1.**

Day 27. The Vibrancy Plan Day 1

Today we will begin the three-day culminating experience for The Power of One Challenge.

You will apply everything you have learned in this course to check in with yourself, then stay connected to yourself, and adopt a healthy, vibrant lifestyle. In addition, you will take five-minute Power Breaks four times daily to use your Power Grind Ins. They will make it far easier to live a life of natural pleasures.

- **Live a vibrant lifestyle.**
- **Use the EBT Tools.**
- **Be at ONE!**

Why

We need a "Vibrancy Reset" in which we not only check in but stay checked in. By weaving a commitment to a healthy lifestyle into your plan, sustaining that new way of life becomes far easier. We feel charged up and motivated!

I did not know how great I could feel. Now that I have experienced it, I want more of this. My reptile wants me to return to my old stagnant, stressed life. Nope. There is no way I'm going to do that!

Past	Now	The Second 30 Days
Not in the Vibrancy Habit	Vibrancy Reset	Vibrancy Habit

How

It's easy! Today as well as for the next two days, the day's learning includes a checklist of activities for a day of vibrancy. First, modify the plan to meet your needs, and then use the checklist as you move through your day. You don't have to do this perfectly to see important results.

Think of this as a time to feast on natural pleasures and outsmart the reptilian brain's drives to keep you addicted to stress. Instead, connect with your inherent strength, goodness, and wisdom. Be at One!

I chose exercise I love, which is walking my dog, and I did Sanctuary Time when I arrived home from work. I went into my bedroom, shut off the light, and curled up in a ball on my bed. I did Cycles in my head and got to One. Dinner was not the usual pasta, bread, and ice cream, but instead a plate of greens, avocados, chicken, and plenty of olive oil. It was delicious. My natural pleasure binge topped it off!

The Vibrancy Plan Day 1

- Read The Vibrancy Plan checklist for Day 1.
- Personalize the plan to meet your needs.
- Enjoy your first day of vibrancy!

Make it Easy

Eat for vibrancy

Establish a pattern of eating that is in harmony with the lifestyle of our hunter-gatherer ancestors, the one that our genes evolved to prefer. We call this the EBT 3-Point Plan, which is eating only when hungry, eating mainly Joy Foods, and taking a 12-hour food rest. Emphasize lean protein, healthy fats, and fiber foods because most people who eat them are satisfied for longer and have fewer blood sugar lows. Add enough Stress Foods to avoid feeling deprived.

Build on your six lifestyle resets

You are already skilled at implementing these changes. During this course, you transitioned to a vibrant lifestyle with six lifestyle resets. It's likely that you will be surprised at how easy this plan is.

Each element has been carefully chosen because it causes positive biochemical changes in your body, such as decreasing cortisol or insulin, or boosting serotonin, dopamine, or oxytocin.

Be sure to personalize your plan. Speed it up and do everything on the list or take a more gradual approach and implement fewer of them. However, err on the side of doing more, as you will feel so much better that you will want to continue it.

Take Power Breaks!

It's essential to keep the Stress Triangle in check so that your reward and stress centers make it easy to enjoy natural pleasures. You now have your four Power Grind Ins, so take five minutes at regular intervals throughout the day to zap those circuits and activate your reward center. You can change your chemistry naturally! Give yourself a dose of healthy chemicals during your Power Breaks and experience how easy it is to live a vibrant lifestyle.

When I thought of putting this all together, I was excited and scared. Then I used the plan – imperfectly but well – and now I feel better than I have in years.

Imagine yourself choosing to activate these healing chemicals throughout the day by using the tools. Also, notice the impact of taking a five-minute Power Break four times today, as you'll identify your amazing learning about using them tomorrow.

Use the checklist on the next page to guide your way. As always, make it fun. YOU now have the Power of One!

Success Check Day 27
The Vibrancy Plan Checklist: Day 1

Today, I . . .

☐ Created my day when I awoke: "I am creating joy in my life"

☐ Made a community connection

☐ Exercised for 10 to 30 minutes in the morning

☐ Ate a Joy Breakfast and drank one or two glasses of water

☐ Did meaningful work in the morning

☐ Ate a Joy Lunch and drank one or two glasses of water

☐ Did meaningful work in the afternoon

☐ Exercised for 10 to 30 minutes in the afternoon or evening

☐ Took Sanctuary Time for 10 minutes

☐ Ate a Joy Dinner and drank one or two glasses of water

☐ Had a natural pleasure binge

☐ Made another community connection

☐ Took a food rest for 12 hours

☐ Created my day at bedtime: "I am creating joy in my life"

☐ Enjoyed balancing sleep for eight hours

Be aware of your EBT practice of Check Ins, Joy Points, and Power Breaks:

Did I check in 10 times?   YES   NO

Did I score 10 Joy Points?   YES   NO

Did I take four Power Breaks?   YES   NO

Total the number of activities you checked in the list above:

Total Vibrancy Points Today _____

<8 = low vibrancy   8-12 = moderate vibrancy   >12 = high vibrancy

My Vibrancy Day 1:   LOW   MODERATE   HIGH

- **My Amazing Learning:**

_____

- **My Biggest Accomplishment:**

_____

- **My Biggest Challenge:**

_____

Congratulations!

You have completed Day 27 of The Power of One Challenge.
Your next step is Day 28. The Vibrancy Plan Day 2.

Day 28. The Vibrancy Plan Day 2

Great work completing the Vibrancy Plan Day 1. You are now in the second day of your Vibrancy Reset.

You are using both your brain state and your lifestyle to improve the chemical cascade that reduces your stress and activates surges of feel-good chemicals like dopamine, serotonin, endorphins, and oxytocin and to separate yourself from the stress-infested, addicted world we live in. Instead of living with these addictive drives (all 5 Circuits are addictions), we are using lifestyle and rewiring to gain more freedom in our lives. This is your opportunity to begin to break free of the stress cycle!

Check to see if you need to increase your Vibrancy Points (be even healthier) or decrease them (ease up a bit). Use your brain state as a guide. Some stress shows that you are changing; too much stress is counterproductive.

Why
Checking in and adjusting your plan is really important, in part because the missing piece of information is how your Power Breaks work.

The Vibrancy Plan Day 2
- Read The Vibrancy Plan checklist for Day 2.
- Personalize the plan to meet your needs.
- Enjoy your second day of vibrancy!

If your Power Breaks are short-circuiting stress and stopping cravings and unwanted drives, then your stress level will be significantly lower. You have more power to change, without triggering a protracted Brain State 5. If you have more bandwidth, then use it!

I forgot to do the Power Breaks during Day 1, and it still worked pretty well. I was running at Brain States 1 to 3 yesterday. It was a great day. I'm going to take four Power Breaks today, and see how much they help.

Take your Power Break Inventory for Day 1

Check whether or not you used each of your four Power Grind Ins during your five-minute Power Breaks throughout the day yesterday.

Notice if you used all of them or were drawn to focusing on one. Everyone is different. Some people use all four each time; others home in on one or two. Experiment. Which way helps you change faster? Your Power Grind Ins will help you win the war against the reptile. It will calm down as you move through Advanced EBT, but it is always a force to be contended with.

During my work day, I use my Mood and Work Power Grind Ins, because they keep me connected and productive, but in the evening I use all four of my Grind Ins. I like the flexibility to use whichever ones help me the most.

How

Today, check if you want to speed it up, slow it down, or keep the plan the same. You may find the second day more challenging, experiencing some detox from the artificial rewards of your previous lifestyle. Flexibility is key. Do not do more than you can. Triggering a protracted 5 State is not the plan – it's not fun or effective.

Plan your Power Breaks at regular intervals throughout the day. You can say your Power Grind Ins to yourself or aloud. Either way, the more passion in your voice, the more emotional amplification you have, the more your wires will change!

I go into the restroom, find a stall, and sit there for five minutes. Nobody sees my face, which is very animated, or that I am waving my arms around. I am completely committed to breaking all four wires in the Second 30 Days, and I want to get a head start NOW.

I use my Power Breaks as a form of Sanctuary Time. I have two stepchildren and a baby and no time to myself. I feel great about taking the four breaks because it impacts my wires, which means it impacts their wires. I'm going to transform my wires for myself and for my family.

The most important outcome from today's plan is for you to know more about how you want to live. Which elements of the plan make life better for you, and which are not realistic or helpful?

Use the checklist on the next page to personalize your plan. It must be fun or you will not stick with it. Enjoy this second day of vibrancy!

Success Check Day 28
The Vibrancy Plan Checklist: Day 2

Today, I . . .

☐ Created my day when I awoke: "I am creating joy in my life"

☐ Made a community connection

☐ Exercised for 10 to 30 minutes in the morning

☐ Ate a Joy Breakfast and drank one or two glasses of water

☐ Did meaningful work in the morning

☐ Ate a Joy Lunch and drank one or two glasses of water

☐ Did meaningful work in the afternoon

☐ Exercised for 10 to 30 minutes in the afternoon or evening

☐ Took Sanctuary Time for 10 minutes

☐ Ate a Joy Dinner and drank one or two glasses of water

☐ Had a natural pleasure binge

☐ Made another community connection

☐ Took a food rest for 12 hours

☐ Created my day at bedtime: "I am creating joy in my life"

☐ Enjoyed balancing sleep for eight hours

Be aware of your EBT practice of Check Ins, Joy Points, and Power Breaks:

Did I check in 10 times?   YES   NO

Did I score 10 Joy Points?   YES   NO

Did I take four Power Breaks?   YES   NO

Total the number of activities you checked in the list above

Total Vibrancy Points Today_____

<8=low vibrancy   8-12=moderate vibrancy   >12=high vibrancy

My Vibrancy Day 2: LOW   MODERATE HIGH

- **My Amazing Learning:**

_____

- **My Biggest Accomplishment:**

_____

- **My Biggest Challenge:**

_____

Congratulations!

**You have completed Day 28 of The Power of One Challenge.
Your next step is Day 29. The Vibrancy Plan Day 3.**

Day 29. The Vibrancy Plan Day 3

As you complete three days of vibrancy, we will transition into using a personalized version of this plan for the next 30 days. This is a moment of opportunity, as incorporating a vibrant lifestyle and transforming these hefty Stress Circuits can lead to a brain and body reset.

The Power Breaks and the natural pleasure binges are winning me over. This is a great way to live!

Today you will transition to the Second 30 Days, check how your Power Grind Ins are working, and ask for support for the Second 30 Days.

Why

The reptile lies in wait. You will be using your prefrontal cortex to deactivate the Stress Circuits stored in the amygdala consistently for 30 days. In a very brief period, you can make solid the amazing work you have done in this challenge! If we do not stick with this and devote these next 30 days to breaking the four major circuits in our brain that attach us to stress WHILE adopting a vibrant lifestyle, we will remain stressed. We may even sense that we have abandoned ourselves. We have missed a golden opportunity. Who will have won? The reptile.

I imagined what I would do if I did not have structure for the next 30 days. It didn't take long. In an instant, I knew that I would go back to my pre-EBT days and give myself the illusion that I would stick with it. I know my reptile and it is pretty fierce. I am staying with the program.

The Vibrancy Plan Day 3

- Read The Vibrancy Plan checklist for Day 3.
- Check how your Power Grind Ins are working.
- Identify your support needs.

Take your Power Circuit Inventory for Day 2

Notice which of the four Power Grind Ins you used yesterday, and which ones worked. Your brain and your Power Grind Ins are unique, so the best indicator of the ideal way to use these Power Grind Ins is how using them impacts you. If one is not helping, update the Power Grind In or try using it at a different time. Experiment. What is the goal? Breaking those circuits. You will know when you have broken them. The attachment is gone, the love affair is over, the excesses become like old news. They may even fade from your memory.

I think I broke my overworking circuit. I believed that I had to work 14 hours a day to make it and not fail, and that was completely wrong. I was working so hard that I was creating problems for myself. I had communication issues with my co-workers because I was at 5. The projects I was choosing did not work out very well. The combination of frying my Work Circuit with these Power Breaks and the lifestyle changes are more rewarding than overworking ever was!

How

Check if you want to speed it up, slow it down, or keep the plan the same. Reflect on what you are learning from these three days, and how the Power Break schedule is working for you. Make any needed changes and consider how important it is for you to access support to make this plan work.

No lone islands – ask for support

As you begin the Second 30 Days, your brain will integrate the vast changes you have made during the first 30 days. During this period of intensive reconsolidating, you will be consistent (but not rigidly so) and passionate. You will be determined, focused, and excited about feasting on natural pleasures and watching every aspect of your life improve. You have worked so hard to complete this challenge that this is your time to cash in on your earnings. If you fold now, you will miss out on a life-changing experience. It is essential that you arrange for support. Relationships are two-way streets, so just the way you help others, they can help you. As your set point rises because of your vibrancy, others around you "catch" your higher state. Helping you, in time, helps them.

I told my boyfriend that I am going to get up earlier and go to the gym, so I can't do errands in the morning. He said okay. I was afraid to ask him (my Merge Circuit operating), but I did it anyway. He didn't like it, but he will like my zest for life down the road.

Sometimes asking for support is not met with joy. Most people like things to stay the same and if you are taking more time for your vibrancy, it may mean more work for them. Most of us over-give to those around us and these folks (quite naturally) like it.

My teenage son groaned when I told him he'd have to cook dinner on Tuesdays so that I would have more time to take care of myself. He made it sound like I was the worst father on Earth. Then he started cooking and he was great at it. He is proud of himself, and I am at One when I come home those nights.

Please reflect on your Vibrancy Plan Day 3 and fine-tune your plan. Keep it flexible, but clear, so that you know what you intend to do going forward. Make it challenging enough so that after 30 days, your Vibrancy Habit will help you move up your set point more quickly and easily.

Success Check Day 29
The Vibrancy Plan Checklist: Day 3

Today, I . . .

☐ Created my day when I awoke: "I am creating joy in my life"

☐ Made a community connection

☐ Exercised for 10 to 30 minutes in the morning

☐ Ate a Joy Breakfast and drank one or two glasses of water

☐ Did meaningful work in the morning

☐ Ate a Joy Lunch and drank one or two glasses of water

☐ Did meaningful work in the afternoon

☐ Exercised for 10 to 30 minutes in the afternoon or evening

☐ Took Sanctuary Time for 10 minutes

☐ Ate a Joy Dinner and drank one or two glasses of water

☐ Had a natural pleasure binge

☐ Made another community connection

☐ Took a food rest for 12 hours

☐ Created my day at bedtime: "I am creating joy in my life"

☐ Enjoyed balancing sleep for eight hours

Be aware of your EBT practice of Check Ins, Joy Points, and Power Breaks:

Did I check in 10 times?   YES   NO

Did I score 10 Joy Points?   YES   NO

Did I take four Power Breaks?   YES   NO

Total the number of activities you checked in the list above:

Total Vibrancy Points Today _____

<8=low vibrancy   8-12=moderate vibrancy   >12=high vibrancy

My Vibrancy Day 3:   LOW   MODERATE   HIGH

- **My Amazing Learning:**

_____

- **My Biggest Accomplishment:**

_____

- **My Biggest Challenge:**

_____

Congratulations!

**You have completed Day 29 of The Power of One Challenge.
Your next step is Day 30. Celebrate The Power of One.**

Day 30. Celebrate the Power of One

In the last 30 days, you have learned how to rewire your own emotional brain. It's time to celebrate what you have accomplished and determine how to make the most of your gains. Please take three steps:

Step 1. Celebrate the Power of One
You have new powers to control your elusive emotional brain. You have learned new tools, and it's time to celebrate that you have completed this foundational course in taking charge of your unconscious mind.

I went to a nearby hilltop at sunset and was in awe of nature, and how comfortable I am with myself. I truly have peace and power from within.

I celebrated by updating my calendar and committing to more Sanctuary Time. I made a special place for Sanctuary Time in an alcove in my house that is quiet and comforting.

I bought myself new clothes. It was in celebration of my new body pride and feeling connected to the deepest part of myself. YES!!!

Step 2. Commit to Raising Your Set Point
You have done the basic work. The foundation has been built. Now it's time to construct the "house." That's the seven rewards that raise the brain's set point for lasting and profound improvements in mood, love, work, habits, and health. This takes as long as it takes but you can complete one course in as little as one month, so consider this a one-year program, however, take longer if you like. The challenge is to commit to becoming wired for JOY, wired at ONE! Consider which of the seven rewards is your ultimate desire . . . and it will motivate you to raise your set point.

I am not going to quit now. I want to reset my brain, particularly because my children have already acquired some of my wires, and the best way to help them update their wires is for ME to update my own! My ultimate reward is Integrity, doing the right thing.

I'm going to raise my set point, and I know that I need structure and support to do it. I have quit other programs. I'm completely "in" on this and my reward is FREEDOM.

Step 3. Share the Tools

EBT is a movement. The #1 epidemic worldwide is the emotional brain in stress. We have the neuroscience to overcome that stress, and make the challenges we face a positive aspect of our lives. The more stress we face and move through, the more our set point rises. Please share EBT in your own time and own way with at least one person. Become part of our mission in a way that works for you. Give back and become part of the solution that the world most needs right now.

I'm inviting family members to try out the tools for a week. A man in my telegroup is part of a family in which 10 members have an EBT practice. His entire family is becoming more connected and healthier. I want that for my family.

I'm going to share this with my daughter who is nine years old and so anxious. I'm going to teach her the Flow Tool. I think I'll call it the Feelings Game!

Celebrate your new power to create joy in your life!

Let's take the Joy Inventory one more time. Changes in all three areas – needs, rewards, and connection – are signs of your raising set point and your enhanced emotional evolution. They are measures of your capacity to experience an exceptional life. Compare your joy to what you experienced at the beginning and middle of this book. Celebrate your progress!

The Power of One Inventory

Needs

In the last week, how often did you meet each of your basic needs?

Purpose
    1 = Rarely   2 = Sometimes   3 = Often   4 = Very Often

Pleasure
    1 = Rarely   2 = Sometimes   3 = Often   4 = Very Often

Comfort
    1 = Rarely   2 = Sometimes   3 = Often   4 = Very Often

Love
    1 = Rarely   2 = Sometimes   3 = Often   4 = Very Often

Safety
    1 = Rarely   2 = Sometimes   3 = Often   4 = Very Often

Total Needs Score _____

Rewards

In the last week, how often did you experience these rewards?

Sanctuary: Peace and power from within
    1 = Rarely   2 = Sometimes   3 = Often   4 = Very Often

Authenticity: Feeling whole and being genuine
    1 = Rarely   2 = Sometimes   3 = Often   4 = Very Often

Vibrancy: Healthy with a zest for life
    1 = Rarely   2 = Sometimes   3 = Often   4 = Very Often

Integrity: Doing the right thing
    1 = Rarely   2 = Sometimes   3 = Often   4 = Very Often

Intimacy: Giving and receiving love
    1 = Rarely   2 = Sometimes   3 = Often   4 = Very Often

Spirituality: Aware of the grace, beauty, and mystery of life

    1 = Rarely   2 = Sometimes   3 = Often   4 = Very Often

Freedom: Common excesses fade

    1 = Rarely   2 = Sometimes   3 = Often   4 = Very Often

Total Rewards Score _____

Connection

In the last week, how often did you connect in this way?

Being aware that I can create joy in my life

    1 = Rarely   2 = Sometimes   3 = Often   4 = Very Often

Choosing to create a moment at One

    1 = Rarely   2 = Sometimes   3 = Often   4 = Very Often

Spiraling up from stress to One

    1 = Rarely   2 = Sometimes   3 = Often   4 = Very Often

Enjoying sensory pleasures

    1 = Rarely   2 = Sometimes   3 = Often   4 = Very Often

Eating healthy food

    1 = Rarely   2 = Sometimes   3 = Often   4 = Very Often

Exercising in ways that are fun

    1 = Rarely   2 = Sometimes   3 = Often   4 = Very Often

Feeling love for myself

    1 = Rarely   2 = Sometimes   3 = Often   4 = Very Often

Feeling love for others

    1 = Rarely   2 = Sometimes   3 = Often   4 = Very Often

Feeling love for all living beings

    1 = Rarely   2 = Sometimes   3 = Often   4 = Very Often

Total Connection Score _____

The Power of One Inventory Summary

Category	Baseline Score	Current Score	Progress	Power of One Range
Needs	_____	_____	_____	15 to 20
Rewards	_____	_____	_____	21 to 28
Connection	_____	_____	_____	27 to 36
Power of One Total	_____	_____	_____	63 to 84

What is your amazing learning about your needs?

_____

What is your amazing learning about your rewards?

_____

What is your amazing learning about your connection?

_____

Moving forward

After celebrating your accomplishments in this course, we will build on them with 30 days of a brain reset. Your brain needs to reorganize around the major changes you have made, making the new circuitry dominant and solid.

This is the Second 30 Days Program. To use it is easy. Focus on transforming all four of your Stress Circuits and train your basal ganglia for a vibrant lifestyle. Then we'll move on to the first reward in Advanced EBT: Sanctuary. Congratulations on completing this course!

Move on to the next chapter to create a sensible and life-changing plan to do the most powerful thing that anyone can do: raise your set point.

Wonderful!

You have completed The Power of One Challenge.
Your Next Step is Raise Your Set Point.

Next Step: Raise Your Set Point

During the last 30 days, you reset your brain so that instead of being stuck in a cycle of stress overload, you have entered a new way of processing life, a cycle of optimal well-being.

Instead of being stuck in the
Stress Overload Cycle . . .

Now, when a stressful stimulus arrives in your brain, you use the tools and switch off that Stress Circuit in favor of a wire that promotes resilience. That wire enables you to meet your most fundamental needs, and rewards you with optimal well-being.

. . . you are now in the
Cycle of Optimal Well-being.

You've made the switch to this new cycle, but much like riding a bucking broncho, your emotional brain will be snorting and kicking a bit. You have created a revolution from within, now you need to give your brain time to reorganize itself around this revolution.

During the next 30 days, you can break the four circuits you selected during this challenge and strengthen the vibrancy habits stored in your basal ganglia. Your reptilian brain will work overtime to convince you that you can skip this time of making solid the circuits that switch off stress overload and activate optimal well-being. However, please don't take the chance that these wires are not strong and secure. Give yourself this small bit of extra time, then launch into the advanced courses and be on fire – raising your set point far more rapidly and with greater ease!

Key steps during the Second 30 Days

What do you do during the Second 30 Days? You use the Vibrancy Plan daily and record what you do. Also, use your Power Grind Ins four times daily and track your progress with breaking all four of your circuits.

This honoring requires NOT taking on any more circuits, but instead making solid your core gains from this challenge. To do that you take five minutes four times daily for a Power Break to use your Grind Ins. Each wire is from a different domain of life. Rewiring all four of these major circuits will strengthen your secure base, so you can be present, aware, and connected. Just the way a table is sturdier with four legs than three, be sure to transform all four of your circuits. This strengthens the all-important connection for optimal functioning between your thinking brain and emotional brain (neural integration) so that you can raise your set point more easily and more rapidly.

Also, the Stress Triangle has calmed down, so you feel emotionally lighter, and more vibrant. To build on your success, continue with the Vibrancy Plan. Consistently practicing vibrancy for 30 days changes the basal ganglia (the brain's habit center), so you will encode the Vibrancy Habit. Research has shown that the repeated use of a lifestyle plan trains the brain to sustain lasting change.

The Second 30 Days

- **Make vibrancy a habit.**
- **Clear away those Stress Circuits.**
- **Prepare to raise your set point.**

I took a break for the Second 30 Days, and followed my version of the Vibrancy Plan. I broke all four of my circuits, too. First, my Mood Circuit transformed, which makes me laugh. I was addicted to depression for how many years? I broke my attachment to depression, and now those mood states are annoying, but they pass. Both my drinking wine wire and my distancing circuit are largely gone. The last one I transformed was my Work Circuit, which was perfectionism. Now I'm ready for Advanced EBT, starting with the Sanctuary course, peace and power from within.

Your set point at One

Congratulations on completing The Power of One Challenge. When you began this challenge, you may have wondered how you could change a neuron in your brain that collaborates with other neurons to trigger you to repeat patterns that you do not like. Now you know how to train a neuron as part of a team effort within to make yourself more resilient, and thus happier and healthier.

Now you are on your way to raising your brain's set point, the most powerful thing that anyone can do. The seven rewards form a solid base for living your best life.

The first advanced course of the method gives you the security of Sanctuary, having peace and power from within. Each advanced course after than builds on that safe place within, and amounts to a neuroscience-based pathway for emotional evolution, as well as optimal well-being.

As your set point rises, you will not only be naturally resilient, but you will have so much energy, wisdom, and power that you can give back, be of service, and use your unique talents in just the way that makes your life complete.

Imagine, your interest in EBT began because you wanted to solve a stress-related problem, and what the tools deliver is an abundance of life's richest rewards. As you use the tools to access these rewards, remember where they came from: science – as well as the magical powers of the elusive emotional brain!

Acknowledgments

This quick course in EBT was 10 years in the writing, as it took piecing together a string of advances in the method to make it possible. The initial impetus for the work came in 2010 with the publication of *Wired for Joy*, which explained the early version of the EBT 5-Point System and reflected my enthusiasm for having discovered the five brain states, not the least of which was unbridled joy.

Late in the writing of that book, new findings in emotional plasticity were forthcoming from New York University, findings that led to the awareness that rewiring the circuits in the brain's "5th Drawer" held the most opportunity for personal transformation.

We reassembled the program to align with this emerging neuroscience and made it simpler, easier, and more fun to use. Meanwhile, technology began taking over healthcare, and my son, Joe Mellin, a business designer, developed a platform for remote EBT services, and helped us see that an online hub of support could provide global access to the tools. He designed an online "emotional gym" for EBT that brought people together to learn the tools solo or to connect in small groups. Dev Singh, now our Chief Technology Officer, and Andrea Singh, EBT's Senior Software Engineer, have developed that state-of-the-art platform over the last six years, bringing their own sensibilities to the design. I am grateful for their creativity, skill, and dedication.

I am thankful for Michael McClure, Director of Member Support, who has contributed to EBT leadership, marketing, and communications for more than eight years, attending to member needs and juggling his many roles with precision and grace. Kelly McGrath has coordinated the method's infrastructure for nearly 20 years and has offered her steadfast support during this transition. Walt Rose led the way in simplifying the method as scalable healthcare, in which members could learn the tools, and potentially avoid excessive reliance on medications, medical procedures, and devices. The empowering nature of the online community appealed to Walt, as he saw it was "people helping people help themselves" to move forward in life.

Early in my work, a colleague, Lee Ann Slinkard, advised me not to write another book until I couldn't stand NOT to write it because there was so much that needed to be shared. We reached that point two years ago, but it took a year to fathom how we could put the entire basic 30-day program into a book. Jill Marsal guided me through writing the proposal, and Colleen Mauro, editor, magazine publisher, and author of *Spiritual Telepathy*, and publishing consultant Eileen Duhné supported our progress in launching this book. Three talented and dedicated editors collaborated on the process of transitioning this course into a book. Frannie Wilson spearheaded the proofing of this publication and brought a fresh eye to the work, and caught me when I explained too much (or too little). She has been tireless in improving the quality of the text and graphics. Michele Welling, MD edited the work, often well into the wee hours of the morning, bringing her medical background to her edits. Jamie Holecek supplied her InDesign and project management experience to the production, and juggled roles to proof and review the instructional design with remarkable dedication. Jami Spittler (Jamison Design), our graphic designer for two decades, provided the cover and interior designs and consulted on the graphics production for this work. As her priorities changed, she helped smooth the transition to our new designer, Steven Isakson, who brought his unique talents to the project. Without each of them, this book would not have been created.

The "pioneers of EBT" for this book and my related book on stress eating include outstanding researchers, each with a body of work that has contributed to the development of the method. The leadership of Charles E. Irwin, Jr., MD in interdisciplinary adolescent health training formed the foundation for the EBT method. Without his dedication to adolescent health, EBT would never have been launched. The core circle of researchers include: Igor Mitrovic, MD, Michael Merzenich, PhD, Lynda Frassetto, MD, Lindsey Fish, MD, Elizabeth Phelps, PhD, Joseph LeDoux, PhD, Bruce McEwen, PhD, Mary Dallman, PhD, Elissa Epel, PhD, Robert Lustig, MD, John Foreyt, PhD, and Nancy Adler, PhD. Without their research and dedication, there would be no EBT.

I am particularly grateful to Patricia Robertson, MD, Sue Carlisle, MD, PhD, Carol Miller, MD, Lori Karan, MD, Kari Connelly, MD, Tracy Fulton, PhD, Melissa Kerr, PhD, Anna Spielvogel, MD, Kim Mulvihill, MD, and Amy Levine, EdD as each has contributed fresh ideas and support for this method at critical junctures in its development. Many EBT clinical leaders have made substantial contributions to this work, including Judy Zehr, LPC, our Director of Community Education, who integrated attachment theory into the conceptual basis of the method, and Michele Welling, MD, who brought her medical perspectives on addiction to EBT, and directs professional certification training. Arinn Testa, PsyD shepherds the method through research planning. Early on, she participated as a trainer in an NIH study on EBT. Mary Croughan, PhD offered guidance about the development of EBT well after her days of analyzing the method's research data had passed. Marion Nestle, PhD, supported the work early on in its transition from pediatrics to family medicine. Dede Taylor advised us through one of our most vulnerable periods and developed our interest in work-site coaching and seminars in EBT. I am grateful to each of them for their generous contributions. I am grateful to Kevin Grumbach, MD, Chair of Family and Community Medicine, and Sam Hawgood, MD, Chancellor, both of UCSF, for their support of the method. Mary Charlson, MD, and Janey Peterson, EdD, of the Center for Complementary and Integrative Medicine, Weill Cornell Medical College advised me on the application of EBT to heart disease and pregnancy research and Kelly Webber, PhD conducted research on the method at the University of Kentucky. Paula Ernst, Tammy Thorton, Lisa McCoy, and Molly Harding were instrumental in supporting an EBT obesity study in association with the public health department in Hagerstown, Maryland.

Many EBT Trainers have contributed to the development of this book, delivering the program and then making important recommendations that have improved its content and process. They include: David Ingebritsen, PhD, LPC, Barbara Gabriel, LPC, Eve Lowry, RD, Denice Keepin, LPC, Deanne Hamilton, MS, RD, Robin Anderson, RD, Micheline Vargas, DrPH, Bonnie Hoag, LPC, Bill Mory, LPC, Sylvia Cramer, DrPH, Carra Richling, RD, and Molly Reno, JD. The memory of psychologist Anne Brown, PhD still influences my thinking about the method.

Special thanks to Seth Kester-Irwin, Nancie Kester, and Charles Irwin for their love and support. Priscilla Christopher, Emily Kearney, Jock Begg, Pamela Steckroat, Janice and Ralph Echenique, Dan Rosenthal, Saunterre Irish, Meghan Decker, Anna O'Connor, Diana Hurlbut, Leah Nafius, Martha Lupe, Sean Foy, Martha Shumway, Tommy Odetto, and Bob Crowder have given to the work in unique and meaningful ways. I am grateful to Lynn and Bruce McDermott, Gail and Bill Hutchinson, Catherine and Dick Krell, Peggy and Jim Galbraith, Jack Grehan, Kela and Carlos Cabrales, Mike Mooney, Skye Reese, and Susie Mooney, Nancy and Jamey Saunders, Jim and Lili

King, Tatihana and George Morales, Justine and Bruce Fairey, Marcia and David Sperling, Keith Chamberlin, Jon Donovan, Brian Strunk, Samantha Wechsler, Lynne Anderson, and Kathleen Wilson for their support during the writing of this book. Beth Tabakin's insights were instrumental to our success during this time of transition. Beth Pawlick has inspired me with her kindness and care. I am very grateful to our exceptional accountant David Bott for his dedication to EBT, and to our business attorney, Bryant Young, and to our intellectual property attorneys Larry Townsend and Steven Nielsen for their crucial advice over the years. Bob Mellin and Sharon Nielsen were instrumental in the early development of EBT when it focused on the treatment of pediatric obesity and its transition into brain training to promote optimal well-being in adults. I am very grateful to them for believing in the method, and helping so many children and families learn the skills. Without their support, there would be no EBT.

My deepest thanks go to my family. My son John and his wife Anastasia's influences have been woven into this book, as both John's understandings from literature and philosophy, and his astute edits of this work have strengthened it considerably. Ana, a pharmacist, is a strong advocate for deriving one's "chemicals" naturally through food ("nutritional power") and a healthy lifestyle rather than from medications. Their son, Henry John, was born just as this book went to press, and already lights up my life. My son Joe and his fiancée Megan share their passions for personal growth as well as systems design and technology with me. Their shared joie de vivre is catching! Megan has brought her Kansas values into our family and enriched us all. My daughter Haley has been a model for me of moving forward authentically in life, and of having sensitivity for animals, teaching me to guide spiders out of the house rather than killing them. She and Joe are now helping people become conservationists, preserving their own acre of land in Oregon or Guatemala to support biodiversity. Still, after more than 40 years, I cherish the memory of my first child, Riley.

When my partner Walt and I met five years ago, he did not fully appreciate the challenges of being with a woman who was in love with EBT. However, soon he shared my passion and became a driving force behind making EBT into scalable emotional healthcare. During these years, Walt has had plenty of "moments of opportunity" to use the stress tools, and, as a result, this book is his accomplishment as much as it is mine. Walt's family, Pete and Erin Rose and their children Paige and Gwen, have become family to me, and bring the fun of making "carrot soup" together and a willingness to be there for one another and share our lives. Walt's son Tom and his wife Caroline and their children Ellie and Tommy have touched me with their commitment to family by moving from Pasadena to Texas as Caroline recovered from a serious health issue. She is now using her experience of recovery in writing her own book and giving City of Hope talks to inspire others.

My father, Jack McClure, passed away peacefully during the writing of this work and showed me how to be brave and live out one's natural life, even when doing so is very hard. The McClure family, my brother Steve and his wife Vivian, Michael and Colleen, Sarah and Ethan, and Lisa have joined my family in continuing the McClure family traditions. My mother, Rosie ("Mackey"), who passed away nine years before my father, and he would be proud of the way their values of taking care of your health, working hard, and loving others now guide all six of their grandchildren.

With the publication of this book and its compatriot book on stress eating, the basic tools of EBT are finally widely available. For the first time in the four decades of developing this method, I can now ride a bike, gallop a horse, or get on an airplane without worrying that if I passed away, the method could pass away with me. That sounds like freedom to me.

I hope you join our mission of bringing EBT to more people to raise their set point and, over time, each do our small but important part to raise the set point of the planet.

Last, I'm grateful to the many EBT participants who apply the tools with enthusiasm, often arriving at new ways to use them, adding to the effectiveness of the method. Also, as they rewire a circuit or spiral up to One, they radiate joy that is contagious and has inspired me as I created this course. I thank them for allowing me to follow their experiences and to share those learnings with you.

Selected Reading

What follows is a list of researchers whose body of work contributed to the conceptual basis of the method and one or more citations of their research. For each researcher, their recent books published in the popular press have been listed first. Several early studies have been included below to show the history of the method.

Hilde Bruch

Bruch, H. & Touraine, G. (1940). Obesity in childhood: V. The family frame of obese children. *Psychosomatic Medicine* 2:142-206.

Mary Dallman

Dallman, M.F. (2010). Stress-induced obesity and the emotional nervous system. *Trends in Endocrinology and Metabolism* 21:159-165.

Antonio Damasio

Damasio, A. (2003). *Looking for Spinoza: Joy, Sorrow, and the Feeling Brain.* Harcourt, Inc.

Fox, G.R., Kaplan, J., Damasio, H., & Damasio, A. (2015). Neural correlates of gratitude. *Frontiers in Psychology* 6:1491.

Damasio, A. & Carvalho, G.B. (2013) The nature of feelings: Evolutionary and neurobiological origins. *National Review of Neuroscience* 14:143-152.

Richard Davidson

Davidson, R.J. & McEwen, B.S. (2012). Social influences on neuroplasticity: Stress and interventions to promote well-being. *Nature Neuroscience* 15:689-695.

Davidson, R.J. (2008). Spirituality and medicine: Science and practice. *Annals of Family Medicine* 6:388-389.

Davidson, R.J., Jackson, D.C., & Kalin, N.H. (2000). Emotion, plasticity, context, and regulation: Perspectives from affective neuroscience. *Psychological Bulletin* 126:890-909.

Paul Ekman

Dalai Lama, Ekman, P. (2008). *Emotional Awareness: Overcoming the obstacles to psychological balance and compassion*. Times Books.

Sauter, D.A., Eisner, F., Ekman, P., & Scott, S.K. (2010). Cross-cultural recognition of basic emotions through nonverbal emotional vocalizations. *Proceedings of the National Academy of Sciences* 107: 2408-2412.

Ekman, P. (2009). Darwin's contributions to our understanding of emotional expressions. *Philosophical Transactions of The Royal Society of London, Series B, Biological Sciences* 364:3449-3451.

Elissa Epel

Blackburn, E. & Epel, E. (2017). *The Telomere Effect: A Revolutionary Approach to Living Younger, Healthier, Longer*. Grand Central Publishing.

Mason, A.E., Laraia, B., Daubenmier, J., Hecht, F.M., Lustig, R.H., Puterman, E., Adler, N., Dallman, M., Kiernan, M., Gearhardt, A.N., & Epel, E.S. (2015). Putting the breaks on the "drive to eat": Pilot effects of naltrexone and reward based eating on food cravings among obese women. *Eating Behaviors* 19:53-56.

Adam, T.C. & Epel, E.S. (2007). Stress, eating and the reward system. *Physiology & Behavior* 91:449-458.

Epel, E.S., McEwen, B., Seeman, T., Matthews, K., Castellazzo, G., Brownell, K., Bell, J., & Ickovics, J.R. (2000). Stress and body shape: stress-induced cortisol secretion is consistently greater among women with central fat. *Psychosomatic Medicine* 62:623-632.

Leonard Epstein

Epstein L.H., Valoski, A., Wing, R.R., & McCurley, J. (1990). Ten-year follow-up of behavioral, family-based treatment for obese children. *Journal of the American Medical Association* 264:2519-2523.

Epstein, L.H., Wing, R.R., Koeske, R., & Valoski, A. (1987). Long-term effects of family-based treatment of childhood obesity. *Journal of Consulting and Clinical Psychology* 55:91-95.

Vincent Felitti

Felitti, V.J., Jakstis, K., Pepper, V., & Ray, A. (2010). Obesity: Problem, Solution, or Both? *The Permanente Journal* 14:24-30.

Felitti, V.J., Anda, R.F., Nordenberg, D., et al. (1998). Relationship of childhood abuse and household dysfunction to many of the leading causes of death in adults: The Adverse Childhood Experiences (ACE) Study. *American Journal of Preventive Medicine* 14:245-258.

Felitti, V.J. (1993). Childhood sexual abuse, depression, and family dysfunction in adult obese patients – a case control study. *Southern Medical Journal* 86:732-736.

Lynda Frassetto

Frassetto, L.A., Schloetter, M., Mietus-Synder, M., Morris, R.C., Jr., & Sebastian, A. (2009). Metabolic and physiologic improvements from consuming a paleolithic, hunter-gatherer type diet. *European Journal of Clinical Nutrition* 63:947-955.

Dacher Keltner

Keltner, D. (2009). *Born to Be Good: The Science of a Meaningful Life*. W.W. Norton.

George Koob

Koob, G.F. & Volkow, N.D. (2010). Neurocircuitry of addiction. *Neuropsychopharmacology* 35:217-238.

Koob, G.F. & Le Moal, M. (2008). Addiction and the brain antireward system. *Annual Review of Psychology* 59:29-53.

Joseph LeDoux

LeDoux, J. (2012). Rethinking the emotional brain. *Neuron* 73:653-676.

LeDoux, J. (2012). Evolution of human emotion: A view through fear. *Progress in Brain Research* 195:431-442.

Robert Lustig

Lustig, R.H. (2017). *The Hacking of the American Mind: The Science Behind the Corporate Takeover of our Bodies and Brains*. Avery.

Lustig, R.H. (2012). *Fat Chance: Beating the Odds Against Sugar, Processed Food, Obesity, and Disease*. Hudson Street Press (Penguin).

Mietus-Snyder M.L. & Lustig, R.H. (2008). Childhood obesity: Adrift in the "limbic triangle." *Annual Review of Medicine* 59:147-162.

Bruce McEwen

McEwen, B. (2002). *The End of Stress as We Know It*. Dana Press.

Picard, M. & McEwen, B.S. (2018). Psychological stress and mitochondria: A conceptual framework. *Psychosomatic Medicine* 80:126-140.

McEwen, B.S., & Gianaros, P.J. (2011). Stress- and allostasis-induced brain plasticity. *Annual Review of Medicine* 62:431-445.

Juster, R.P., McEwen, B.S., & Lupien, S.J. (2010). Allostatic load biomarkers of chronic stress and impact on health and cognition. *Neuroscience and Biobehavioral Reviews* 35:2-16.

McEwen, B.S. (2009). The brain is the central organ of stress and adaptation. *NeuroImage* 47:911-913.

Laurel Mellin

Mellin L. (2010). *Wired for Joy: A Revolutionary Method for Creating Happiness from Within.* Hay House, Inc.

Mellin, L. (2013). *Emotional plasticity theory: Preliminary evaluation of changes in stress-related variables in obese adults.* (Northcentral University). ProQuest Dissertations and Theses, 307.

Mellin, L., Croughan, M., & Dickey, L. (1997). The Solution Method: 2-year trends in weight, blood pressure, exercise, depression and functioning of adults trained in developmental skills. *Journal of the American Dietetic Association* 97:1133-1138.

McNutt, S.W., Hu, Y., Schreiber, G.B., Crawford, P.B., Obarzanek, E., & Mellin, L. (1997). A longitudinal study of dietary practices of black and white girls 9 and 10 years old at enrollment: the NHLBI Growth and Health Study. *Journal of Adolescent Health* 20:27-37.

Mellin, L., Irwin, C., & Scully, S. (1992). Prevalence of disordered eating in girls: A survey of middle-class children. *Journal of the American Dietetic Association* 92:851-853.

Mellin, L., Slinkard, L.A., & Irwin, C.E., Jr. (1987). Adolescent obesity intervention: Validation of the SHAPEDOWN program. *Journal of the American Dietetic Association* 87:333-338.

Michael Merzenich

Merzenich, M. (2013). *Soft-Wired: How the New Science of Brain Plasticity Can Change Your Life*. Parnassus Publishing.

Merzenich, M.M., Van Vleet, T.M., & Nahum, M. (2014). Brain plasticity-based therapeutics. *Frontiers in Human Neuroscience* 8:385.

Mahncke, H.W., Connor, B.B., Appleman, J., Ahsanuddin, O.N., Hardy, J.L., Wood, R.A., Joyce, N.M., Boniske, T., Atkins, S.M., & Merzenich, M.M. (2006). Memory enhancement in healthy older adults using a brain plasticity-based training program: A randomized, controlled study. *Proceedings of the National Academy of Science U.S.A.* 103:12523-12528.

Temple, E., Deutsch, G.K., Poldrack, R.A., Miller, S.L., Tallal, P., Merzenich, M.M., & Gabrieli, J.D. (2003). Neural deficits in children with dyslexia ameliorated by behavioral remediation: Evidence from functional MRI. *Proceedings of the National Academy of Science U.S.A.* 100:2860-2865.

Igor Mitrovic

Kurtzman, L. (2014). Neurobiologist Shares Personal Journey, Life Lessons in 'Last Lecture.' *UCSF News*. www.youtube.com/watch?v=uKjvQSBaWKQ

Mitrovic, I., Fish de Peña, L., Frassetto, L.A., & Mellin, L. (2011). Rewiring the stress response: A new paradigm for health care. *Hypothesis* 9:1:e1-e5.

Mitrovic, I., Mellin, L., & Fish de Peña, L. (2008). *Emotional brain training: The neurobiology of brain retraining for promotion of adaptive behaviors and state of well-being*. pp. 1-19. Institute for Health Solutions.

Bruce Perry

Perry, B.D. & Szalavitz, M. (2006). *The Boy Who Was Raised as a Dog: And Other Stories from a Child Psychiatrist's Notebook-What Traumatized Children Can Teach Us About Loss, Love, and Healing*. Basic Books.

Perry, B.D. & Hambrick, E.P. (2008). The neurosequential model of therapeutics. *Reclaiming Children and Youth* 17:38-43.

Perry, B.D. & Pollard, R. (1998). Homeostasis, stress, trauma, and adaptation. A neurodevelopmental view of childhood trauma. *Child & Adolescent Psychiatric Clinics of North America* 7:33-51.

Elizabeth Phelps

Raio, C.M., Orederu, T.A., Palazzolo, L., Shurick, A.A., & Phelps, E.A. (2013). Cognitive emotion regulation fails the stress test. *Proceedings of the Natural Academy of Sciences* 110:15139-15144.

Schiller, D., Monfils, M.H., Raio, C.M., Johnson, D.C., LeDoux, J.E., & Phelps, E.A. (2010). Preventing the return of fear in humans using reconsolidation update mechanisms. *Nature* 463:49-53.

Hartley, C.A. & Phelps, E.A. (2010). Changing fear: The neurocircuitry of emotion regulation. *Neuropsychopharmacology* 35:136-146.

Delgado, M.R., Nearing, K.I., LeDoux, J.E., & Phelps, E.A., (2008). Neural circuitry underlying the regulation of conditioned fear and its relation to extinction. *Neuron* 59:829-838.

Stephen Porges

Porges, S., (2011). *The Polyvagal Theory: Neurophysiological Foundations of Emotions, Attachment, Communication, and Self-regulation*. W.W. Norton.

Porges, S. W. & Furman, S. A. (2011). The early development of the autonomic nervous system provides a neural platform for social behavior: A polyvagal perspective. *Infant and Child Development* 20:106-118.

Alan Schore

Schore, A.N. (2009). Relational trauma and the developing right brain: An interface of psychoanalytic self psychology and neuroscience. *Annals of the New York Academy of Sciences* 1159:189-203.

Schore, A.N. (2005). Back to basics: Attachment, affect regulation, and the developing right brain: Linking developmental neuroscience to pediatrics. *Pediatric Reviews* 26:204-217.

Peter Sterling

Sterling, P. (2014). Homeostasis vs. allostasis: Implications for brain function and mental disorders. *Journal of the American Medical Association Psychiatry* 71:1192-3.

Sterling, P. (2004). Principles of allostasis: Optimal design, predictive regulation, pathophysiology, and rational therapeutics. In J. Schulkin (Ed.), *Allostasis, Homeostasis, and the Costs of Physiological Adaptation* (pp. 17-64). Cambridge University Press.

Janet Tomiyama

Tomiyama, A.J. (2019). Stress and obesity. *Annual Review of Psychology* 70. doi.org/10.1146/annurev-psych-010418-102936.

George Vaillant

Vaillant, G. (2008). *Spiritual Evolution: How We Are Wired for Faith, Hope, and Love*. Broadway Books.

Kelly Webber

Webber K.H., Mellin L., Mayes L., Mitrovic I., & Saulnier M. (2018). Pilot investigation of 2 nondiet approaches to improve weight and health. *Alternative Therapies in Health and Medicine* 24:16-20.

Webber, K.H., Casey, E.M., Mayes, L., Katsumata, Y., & Mellin, L. (2016). A comparison of a behavioral weight loss program to a stress management program: A pilot randomized controlled trial. *Nutrition* 32:904-909.

Your EBT Experience

The goal of EBT is to raise the brain's set point for optimal well-being. To reach that goal more easily and more rapidly, please select one or more of the following options:

☐ **Join the EBT Online Community***

Visit ebt.org and receive a 25% discount on the Online Plus membership. Use coupon code stressoverload. With this membership, you will have access to our app, videos, workshops, and forum boards. Learn more about options for coaching, weekly telegroups, and intensives.

☐ **Participate in a Chat with Dr. Laurel session**

If you have questions about EBT, Dr. Laurel Mellin offers regular, free drop-in question and answer sessions for readers of *The Stress Overload Solution*. Visit **ebtbook.com/stressoverload**.

☐ **Visit the Brain Based Health Blog**

For the latest science and news about EBT, visit **brainbasedhealth.org**

☐ **Access this book's companion downloads**

If you would like to download complimentary materials to record your progress with this Challenge, visit **ebtbook.com/stressoverload**.

☐ **Develop a circle of support for raising your set point**

Ask your family members and friends to take the Challenge with you. If you are in a relationship, consider inviting your partner or spouse to join the Challenge. Are you a member of a book club? Select this book or *The Stress Eating Solution* and support one another.

☐ **Learn more about certification (for health professionals)**

If you are a health professional who would like more information about certification as an EBT Provider or EBT Mentor, visit **ebtbook.com/stressoverload**.

*membership in the EBT Online Community is recommended for all book readers

My Power Grind Ins

Take a Power Break four times per day and use the Power Grind Ins that you are drawn to using. Experience freedom and a joyful, vibrant life!

My Power Grind In: Mood

I cannot get my _____ from _____ .

That's ridiculous! I cannot get my _____ from _____ .

I get my _____ from:

Connect: _____ .

Approach: _____ .

Reward: _____ .

My Power Grind In: Love

I cannot get my _____ from _____ .

That's ridiculous! I cannot get my _____ from _____ .

I get my _____ from:

Connect: _____ .

Approach: _____ .

Reward: _____ .

My Power Grind In: Work

I cannot get my _____ from _____ .

That's ridiculous! I cannot get my _____ from _____ .

I get my _____ from:

Connect: _____ .

Approach: _____ .

Reward: _____ .

My Power Grind In: Habit

I cannot get my _____ from _____ .

That's ridiculous! I cannot get my _____ from _____ .

I get my _____ from:

Connect: _____ .

Approach: _____ .

Reward: _____ .

Printed in Great Britain
by Amazon

38434436R00176